with best wish

Jacqueline and

Wright

SHOTOVER
The Life of an Oxfordshire Hill

Edited by Ivan Wright and Jacqueline Wright

Written by
Lawrence Bee, Marc Botham, Steve Gregory, Eleanor Hawtree, Eliza Howlett,
Linda Losito, Tim Newton, Antonia Whitehead, Ivan Wright and Jacqueline Wright

With editorial assistance from
Timothy Bartel and Marion Couldrey

Book management team
Lawrence Bee, Helen Carter, Marion Couldrey, Ivan Wright and Jacqueline Wright

Shotover Wildlife

Published by

piscespublications

Published 2018 for Shotover Wildlife by Pisces Publications

First published 2018.

British-Library-in-Publication Data
A catalogue record for this book is available from the British Library.

ISBN 978-1-874357-87-2

Designed and published by Pisces Publications

Visit our bookshop
www.naturebureau.co.uk/bookshop/

Pisces Publications is the imprint of NatureBureau, 36 Kingfisher Court, Hambridge Road, Newbury, Berkshire RG14 5SJ
www.naturebureau.co.uk

Printed and bound in the UK by Gomer Press Ltd

COVER PHOTOGRAPHS
Front cover **Downy Birches *Betula pubescens* on Horspath Common** [Jacqueline Wright]
Back cover   **Aerial view of Shotover Hill** [Martin Kennedy]

All photographs within this book belong to Jacqueline Wright unless otherwise stated.

To David Steel (1951–2006)

His foresight, resoluteness and wisdom laid the foundation for a lasting recognition of Shotover as an exceptional place for wildlife.

The authors

Lawrence Bee is an ecological consultant and educator. He is the author of the Field Studies Council's *Guide to House and Garden Spiders* and co-author of *Britain's Spiders: A field guide*. He regularly teaches on Field Studies Council courses throughout the UK.

Marc Botham has worked as an ecologist for the Centre for Ecology & Hydrology in Oxfordshire for over ten years, specializing in Lepidoptera, and working closely with the UK Butterfly Monitoring Scheme. He has been greatly involved in surveying moths throughout the Upper Thames region and became involved with Shotover Wildlife in order to study moths at Shotover.

Steve Gregory developed his passion for natural history as a child. In the 1990s he worked for the Oxfordshire Biological Record Centre where he was encouraged to develop his entomological bias. Now an ecological consultant, Steve is organizer of the British Woodlouse Recording Scheme and author of *Woodlice and Waterlice in Britain and Ireland*. He remains an active recorder in Oxfordshire.

Eleanor Hawtree grew up near Shotover, and the Hill has been a place of great significance throughout her life. She has been a member of Shotover Wildlife since its inception, contributing to botanical surveying, conservation work, publications and website management. Eleanor is a qualified teacher with a degree in Environmental Biology.

Eliza Howlett is Head of Earth Collections at the Oxford University Museum of Natural History, where she is primarily responsible for fossils but also has oversight of minerals and rocks. She is particularly interested in the history of palaeontology from 1650 to 1900, including figures such as William Buckland and Robert Plot.

Linda Losito roamed Shotover as a child, before becoming a biology teacher and author of natural history books. She also contributes her time and beetle identification skills to the many campaigns protecting Oxfordshire's threatened green spaces. Currently, Linda is helping to survey the distribution of dung beetles throughout the UK.

Tim Newton discovered beetles in 1969 while at school. An invitation from the Natural History Museum (London) to look at their Coleoptera collections resulted in a passion which has not diminished over almost five decades. Tim runs workshops for Wildlife Trusts and Societies, and undertakes saproxylic survey work for a variety of landowners.

Antonia 'Toni' Whitehead was a lecturer and senior manager in psychology but on retirement her interest in birds came to the fore. She directed Shotover Wildlife's bird surveying and data protocols and was principal author of *The Birds of Shotover* (2003). Toni died in 2015 shortly after completing the draft of the chapter on birds for this publication. The chapter is dedicated to her memory.

Ivan Wright worked in meteorology with the Natural Environment Research Council until early retirement in 1995. Through a passion for informed conservation at Shotover, he has become a naturalist and hymenopterist. Ivan is now a consultant entomologist for Oxfordshire and the Oxford University Museum of Natural History and has been chairman of Shotover Wildlife since 1999.

Jacqueline Wright is a self-taught botanist and ecologist and came to wildlife through discovering the inspirational atmosphere of Shotover. She has specialized in mosses and liverworts, becoming County Recorder in 2002. Alongside her nursing career, Jacqueline is also an artist and wildlife illustrator and has produced drawings for several books.

Contents

Preface

Despite the enduring popularity of Shotover Hill, remarkably little has been published about it. Indeed, until the mid-1980s there were only two publications which dealt at any length with Shotover and the associated royal forest, and then only with aspects of their physical and social history: *Headington Quarry and Shotover* (Coppock and Hill, 1933), produced locally by the Women's Institute, and *A History of the County of Oxford: Volume 5, Bullingdon Hundred* (Lobel, 1957).

All this changed, however, with the publication in 1984 of David Steel's seminal book, *Shotover: The Natural History of a Royal Forest*. This deceptively modest volume not only sketched the long social history of Shotover Forest but also provided the first detailed account of its remaining habitats and their associated flora and fauna. More importantly, it had at least one far-reaching consequence. The text was easily modified to form an outline management plan for Shotover Country Park (Steel, 1988) — the public space that had been formally designated by that name since 1973. The management plan, in turn, played a major role in the designation of Shotover Country Park as a Site of Special Scientific Interest (SSSI) by the Joint Nature Conservancy Council (JNCC). That status officially recognizes the importance of the area for wildlife and also establishes a basic framework of legal protection from activities that would compromise the special wildlife interest of the SSSI.

David Steel's writing also played a large part in the genesis of the community organization Shotover Wildlife by inspiring local amateur botanist Jacqueline Wright to begin surveying flora in the SSSI in 1995. Shotover Wildlife was launched in August 1999 by Ivan and Jacqueline Wright to bring together local naturalists for the surveying and study of species, and to apply that knowledge for optimal conservation. An important additional objective has been to disseminate the results through community leaflets and published reports. The resulting accumulation of written material about the wildlife of Shotover raised the possibility of producing a sequel to *Shotover: The Natural History of a Royal Forest*.

Our hopes for that sequel have now been fulfilled. Moreover, as David Steel's book was one of the first hardbacks to be launched by the newly founded Pisces Publications, it is wholly fitting that the sequel should be produced by the same highly respected wildlife publishing company. This achievement, however, is tinged with sadness as we had always hoped that a Foreword to our book would be written by David, our inspiration and first supporter. Nevertheless, we see the publication of this volume as a continuation of his work, and hope that others will be inspired by it, and the work of Shotover Wildlife, in the years to come.

Ivan and Jacqueline Wright
Horspath 2018

Acknowledgements

This book is based upon the contributions of a great many wildlife enthusiasts, the vast majority of whom have volunteered their time and expertise toward the common goal of wildlife conservation at Shotover. Without their hard work and dedication this book would not have been possible.

Supporters

The infrastructure for the production of the book has been provided by the community organization Shotover Wildlife. Since its founding in 1999, and throughout the production of this book, support for its objectives has been outstanding, particularly from Shotover Wildlife members and the wider community of those who care for wildlife. For their various most valuable contributions, the editors are especially grateful to the following, including past and present committee members of Shotover Wildlife (committee):

Jane Applegarth, Ruth Ashcroft, Timothy Bartel (committee), Lawrence Bee (committee), George Bloom, Michael Bloom, Nicola Bourdillon and family, Malcolm Brownsword, John Campbell, Carlo Charlesworth, Anthony Cheke, Nina Chelms, Katherine Child, Edith Clift, Bonnie Collins (committee), Chris Cornforth, Marion Couldrey, Graham Diggle, Paul Dunstan (committee), The Edina Trust, Isobel Gilham, Sarah Gray (committee), Owen Green, David Guyoncourt, Jane Haigh, Peter Harbour, Eleanor Hawtree, John Hawtree, Birgit Hontzsch, Barry Hudson, Jackie Hudson, Angela Julian (committee), Andrew Kay, Janet Keene, John Killick, Andrew Lack, Shirley Leach, Alison Leaf (committee), Susan Lewis, Dave Linzey, Rachel Locklin (committee), Darren Mann, Serena Marner, Phil Mead, Rob Morby, Sue Oldfield, Roger Parker, Phil Powell, Gary Powney (committee), Dave Powney (committee), Kate Prudden (committee), Betty Purves, John Purves, Rebecca Read, Dot Reich, Alex Rey (committee), Debbie Reynolds, Mark Reynolds, Ruth Russel, Ian Smith, Xenia Snowman, Marianne Stanley, Alan Stubbs, Roger Thomas, Stewart Thompson,

Alan Todd, Keith Tomey, Antonia Whitehead, Andrew Wilkinson, Peter Wilkinson, Nick Willcox, Pip Willcox, Walter Wright, Roger Wyatt and Wiltrud Young.

Surveyors and other specialists

The authors are greatly indebted to the many surveyors and specialists who have contributed their time and expertise over the past 20 years to build the extensive volume of data and information on which this book is based:

Michael Ackland, Keith Alexander, Simon Anson, Jane Applegarth, Michael Archer, Brian Armstrong, Ruth Ashcroft, Jim Asher, J.S. Baker, Max Barclay, S. Barlow, Kate Barnett, P.R. Barnett, Timothy Bartel, Lawrence Bee, Joe Bennet, Jeremy Biggs, Hannah Bilston, George Bloom, John Bolt, Marc Botham, Andrew Burdock, Jill Butler, John Campbell, Helen Carter, Peter Chandler, June Chatfield, Caroline Cheeseman, Anthony Cheke, Gareth Clay, Sam Claydon, Graham Coleman, Bonnie Collins, Dom Collins, Richard Comont, Marion Couldrey, M.L. Cox, Peter Creed, Nigel Cuming, Rob Curtis, Gus David-Smith, Rod d'Ayala, Jonti Denton, Graham Diggle, Tony Drane, Katherine Drayson, Trevor Duke, Mary Elford, Susanne Eti, Jim Fairclough, Emeline Favreau, Paul Fernborough, Jim Flanagan, Bob Fleetwood, Richard Fortey, Stephen Freeman, Liz Fricker, Matt Fry, David Gibbs, Marion Gillie, Tony Gillie, Peter Gillott, James Glendenning, Sarah Gorman, Andy Gosler, Claudia Gray, Sarah Gray, Ted Green, Dick Greenaway, Steve Gregory, Marian Griffiths, Anne Grimm, Simon Grove, Jane Haigh, Andrew Halcro-Johnston, Andrew Halstead, Clive Hambler, Brian Harding, Pat Hartridge, Martin Harvey, Peter Harvey, Cathie Hasler, Nick Havely, Eleanor Hawtree, Andrew Heaver, Alan Hills, Katrin Hochberg, Sarah Hodgetts, James Hogan, Birgit Hontzsch, Eliza Howlett, David Hughes, John Hyde, Euan Inglis, John Ismay, Caroline Jackson-Houlston, Paul Jeffery, Pat Jeffs, Carolyn Jewell, Sam Jones, Steve Jones, Angela Julian, A. Kannard, Susanna Kay, Janet Keene, S. Kelly, John Killick, Tim King, Peter Kirby, Elizabeth Kreager,

Andrew Lack, Curt Lambeth, Camilla Lambrick, Jill Lang, Andy Lawfield, Allan Lawson, Shirley Leach, Alison Leaf, Anthony Levison-Gower, Devi Lingham, Rachel Locklin, Linda Losito, Stuart Mabbutt, Wendy MacEachrane, Darren Mann, Deborah Marchant, Rachel McDonald, Camilla Mitchell, Dave Molloy, Nicola Montalto, Alison Muldal, Erin Murton, H. Netley, Richard Newton, Tim Newton, Pascale Nicolet, B. Nind, Carl Noyce, Sue Oldfield, Oxfordshire Mammals Group, Sean O'Leary, Chris O'Toole, Denise Pallett, Roger Parker, Audrey Parsons, Mark Pavett, Ben Payne, Russell Payne, Ray Pearce, Sharon Pilkington, R.M. Pomfret, Keith Porter, Liz Powell, Dave Powney, Gary Powney, Kate Prudden, James Rainey, P. Rainsden, Chris Raper, S. Rawlings, Rebecca Read, David Redhead, Claire Rennie-Lis, Alex Rey, Janet Ridout-Sharp, Anthony Roberts, Sarah Roberts, Amy Robinson, Sarah Rose, Amaryllis Roy, Ruth Russel, Rob Ryan, Albert Sallu, Claire Sampson, Jo Savage, D. Schafer, Jo Shackleton, Mary-Clare Sheahan, Zoë Simmons, Lucy Small, Arthur Smith, Matt Smith, Xenia Snowman, K. Southern, Jodie Southgate, Amoret Spooner, Carl Sprake, Arthur Spriggs, Sandra Standbridge, Marianne Stanley, Caroline Steel, Ian Stevenson, Doris Stogdale, Michael Swaine, Thurston Tallack, Jim Tallett, Mark Telfer, Reg Tipping, John Tomlinson, Martin Townsend, Daniel Tritton, Darren Twort, Robert Twycross, John Uren, Dorothy Vincent, Arthur Warland, Marion Warland, Steven Washington, Ceri Watkins, Charlie Webb, Justin Webber, Antonia Whitehead, Peter Whitton, Peter Wilkinson, Nick Willcox, Pip Willcox, Rebecca Willetts, Alex Williams, Colin Williams, Steven Williams, Mike Wilson, Dave Wilton, Sula Wiltshire, Ivan Wright, Jacqueline Wright, Wiltrud Young and Nicole Youngs.

Landowners

Finally, the authors are grateful to the owners, tenants and managers of land on Shotover Hill who have granted permission to visit, survey and gather wildlife information: Gill and Donald Gray, Robert McHenry, Phil Mead, Lt. Col. Sir John Miller, Oxford City Council, Alexander Stanier, Doris Stogdale, David Walker and Denis Walker.

Extent of the survey area

The region referred to in this volume as Shotover or 'the Hill' is the 940 hectares bounded by the London Road (A40) on the northern boundary, the Oxford ring road to the west, Horspath Road to the south and Littleworth and Wheatley to the east [see Fig. a, below]. This area is similar to that defined by Shotover Wildlife in *The Birds of Shotover* (Whitehead *et al.*, 2003) as the extent of surveying interest for birds; in this book, the isolated western half of Magdalen Wood is not included. Within the survey area are Shotover Country Park and the Brasenose Wood and Shotover Hill Site of Special Scientific Interest (the SSSI), which share almost the same boundaries and cover 113 and 110 hectares respectively [see Fig. b, opposite].

Before 1974 Oxfordshire was smaller than today's 'modern' Oxfordshire and did not then include that part of old Berkshire that is north of the Berkshire Downs. However, the boundaries of pre-1974 Oxfordshire have been retained for contemporary biological recording in Britain (as Vice County 23). Therefore, references to Oxfordshire published before 1974, as well as some biological references since (for example, Killick *et al.*, 1998), apply to the pre-1974 extent of the county. In this book 'pre-1974 Oxfordshire' is used for the smaller recording area.

Source data

The principal source of material for the book is the recording, research and analysis undertaken by a great many dedicated naturalists, mostly

Figure a Principal place names and areas surveyed Ivan Wright/©Crown copyright 2018 OS 100057706

members of Shotover Wildlife, who have been studying wildlife on the Hill since the founding of the organization in 1999. Additional information has been distilled from historic records, a considerable volume of data coming from naturalists working in the late 19th and early 20th centuries. Most of the historic information has been extracted from early publications, supplemented significantly, however, by hitherto unpublished source material (diaries and specimen labels) at the Oxford University Museum of Natural History. We have taken care to avoid relying on information without first consulting the original source material wherever possible.

Clearly species recorded in past years cannot all be assumed to be living on the Hill today. For this book we have adopted a threshold date of 1995; if a species was extant before this date and not recorded since, it cannot be assumed that it has remained at Shotover. This threshold applies, for example, to all the species listed by David Steel in his book (Steel, 1984: Appendices 2–16).

Therefore, our reporting of which species currently exist on the Hill relies predominantly on the records accumulated by Shotover Wildlife since 1995, and we acknowledge that some relatively common and widespread species are likely to have been overlooked, particularly among the invertebrates. Moreover, some groups of species that are well represented in data from earlier years have since gone unrecorded because the specialist identification skills are no longer available.

There are 13,800 known wildlife records for Shotover prior to 1995, including 3,800 species. In the 23 years since then, over 130,000 records have been assembled, with 2,000 previously extant species confirmed and at least 2,100 new species added, making the all-time total number of species recorded for Shotover currently over 5,900.

References and species nomenclature

The book is intended to be as accurate and informative as possible, while remaining unencumbered by excessive references and

Figure b Location names in and around Shotover Country Park Ivan Wright/©Crown copyright 2018 OS 100057706

technical terms. References to further reading are mostly confined to texts that are specific to Shotover and the local or county context. It is assumed that the reader can investigate more general references elsewhere. The common English name of a species or taxonomic family is used wherever possible. As a rule, Latin names are also given in the chapters dealing with that species group but only at the first mention. English names of species are capitalized (for example, Silver Birch) but not species groups (for example, birches).

Introducing Shotover

Ivan Wright and Jacqueline Wright

From any of the viewpoints in the centre of Oxford, Shotover Hill dominates the eastern horizon. The road from Oxford to Shotover, once the main road to London, rises 110 metres from Magdalen Bridge, finally climbing Fiddlestone Hill to reach the summit. Over the years innumerable scholars, luminaries and dignitaries have travelled this ancient route. At the top today is a public park and nature reserve, scarcely five kilometres from the centre of Oxford, offering a natural space that is well known and much loved, its appeal undiminished by the trees that now obscure the view back towards the spires of Oxford.

There are, of course, many different reasons to visit Shotover, among them the enjoyments of walking, running, picnicking and playing games.

Perhaps more subtly there is also the desire to climb a hill and experience the exhilarating view from the top, or to seek the calming tranquillity of natural surroundings. Indeed, access to the countryside is indispensable to the health and well-being of society, and Shotover is one of the best places around Oxford to satisfy that need. Yet Shotover is not unique in this respect; if necessary these outdoor activities can all be pursued elsewhere in Oxfordshire. But where Shotover is unique, and of exceptional value, is in its assemblage of wildlife and habitats: on these particular soils, in this particular county and at its particular inland position in Britain. One of the main purposes of this book is to show how and why Shotover Hill is both regionally

The mature trees and open spaces of Shotover Hill are just a short distance from the bustle of Oxford City

and nationally exceptional. The distinctiveness of a major portion of the southern slopes is acknowledged by its designation as a nature reserve but even outside the reserve the varied and extensive tracts of private land greatly enrich the wildlife diversity of the Hill.

Again and again, the true importance of Shotover Hill for wildlife diversity needs to be restated — not as mere rhetoric or unfounded hyperbole but from an informed position — so that future generations may inherit a proper appreciation of the value of Shotover's wildlife and its heritage. This embraces far more than an appreciation of the trees, birds, butterflies and flowers that most of us admire; it also includes, for example, the beetles, mosses, snails and fungi, all of which make their own crucial contribution to a robust ecology. It has often been remarked that for the majority of people, the year-round enjoyment of the countryside is easily satisfied by less than five per cent of its species while the remaining 95 per cent are aesthetically irrelevant.

Yet the loss of even a small fraction of the 'hidden' 95 per cent would soon degrade the few species that most people require for a pleasant and uplifting experience of the countryside.

We live in an age when any reassessment of wildlife, both nationally and internationally, reveals a worrying loss of diversity and an alarming vulnerability of many species to further decline. This fact is often overlooked at the smaller or more local level, yet it is true on any scale, including at Shotover. In his book about Shotover, David Steel makes an impassioned plea for members of the public to be vigilant in saving the countryside from damage [see page 241]. Three decades later, his plea has lost none of its urgency. The difference now is that public authority budget cuts have overwhelmingly reduced official concern for wildlife and biodiversity, so that the responsibility for safeguarding the natural world now depends largely on the knowledge and determination of the community.

Professional and amateur naturalists studying the grassland ecology of Mary Sadler Field

A natural history

Ivan Wright

The habitats on Shotover Hill have been shaped by millennia of human influences, whether social, political, economic or industrial; hunting, farming and quarrying have all left their mark. What follows is an overview of Shotover's history in terms of its wildlife habitats, describing the influences that have shaped the natural legacy that remains after thousands of years of human intervention.

From around 2,500 BCE, the landscape around Shotover saw profound changes during the Neolithic, Bronze and Iron Ages, bringing to an end about 10,000 years of post-glacial woodland maturity and natural stability. Primary woodland was cleared as human settlement gradually increased and, for strategic purposes, priority was probably given to clearing trees on high ground, including Shotover Hill, as well as around major river crossings. Where occupation coincided with workable soils, additional tracts of woodland were cleared for crops and pasture as a more settled, agriculture-based society developed.

At Shotover in particular, the quarrying of minerals was an additional lure for settlers. During the period of Roman occupation, ending around 400 CE, interventions included the open-cast excavation of sand and clay for pottery, the cutting of timber to fuel the many dwellings and kilns, the extraction of the pigment yellow ochre and the development of an associated transport infrastructure in support of all this industry. Yet apart from a few surviving artefacts (flints and potsherds), the thousands of years of pre-Saxon occupation at Shotover have left hardly any lasting signs in the wildlife habitats of today. For example, an ancient woodland may be revered today for being 1,000 years old, yet the land on which it stands could have been cornfields or sheep pasture for twice that period, or more, before being abandoned to revert to woodland.

By the time of the Norman Conquest of 1066 much of southern England had already been partitioned into areas of baronial land and hunting forest — including the environs of Shotover. Those claiming ownership of the land would have imposed some form of feudal forest rule and a woodland-based economy prevailed. However, with the arrival of the Normans, written records of land usage began to appear (notably the Domesday Book of 1086) and, through a combination of administrative efficiency and William the Conqueror's fondness for hunting, the king's forests became more clearly defined in extent and more closely protected by new forest laws. In this way, the basis for a future habitat — ancient woodland — was established in England, and some of the oldest surviving trees in the country may date from that period. The reference to Shotover in the Domesday Book (as 'Scotorne') was to document the number of settlements or 'hides' that the king's land could support for taxation purposes, and establishes that Shotover Hill was at that time already in the king's ownership.

By the 14th century the wooded countryside immediately north-east of Oxford had become generally known as Shotover Forest. Before this time the name appeared in various forms but the etymological origins are very uncertain (Alexander, 1912: p. 186). The first published delineation of the Shotover Forest boundary was a commissioned 'perambulation' in 1298 which outlines an area of about nine square miles (2,330 hectares) extending eastwards from Oxford's Magdalen Bridge to Wheatley and north to Woodeaton (Steel, 1984: p. 10), and approximates to the old parish boundaries of Headington, Shotover and Stowood (Roberts, 1963). Many of the boundaries described in 1298 can still be found on a modern map, coinciding in a few places with boundaries in and around Shotover Country Park [see Fig. 1, page 4].

Along with many other perambulations at that time, the purpose of the 1298 document was to settle the disputed boundaries of the royal forest, and in all likelihood severely constrained the king's desire to increase the extent of hunting forest. Indeed, for over 100 years since the reign of Henry II (d. 1189), the kings of England had been trying, with ever-diminishing prospects of success, to acquire land to create a great

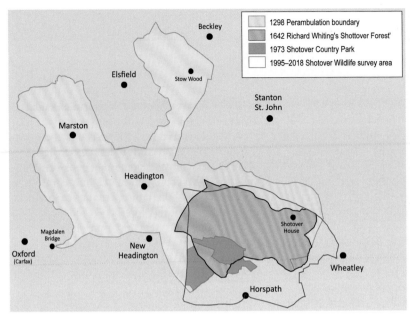

Figure 1 The boundaries of the royal forest in 1298 and 1642 together with Shotover Country Park and the areas surveyed by Shotover Wildlife from 1995–2018
Ivan Wright/©Crown copyright 2018 OS 100057706

Map legend:
- 1298 Perambulation boundary
- 1642 Richard Whiting's Shotover Forest'
- 1973 Shotover Country Park
- 1995–2018 Shotover Wildlife survey area

Map labels: Beckley, Elsfield, Stow Wood, Stanton St. John, Marston, Headington, Shotover House, Magdalen Bridge, Oxford (Carfax), New Headington, Wheatley, Horspath

continuous hunting forest from Oxfordshire to Lincolnshire. However, in 1297, the year before the perambulation, Edward I had been forced to reaffirm his commitment to both Magna Carta and the 1271 Charter of the Forest in exchange for new taxation legislation. This necessarily required a formal record of the limit to the king's land and forest jurisdiction. Consequently, that part of Shotover Hill within the newly defined boundary remained woodland — at least officially — for the following 350 years (until disafforestation, the forest's reduced legal status to ordinary land), whereas the flatter ground outside the royal forest was some of the first land on the Hill to be hedged for agricultural purposes. For example, the hedgerows that define the fields between Brasenose Wood and Horspath village are over 400 years old and are still in place today [see page 39].

Although the royal forests were a significant source of timber, venison and revenue for the English monarchs, a preoccupation with domestic and international politics led to their widespread neglect during the Tudor and early Stuart periods. By the early 17th century Shotover Forest had become greatly reduced in area. Much of the land, especially around Headington, had been granted to local beneficiaries, and the fragmentation into agricultural and domestic uses probably rendered forest law quite inapplicable in these places. Most

notably, on the north side of the Hill, in 1613 the bailiwick of Shotover Forest was awarded to Sir Timothy Tyrell the elder (1575–1632) by James I. The reason for this award is generally thought to be compensation for a hunting accident, inflicted by the king's young son Henry, Prince of Wales, causing Tyrell to lose the use of one of his hands.

A map of *Shottover Forest in the Countie of Oxon* [opposite] surveyed by Richard Whiting shows that in 1643 the extent of the royal forest had become reduced to just over two square miles (520 hectares), less than a quarter of its extent of 1298 [see page 3 and Fig. 1]. This new survey may have been commissioned in anticipation of eventual disafforestation. In terms of current place names, the forest of 1643 encompassed Shotover Hill, Risinghurst, Littleworth and the Shotover Estate but no longer included Brasenose Wood, Magdalen Wood, Stowood, Marston and Headington. The greater part of today's Shotover Country Park, between The Plain and Brasenose Wood, and including the fields below Westhill Farm, was then a single parcel within the royal forest called Horspathe Copise. Permanent enclosure was not permitted in the royal forest; however, the boundaries of the nine 'copise' parcels on Whiting's map are shown as hedgerow or lined with trees, and most of these old forest boundaries still remain.

There is little indication of the land use within the Shotover Forest of 1643, for although

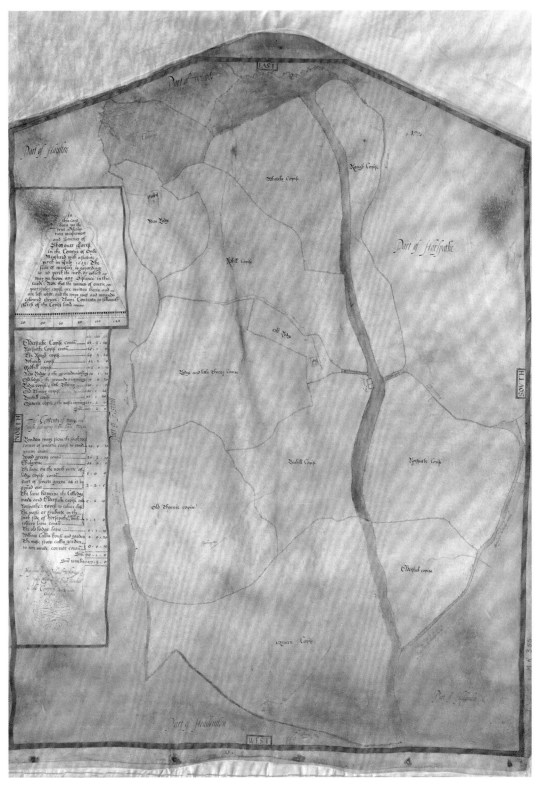

Richard Whiting's 1643 map of 'Shottover Forest' ©The National Archives, ref. MR1/355

most of the parcels are referred to as 'copise', this may not be a reliable indication of their usefulness for coppicing (whereby small woodland trees or shrubs are cut regularly to provide fuel and straight poles). Quite apart from the relatively unproductive sandy soils on the Hill, the condition of the woodland had become much degraded during the first half of the 17th century due to excessive felling (Steel, 1984; Lobel, 1957). In 1629 a survey of timber for the royal shipwrights numbered 27,000 trees at Shotover — *"some very fit for the navy"* — and the ensuing extraction would have resulted in considerable woodland clearance and waste. Also, the incumbent bailiff and 'Keeper of the Shotover Forest', Sir Timothy Tyrell the elder, was misappropriating large quantities of oak, including for the repair of the old Shotover House (Lobel, 1957).

It is clear, therefore, that even before the onset of the English Civil War in 1642, some, if not most, of Shotover woodland would have been devoid of large timbers of any quality. The cutting of small-wood would have remained an important local industry considering the high demand for wood-fuel — a valuable output for Shotover in an otherwise agricultural landscape. But finally, in 1660, after further ravages from the Civil War (in particular the siege of Oxford), an over-exploited and bedraggled Shotover was disafforested from royal forest law. About 40 per cent was awarded by the Crown to those with rights of common and the portion that remained Crown land (little more than is occupied by the Shotover Estate of today) was leased with *"the lessees being encouraged to build and plough"* (Steel, 1984: p. 16).

For 85 years after disafforestation (1660–1745) the Crown land was rented by the descendants of Sir Timothy Tyrell the elder. The grounds of Tyrell's first Shotover House (preceding the current building) were later landscaped in the 1730s, by William Kent (Mowl, 2007), and remain today as formal gardens surrounded by wood pasture (grazed land with trees). The rest of the estate was given over to the grazing of sheep and cattle, as encouraged by the landlord.

Throughout the 18th and early 19th century the Shotover Estate was a grand and important venue. The current Shotover House was completed in 1718, and in 1742 the leasehold passed by marriage to the family of Augustus Schutz (*c.* 1693–1757), a courtier of George II. Schutz bought the freehold of the estate from the Crown in 1745. With the death of Schutz's grandson Thomas in 1839 the estate passed indirectly to his cousin's family (George Drury) but by then the Tyrrell–Schutz dynasty had effectively come to an end; the Druries only occupied the estate for a further 15 years. In the three decades that followed 1839 the Shotover Estate was clearly losing money and large parts of it were sold off as separate farmsteads. By the time the greater part of the remaining estate was bought by James Miller in 1871 the preceding owner, George Gammie, had gone bankrupt.

From the late 18th century Shotover Hill began to attract eminent artists from Oxford and for the first time pictorial representations of the habitats began to appear. With the change to

Quarries at Shotover, near Oxford (c.1816) by William Turner of Oxford
©The Samuel Courtauld Trust, The Courtauld Gallery, London

Gravel Pit on Shotover Hill, near Oxford (c.1818) by
William Turner of Oxford
©Ashmolean Museum, University of Oxford

grazing, the view of Oxford from Shotover had
become unobscured by trees (unlike today) and
was a popular subject for artists. John Malchair's
Oxford from Shotover Hill, from Recollection
(1791) [see box right] is one of the earliest
depictions and, although drawn from memory,
it recalls open pasture with taller vegetation
further downhill. The striking impression from
the more detailed landscapes by William Turner
of Oxford, *Quarries at Shotover, near Oxford*
(*c.* 1816) [left] and *Gravel Pit on Shotover Hill,
near Oxford* (1818) [above], is the stark paucity
of trees on the flat plateaux of the Hill [see also
box, page 34] — no longer coppice but pasture.
All but a few large trees appear to have gone and
only the steeper ground is occupied by taller
vegetation, possibly coppice or rough grazing.
With the exception of a few discrete woodland
areas such as Brasenose and Magdalen Woods,
Shotover Hill had become a landscape with very
few mature trees.

Enclosure was awarded to 'Shotover Hill'
in 1824 and to Horspath in 1858 but little is
known of the subsequent parcelling of land after
these dates (Lobel, 1957); indeed, much was
already enclosed [see for example page 39]. In
time, therefore, under the pastoral agriculture
of the various farms, together with some arable
cropping where the soils permitted, the fields
and hedgerows of 19th-century Shotover became
established and, with a few exceptions, are much
the same today [see page x]. A few hedgerows
and small woodland copses were added in the
late 19th century and some urban expansion
occurred in the early 20th century. However, the
dominant exception is the area now occupied

by the Country Park and SSSI in which former
pastures have naturally succeeded to mixed
secondary woodland [see box, page 31].

Meanwhile, for millennia, open-cast
quarrying for clay, sand, stone and the valuable
pigments of yellow and red ochre were all
important industries on the Hill. Clay was
extracted for pottery during the Roman
occupation and the earliest known reference
to the quarrying of stone is from the early 14th
century in West Field, west of Wheatley. In 1303,
according to Wood (1890), "*as much quarry
ground called Cherlegrave in Whately parish
near Oxford that contained 100 feet in length
and as many in breadth*" was given by Edward I
to the Black Friars. However, throughout the
17th, 18th and 19th centuries mineral extraction
increased to a much larger scale than hitherto.
The number and size of quarries and work yards
during these centuries, as shown on old maps,
early photographs [see page 8] and paintings [see
pages 6 and 7], indicate that these industries and

John Malchair

Joannes Baptist Malchair (*c.* 1730–1812) was born
in Cologne, Germany, but came to England in
his mid-twenties and from 1759 was a much-
respected musician and drawing master in
Oxford. Although he visited and sketched
Shotover many times, his well-known view
of Oxford from the top of Shotover Hill was
painted when he was 61 years old and probably
experiencing the first signs of the blindness that
would accompany his final years. Nevertheless,
this was a popular and frequently painted scene
by artists at that time and Malchair produced at
least two representations from memory for his
friends (Harrison, 1998).

Oxford from Shotover Hill, from recollection (1791) by
John Malchair ©Ashmolean Museum, University of Oxford

One of the many former brick and tile works around Shotover

This 1915 photograph shows a brick yard where now the Oxford ring road passes under Old Road, Headington. The view looks north-west with, in the distance (from left to right), part of central Headington, the trees bordering Bury Knowle Park and the high ground at Elsfield.

their infrastructures would have had a significant impact on habitats overall. For example, much more bare soil would have been exposed, and local hydrology and microclimates would have been modified to a greater or lesser extent.

The second half of the 20th century witnessed sweeping structural changes in all sectors of society. Sheep grazing and mineral extraction at Shotover became unprofitable and the sloping sandy ground declined in commercial value. Also, leisure time, public access to the countryside and affordable motorized transport were all on the increase, bringing more people into the countryside for a great variety of pursuits, not all of them sympathetic to natural habitats. In the wider surrounding countryside, intensive mechanized farming, with its larger fields, heavier equipment and chemical fertilizers, created a rural environment that is considerably more hostile to much of our wildlife. It is therefore understandable that, in the mid-20th century, concern for biodiversity began to strengthen and the concept of nature reserves and wildlife conservation developed out of the 19th-century enthusiasm for the natural world (Sheail, 1998).

All of the current wildlife habitats at Shotover are a product of the land-use history. Pasture is still a major component of land area, including the many horse paddocks distributed across the Hill, beef-cattle grazing and the extensive and historic wood pasture of the Shotover Estate. The only relics of an era of royal hunting are a few very old trees, some small parcels of ancient woodland and many of the original boundaries. Commercial agriculture has removed most traces of the woodland antecedence; the exceptions are where the ground was too wet or infertile, or where active coppicing lingered on through the 20th century. Fortunately, the roads, tracks, boundary banks and hedgerows, which are so much a part of the historic landscape and wildlife ecology, have remained more or less the same for centuries.

In places new habitats have matured. The trees that have germinated in the old sheep pastures, especially in the Country Park, form a tall secondary woodland that is now many decades old. Some human habitation has been built on wildlife habitat but not to any great extent, and in many places large domestic gardens, and small ones *en masse*, make a significant ecological contribution of their own. With a few exceptions, evidence of the busy and widespread quarrying industry has disappeared; certainly, most of the infrastructure has vanished and some of the pits have been built on or have become overgrown with vegetation. The exceptions are the deep clay pits on the north-western slopes, now filled with water, which provide some of the few permanent ponds on the Hill.

Lawrence Bee, Eliza Howlett and Ivan Wright

Geology

The foundation strata

On the eastern margins of the city of Oxford, Shotover Hill rises to a height of around 170 metres above sea level. While the surrounding areas have undergone both urban and agricultural development the Hill itself has remained for the most part an oasis for wildlife, providing for a wealth of species in a variety of habitats. Although the rich biodiversity of Shotover is largely the product of its land-use history over recent centuries [see page 3], the primary foundation is the contrasting geological strata laid down during its formation, particularly during the Jurassic and Cretaceous Periods (199–66 million years ago). Throughout this time the rock strata which now make up the Hill were deposited in conditions very different from those we know today.

For long periods, southern Britain was affected by global tectonic movement and the Oxford area was submerged under various seas which differed in both extent and depth. The astrophysicist Milutin Milanković (1879–1958) argued that the periodic fluctuations in sea level during the Jurassic and Cretaceous Periods resulted from planetary positioning and changes in the Earth's axis of rotation and orbit around the Sun. These changes produce variations in the amount of solar energy reaching the Earth's surface, thus causing the long-term climatic changes that affect sea levels across the Earth. Shallow seas, such as those over the Oxford area, would be particularly sensitive to these fluctuations, influencing the fossils and rocks that we see today at Shotover.

The underlying landmass on which Shotover's Jurassic and Cretaceous strata were deposited is a bed of rock from the Devonian Period (420–360 million years ago) known as the London Platform, which extends eastward under London and Kent with the Oxford area on the western margin (Horton *et al.*, 1995: p. 3). At the beginning of the Middle Jurassic Period, about 170 million years ago, a relatively shallow sea with warm clear waters covered the present Oxford area, with part of the London Platform rising above the water to the east, the Welsh

Shotover Hill viewed from the north with Wheatley on the left (behind Red Hill) and to the right the steep slope of Fiddlestone Hill which begins the long descent into Oxford

landmass to the north-west, and the Cornubia landmass to the south-west in the modern area of Cornwall and Devon (Powell, 2005: p. 25).

Throughout the Upper Jurassic Period (166–144 million years ago) southern Britain was subjected to widely fluctuating sea levels and associated rock-forming deposits. Initially, sea levels rose dramatically by tens of metres, leaving part of the London Platform just above sea level. However, the rising waters eroded a great volume of mud away from the Platform to form the Oxford Clay — a deep stratum which now underlies Shotover and Oxford city. Then, after about 10 million years, sea levels began to rise and fall, the waters losing some of their depth overall, with alternating periods of shallow sea, off-shore coral formation and coastal lagoons; these conditions deposited, respectively, further clay, limestone and coarse sand to form the Corallian Formation. These are the lowest and oldest of the strata now exposed around the perimeter of the Hill.

Overlying the Corallian Formation is a seam of Ampthill Clay laid down about 160–155 million years ago, just as sea levels began to rise again, and spanning the transition from the Oxfordian to the Kimmeridgian stages of the Upper Jurassic Period. Superimposed on the pale-brown Ampthill Clay are the blue clays and fine sands that today make up the bulk of Shotover Hill, all of them dating from the Kimmeridgian age (155–152 million years ago). At the end of the Jurassic Period, sea levels fell away again and warm shallow lagoons developed in which corals gained dominance. These corals eventually formed the Portland Limestone beds, which contain large bivalves and ammonites. In the Lower Cretaceous Period that followed, 144–100 million years ago, continuing tectonic movements over much of the planet's surface transformed a great deal of north-west Europe into land. The Oxford area, however, was still mostly submerged under coastal seas, and coarse sand was still being deposited — the Whitchurch Sand Formation.

In brief, during the Jurassic and Lower Cretaceous Periods, conditions varied considerably at the land's surface: at times it was almost dry, while at others it was dotted with warm shallow coastal lagoons or covered with shallow seas or deep calm water. The climate, while fluctuating throughout this time, included warm tropical periods when marine flora and fauna flourished.

The formation of a hill
The rock strata at Shotover reflect the variety of sediments laid down in different marine conditions. Originally these strata would have

Figure 2 Shotover Hill in section, see section line X---X **in Fig. 3, opposite** Ivan Wright/©Crown copyright 2018 OS 100057706

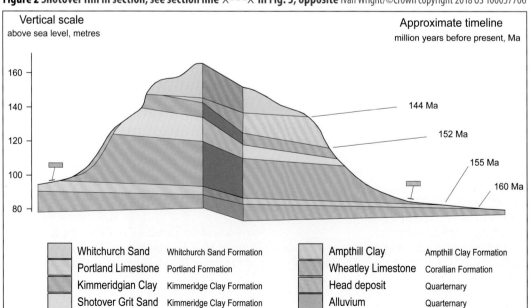

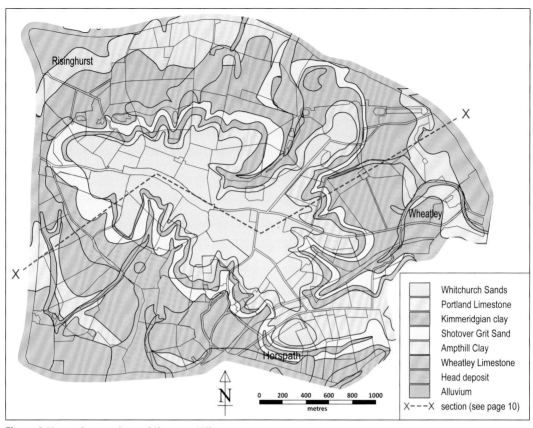

Risinghurst

Wheatley

Horspath

N

0   200   400   600   800   1000
metres

Whitchurch Sands
Portland Limestone
Kimmeridgian clay
Shotover Grit Sand
Ampthill Clay
Wheatley Limestone
Head deposit
Alluvium
X---X   section (see page 10)

Figure 3 **The surface geology of Shotover Hill** Permit Number CP16/054 British Geological Survey ©NERC 2016. All rights reserved

been vast horizontal sheets of sediment on the sea bed; however, a cross-section through Shotover Hill from west to east [see opposite, Fig. 2] would show the strata dipping towards the east. This tilting of the strata occurred during the massive movements of the planetary tectonic plates (Powell, 2005: p. 72), mostly much later in the Miocene Epoch (23–5 million years ago). The pressure of the northward-moving African Plate pushing against the Eurasian Plate, which caused the dramatic uplift of land in southern Europe that formed the Alps, produced more modest effects much farther north in southern England. Nonetheless, land surfaces were raised above the existing sea levels and the strata laid down during the Jurassic and earlier Cretaceous Periods were bowed and tilted.

Although tectonic forces played their part in raising the general ground level, the Hill itself was not formed by these movements but instead is all that remains of the sedimentary layers after the surrounding land was eroded away. At the

end of the Pleistocene Epoch (2.5 million to 12,000 years ago), as the ice of the last glaciers retreated, most of the sands and clays laid down during earlier epochs were scoured away by surging meltwater, leaving the high ground of Shotover, and Cuddesdon and Garsington to the south-east, standing in isolation on the underlying beds of Corallian limestone (including Coral Rag) and Oxford Clay. In the valley bottoms and along the lower slopes of the hill is a superficial deposit of glacially eroded material — a mixture of clay and other sediments called Head [see Fig. 3].

The Jurassic strata at Shotover
The main bulk of Shotover Hill consists of a deep stratum of the Kimmeridge Clay Formation, around 40 to 50 metres thick, which outcrops at Brasenose Wood, Risinghurst and Shotover House [see Figs. a, b and 3]. This smooth blue clay once supported a thriving local brick industry which has left traces of its quarrying

activities at ponds near Risinghurst and in the name of two roads — Kiln Lane — in Risinghurst and Wheatley. In places, these clay beds are also rich in fossils. Oyster species, for example *Deltoideum delta* and *Nanogyra virgula*, are predominant but a variety of other bivalves, as well as gastropods and ammonites, has also been discovered and many examples can be seen in the Oxford University Museum of Natural History (OUMNH).

Contained within the clay of the Kimmeridge Clay Formation is a bed of Shotover Grit Sand (more generally termed Pectinatus Sand) 10 to 20 metres deep, which separates a thin upper seam of clay from the bulk of Kimmeridgian clay beneath. This fine-grained sand outcrops all around the Hill and is most apparent at The Sandpit; it is also the stratum in which large rounded boulders, known as doggers [see box below], have formed. Many of these boulders have become exposed, either from

quarrying or from the erosion of the surrounding sand, and some of the largest have stood in the same place for centuries. Not surprisingly, individual landmark doggers — especially those with curious shapes — have attracted folk names, such as the Giant's Loaf, which has a waist like a cottage loaf. It is possible that Fiddlestone Hill [see Fig. b, page xi and map (to the left of 'Elderftub copise'), page 5] was named after a similarly waisted dogger.

Overlying the Shotover Grit Sand is the upper seam of Kimmeridgian clay (also known regionally as Swindon Clay) which is typically only a few metres thick at Shotover and situated quite high on the Hill — at its highest only 20 metres below the summit. As an impermeable layer, the Swindon Clay forms a barrier to the water that percolates through the overlying Whitchurch Sand, giving rise to the 'halo' of springs around the Hill and the critical supply of spring water for the marshes below [see page 20].

Doggers

Within the Shotover Grit Sand — and conspicuous at The Sandpit — are the large sandy boulders known as 'doggers'. The details of their formation are uncertain but, in essence, they are thought to form in the first few million years following the deposition of a sandy stratum that contains shells and shell fragments. While this mixture is still under water, the shells dissolve to produce a solution of calcium carbonate. Wherever the solution is sufficiently concentrated the calcium carbonate crystallizes back into a solid, initially on small nuclei — such as a sharp shell fragment — and thereafter preferentially on a pre-existing encrustation of crystals. As each mass grows concentrically, it incorporates the surrounding sand to form a hard, often spherical, concretion. This slow accumulation of rock is not unlike that of stalactites and stalagmites, which grow from the calcium carbonate-rich water that drips through caves — though without the incorporation of sand.

Apart from the folk names of individual stones (such as Giant's Loaf), the doggers *en masse* have attracted local names of legend such as Giants' Marbles and Matilda's Tears. The giants are supposed to have thrown the 'marbles' at each other as well as over the top of the Hill. The boulders are also said to be the fossilized tears of the Empress Matilda, daughter of Henry I. In 1141, she was in bitter dispute with her cousin Stephen over the crown of England, and was obliged to flee London to seek refuge in Oxford. When she reached Shotover Hill, so the story goes, Matilda wept tears of joy at her first sight of Oxford, and safety.

Doggers exposed by erosion at The Sandpit

Doggers recently excavated from the Shotover Grit Sand near Fiddlestone Hill

The Portland Limestone beds, deposited in lagoons at the end of the Jurassic Period, outcrop as a thin seam around most of the Hill; the exception is a short section at The Larches on the western side of the Hill, where the limestone and the Swindon Clay (Kimmeridgian) are obscured by the Cretaceous capping [see Fig. 3]. Yet although the limestone seam does not come to the surface all around the Hill, its influence can be detected on every side. For example, due to its resistance to erosion, the steepest slopes on the hillside coincide with the limestone seam, especially at Fiddlestone Hill and the track that descends into Horspath, and plants that prefer a calcareous soil — such as Beech trees — tend to be found in greater number where this stratum outcrops [see Fig. 6, page 45].

The Cretaceous capping at Shotover

Above the Portland Limestone, at the top of Shotover Hill, lies the earliest of the Cretaceous formations. The Whitchurch Sand Formation, sometimes known as Shotover Ironsand, forms a bed nearly 20 metres deep of sands, clays and ironstones, varying in colour according to

A sample of Shotover Ironsand showing a characteristic range of colours

the amount of iron oxides present, from grey or white through to yellow or dark purple. At the base of this stratum are the seams of red and yellow ochre for which Shotover has been renowned for centuries [see box, page 14].

In *The Natural History of Oxfordshire* (1677), Dr Robert Plot (1640–96), the first Keeper of the Ashmolean Museum, mentions ochre as one of the important commercial minerals of Oxfordshire. He reports that the yellow ochre at Shotover is superior to that found in other localities, such as at Garsington and near Witney, and further claims that *"it being accounted the best in its kind in the world"*. He continues: *"They dig it now at **Shotover** on the **east** side of the **Hill**, on the right hand of the way leading from **Oxford** to **Whately** . . . The **vein** dips from **East** to **West**,* and lies from seven to thirty feet in depth, and between two and seven inches thick; enwrapped it is within ten folds of **Earth**, all which must be past through before they come at it; for the **Earth** is here . . . of a **bulbous** nature, several folds of divers colours and consistencies, still including one another, not unlike the several coats of a **Tulip** root, or **Onyon**."* (Plot, 1677: p. 55–56)

Also extracted at this time, from just below the seam of best-quality ochre, were inferior red and yellow ochres which required additional processing before they could be traded as pigment. The windmill at Wheatley was

The title page of Dr Robert Plot's *The Natural History of Oxfordshire* (1677) ©OUMNH, University of Oxford

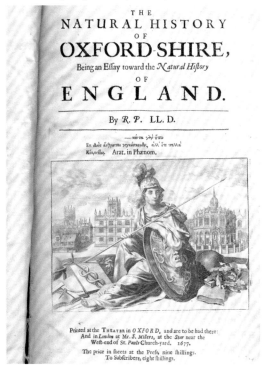

THE
NATURAL HISTORY
OF
OXFORD·SHIRE,
Being an Essay toward the Natural History
OF
ENGLAND.

By R. P. LL. D.

Εκ Διὸς ἀρχώμεσθα μεγαλήτορος, ὃν ᾽εν πολλά
Κίνωσις. Arat. in Phænom.

Printed at the THEATER in OXFORD, and are to be had there:
And in London at Mr. S. Millers, at the Star near the
West-end of St. Pauls Church-yard. 1677.
The price in sheets at the Press, nine shillings.
To Subscribers, eight shillings.

---

* Plot's description of the dip in the ochre vein might seem erroneous, given the overall west–east declination of strata on the Hill [see page 11] but local variation in the folds of strata is not uncommon [see for example Turner's painting of a gravel pit on page 7].

converted for such work in later years and an auxiliary drive from within the mill powered an external grinder; the machinery was still in place on the south side of the mill in 1907.

The post-glacial deposits at Shotover

The post-glacial Head deposit at Shotover is a mixture of clayey sand and clay with poor permeability and is generally associated with damp ground. It occurs on the lower slopes of the Hill, especially on the south-western side, underlying The Ridings and the meadows below Westhill Farm [see Fig. 3]. Much of the deposit obscures the lower spring line [see page 20] and creates a confused distribution of springs and marshy flushes. The Head material also fills the

Ochre

Natural ochres occur in many forms but all are chemical derivatives of iron oxide and have been used as a rich yellow or brown pigment for millennia — including in the Palaeolithic cave paintings of Lascaux in France. Some of the purest and most valued ochres are produced by 'supergene enrichment', a natural process in which minerals in one layer of rock are dissolved and are then washed down and accumulate in a lower stratum of different rock. At Shotover the highest-quality ochre has been formed in this way: over time, oxides of iron have been washed down from the orange sand of the Whitchurch Sand Formation that caps the Hill and have stained the fine white clay lying several metres beneath.

This most useful mineral in its purest form requires little preparation for immediate use as a water colour pigment and, after heating, produces a continuum of warm colours, from its natural golden yellow through to orange and brown to deep purple.

Pieces of ochre from Horseshoe Field

A study of pigment ochre by Nicola Montalto (2010), which included samples from Shotover, Norfolk, Cyprus and India, analyzed the chemical composition of four different samples of Shotover ochre — each from a different location on the Hill. The samples were selected for their yellow colour, fine-grained texture and staining qualities. Although the chemical composition of the four samples varied significantly, the concentration of iron oxide in two of them (as goethite, $FeO(OH)$) was higher than any other ochre sampled in the study. Montalto has suggested (2008, pers. comm.) that after more than 300 years, Plot's bold claim for the superior quality of Shotover's natural ochre [see page 13] may still be true today.

A range of colours from a single piece of yellow ochre, shown here powdered, heat treated and ready for making into paint ('Fun with Geology' Shotover Wildlife 2006)

From rock to paint in 15 minutes (also note the plaster sprocket freshly cast using sand from The Sandpit) ('Fun with Geology' Shotover Wildlife 2006)

steeper valleys of the Hill, thereby supporting the flower-rich marshes and streams of Long Marsh, Holme Ground, Long Bog and The Spinney.

Fossils and geological history
Discovering Shotover's strata
Fossils are a fascinating link with the distant past and have been collected and studied at Shotover for more than 300 years. The identification of fossils underpins the study of geology and helps untangle the riddle posed by the rocks under our feet. Indeed, the petrified remains of ancient plants and animals are indispensable for understanding the sequence and circumstances of rock formation.

Probably the earliest description of the strata at Shotover was that published in Plot's *The Natural History of Oxfordshire* (1677: p. 56). This was revisited by John Pointer, Chaplain of Merton College Oxford from 1693 to 1732, in the manuscript catalogue of his 'Museum Pointerianum' transcribed in Robert Gunther's *Early Science in Oxford* (1925: p. 495–6). The catalogue lists the *"21 Stratum of Layers of Earth, Sand, & Shells, to be passd thro' before you come to the Oker"* — 11 more subdivisions than Plot's 10 [see page 13]. Remarkably, Pointer's 21 associated rock samples, probably collected around 1720, are still in existence. Having been bequeathed to St John's College Oxford in 1754, they were rescued from the dirt of a cellar by Gunther in 1924, and have been on loan to Oxford's Museum of the History of Science ever since. They are described in Walker's *The Natural History of the Oxford District* (1926: p. 334) as *"the oldest stratigraphical collection in the world"*, though whether this is strictly true is open to debate. The series of rock samples is certainly one of the earliest to document the order of strata but we have no way of knowing whether Pointer understood that the order related to geological time rather than the contemporary competing explanation of gravitational settling following the biblical Deluge.

Between 1800 and 1805, the eminent geological surveyor William Smith mapped the sandy hills that run along the north side of the London Basin, including Shotover Hill. He associated their strata with the ironsands of Wiltshire, Kent and Sussex, and on his 1815 map — the first geological map of England

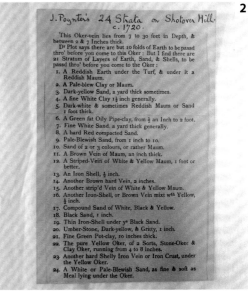

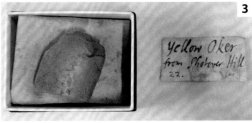

Rescued from an Oxford cellar in 1924, 'This is perhaps the oldest stratigraphical collection now extant' (Gunther, 1925). (1) Pointer's 300-year-old collection of Shotover rock samples in sequence (fifth to seventh columns in the drawer). (2) Pointer's annotations transcribed by Gunther. (3) Shotover ochre with Pointer's original label
Ivan Wright. Reproduced courtesy of the Museum of the History of Science, University of Oxford

and Wales — he placed them chronologically between the Portland rocks and the younger Gault Clay. The rest of the 19th century saw further work devoted to understanding the complex stratification at Shotover. William Fitton published an early description of the upper layers of the Hill (Fitton, 1836: p. 274–5, 277–8), followed by a more extensive account by John Phillips (nephew of William Smith, and first Curator of the Oxford University Museum of Natural History), which included a description of the deeper beds of Oxford Clay that had been exposed by the railway cutting at Horspath (Phillips, 1871: p. 412–4).

C. J. Bayzand's 1926 generalized vertical section of the geology of Shotover ©OUMNH, University of Oxford

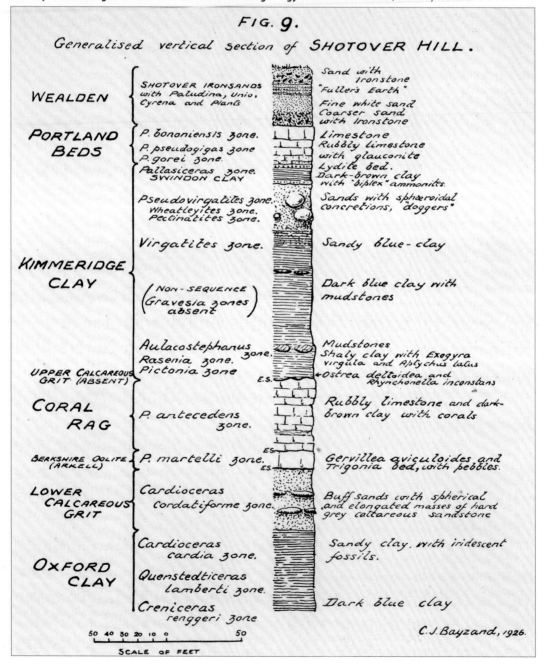

Meticulous study of Shotover's strata continued in the early 20th century with W.J. Sollas (Professor of Geology at Oxford from 1897 to 1936) and C.J. Bayzand (University Demonstrator in Geology from 1920 to 1948). Their work, including a generalized vertical section [opposite], was published as part of a chapter on the Jurassic System in Walker's *The Natural History of the Oxford District* (1926: p. 48), and some of Bayzand's photos of Shotover are preserved in the archives of the Oxford University Museum of Natural History. Some 20 years later, at a time when many of the quarries at Shotover were closing, W.J. Arkell redescribed the succession of strata in *The Geology of Oxford* (1947: p. 102–33). He listed Kimmeridgian beds at the Shotover brickworks [see pages x and 8] at the west end of Shotover; Corallian beds in the old quarries below the brickworks; Portlandian beds in the sandpits above the brickworks and on either side of the old coach road over Shotover Hill; and ironsand and ochre in the old ochre pits on the Shotover Estate. The most recent and comprehensive description of the stratification at Shotover is given by Horton *et al.* (1995).

Shotover fossils

Wherever minerals are quarried there is always the prospect of finding new fossils, each adding to our knowledge of life on Earth in the distant past, and the quarrying around Shotover is no exception.

The earliest fossils to be recorded from the area were those described by Plot (1677) and included corals (described as *Astroites*, *Echinites minutus* or the roots of plants), bivalves (*Trichites*, *Ostracites* and Escallop-stones), serpulids (Worm-stones) and a gastropod (Snail-stone), all found in rubblestone quarries in the Wheatley Limestone at the foot of the Hill. Plot also referred to huge concretions (*Orchites*) in the ironsands on the western side of the Hill, which he described as being shaped like giant pairs of testicles and in one case a foot. The 'foot' is pictured in Plot's Table VIII [above] along with an example of 'testicles' from west Oxfordshire (now recognized to be part of a thigh bone of the dinosaur *Megalosaurus*). Notwithstanding Plot's simple biomorphic descriptions, he did realise that the Shotover concretions were not petrified body parts but naturally formed stones. Plot's successor as Keeper of the

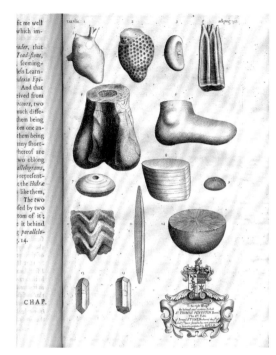

The earliest fossils recorded from Shotover include the 'foot' (6) illustrated by Plot (1677) together with the end of a dinosaur thigh bone (4) similar to that found at Shotover ©OUMNH, University of Oxford

Ashmolean Museum, Edward Lhwyd, kept up the tradition of collecting at Shotover, and his book *Lithophylacii Britannici Ichnographia* (1699) described minerals and fossils in the Ashmolean collections, including two of the Shotover corals illustrated in Plot (1677) and a piece of fossil wood (*Xylosteon*).

Many more Shotover specimens are listed in a catalogue of fossils presented to the Ashmolean in 1765 by Joshua Platt. The distance science had travelled since 1677 is apparent from the more advanced descriptions of some of the finds: "*The lower Valve of an Oister odly formed by adhering to some other Subject*", "*A mass of large Vertebrae of a Fish*", "*Tibia or Shinbone of the Hippopotamus*". However, as all these specimens came from the Kimmeridgian clay, the Hippopotamus shinbone is more likely to be some element of a Pliosaur, a large marine reptile typical of the Kimmeridgian Age. The manuscript catalogue is transcribed in MacGregor *et al.* (2000: p. 229–38).

In the 19th century, William Buckland (Reader in Geology at Oxford from 1819 to 1856) also collected fossils at Shotover and would

A lithograph depicting one of William Buckland's excursions to Shotover to teach geology and collect fossils
©OUMNH, University of Oxford

Buckland can be seen on horseback pointing towards Oxford with the aid of a large bone. Reproduced in Elizabeth Gordon's *The Life and Correspondence of William Buckland* (1894).

often go out on horseback to lead his students on excursions to the Hill. According to his daughter Elizabeth, Buckland "*delighted in giving a new class of equestrian listeners a practical lesson in geology, by sticking them all in the mud to remember the Kimmeridge clay*" (Gordon, 1894). The Buckland collection in the Oxford University Museum of Natural History contains several specimens from Shotover, including a skull of the marine crocodile *Metriorhynchus palpebrosus* from the Kimmeridgian clay (Buckland, 1836).

Not all Shotover fossils have come from the clay. Around 1833, the Revd. Harry Jelly was the first to notice and collect small fossil shells from the Whitchurch Sand Formation, and these were attributed by Hugh Strickland — later to become Buckland's deputy — to the freshwater gastropod *Paludina* (now known as *Viviparus*). After much searching, Strickland himself found a remarkable specimen of the bivalve *Unio* in the ochre-rich sands near the summit of the Hill, also preserved in the Oxford University Museum of Natural History. In 1853 Strickland was tragically killed by a train while examining a railway cutting in Nottinghamshire, and John Phillips was appointed Deputy Reader in Geology in his place. The following year Phillips took his class of students to Shotover "*and engaged 30 or 40 busy hands to renew the search in the ironsands*" (Phillips, 1871: p. 412). This approach clearly paid off: over several trips the class collected a small

number of bivalves and gastropods and a great deal of fossilized wood. Phillips also acquired material from the Kimmeridgian clay, including a pelvic bone of a Pliosaur in 1858. Phillips describes Jelly's work at Shotover, as well as his own, in *Geology of Oxford and the Valley of the Thames* (Phillips, 1871).

More extensive collections from Shotover were put together by the antiquarian bookseller James Parker between 1854 and 1884. Parker's collection, now in the Oxford University Museum of Natural History, contains around 400 Shotover fossils, many with details of the site where they were found, such as Pether's Pit, Shotover Kiln Pit and Hedges' Large Pit (all in the Kimmeridgian clay). The collection contains numerous Pliosaur bones, including a skull of *Liopleurodon* collected from Coppock's Pit around 1872. Parker's daybooks, which accompany the collection, describe his own excursions to Shotover and his purchases from local collectors, named in the books as "*Old Man (Jones)*", "*Best*" and "*Mr Wood*".

All the clay- and sand-pit workings at Shotover are now closed, which means that new fossils are rarely found, but the historic collections continue to attract significant research interest. The crocodile skull described by Buckland in 1836 was recognized by John Phillips as a new species, which he called *Stenosaurus palpebrosus* (Phillips, 1871: p. 319), denoting the Shotover skull as the holotype

In 1871 the skull was recognised as the defining specimen of a hitherto unknown species.

specimen — that is, the specimen on which the species description is based. The skull has been referred to by numerous authors under the name of *Metriorhynchus palpebrosus*, including Woodward (1885) and Grange and Benton (1996). More recently, Mark Young published a description of five teeth of the marine crocodile *Dakosaurus* from the Kimmeridgian clay of Shotover, the earliest known occurrence of this genus (Young *et al.*, 2014), and re-examination of other historic material may well reveal further hidden treasures.

Hydrology

Although the movement of water in and around Shotover is rather complex, the overall hydrology of the Hill is relatively straightforward, as the Hill rests upon a foundation of impermeable clay and no streams or rivers enter the region. The water balance of the Hill is, therefore, a well-defined system, and since it amounts to only a few square kilometres of small valleys and streams, human intervention can have a significant influence. For this reason, not only is hydrology a key determinant of the ecology

The dam at Long Marsh was restored by Shotover Wildlife in 2001 and then raised in 2017

of the Hill but it is also possible, intentionally or inadvertently, to change local wetness radically, meaning that the balance of water flow is an important consideration in wildlife conservation.

Almost all of the water input to Shotover arrives as precipitation. The only exceptions are infrequent leaks and discharges from the reservoirs and their supply pipes, the effects of which are negligible overall but can be locally significant. Water can only leave the Hill by stream flow or evaporation because the underlying clay prevents any loss by downward percolation to deeper water-bearing rocks, and any extraction from the remaining private wells on the Hill is likely to be insignificant. Apart from water extracted by plant roots, all the precipitation and runoff that infiltrates the sandy soils will reappear further down the Hill — often at a spring — wherever the percolating water meets a seam of impermeable clay.

Shotover is capped with 250 hectares of porous Whitchurch Sand and Portland Limestone [see Fig. 2, page 10]. Generally, water percolates readily into this topmost stratum, and only flows over the surface during the heaviest rain. However, as the cap is nowhere more than 30 metres deep the percolated water is forced to emerge, still quite high on the Hill, at the next stratum down — a seam of Kimmeridgian clay (the Swindon Clay, see page 12). The interfacing of these two strata, therefore, forms a halo of springs, marshes and flushes around the Hill which include the majority of spring water outlets, including those in the Country Park and the Shotover Estate. Since the geological strata tilt downwards to the east, by far the fastest-flowing springs emerge on the eastern side of the Hill between Horspath and Littleworth.

Underlying the seam of Kimmeridgian clay, and extending out some distance from it in most places, is a further 150 hectares of porous sandy soil (Shotover Grit Sand, see page 12). Since the overlying seam of clay is mostly only one or two metres deep, water from many of the slower-flowing springs above the clay soon re-enters the sandy ground [see below], especially in the summer. Further down the Hill, the next layer of Kimmeridgian clay creates a second spring line; the water flowing out here is a combination of direct precipitation on the Shotover Grit Sand and the water that re-entered the ground from

One of the strongest-flowing springs rises east of The Piggery and flows towards Wheatley

Spring water in Johnson's Piece re-entering the ground where the Kimmeridgian clay meets the Shotover Grit Sand

the upper spring line. These springs are less numerous, and are found in the Shotover Estate and the C.S. Lewis Community Nature Reserve and around Spring Lane in Horspath.

On the west side of Shotover the upper seam of Kimmeridgian clay does not outcrop at the surface, and so the upper spring line disappears for about 400 metres [see Fig. 3, page 11]. Much of the precipitation that enters the ground on Mary Sadler Field and The Larches does not return to the surface until it reaches the clay of Magdalen Wood, which accounts for the large wet flush just west of The Ridings. This juxtaposition of two porous sandy strata may also account for the strength of the springs in the C.S. Lewis Community Nature Reserve and the dampness of Tews Ground.

Once flowing water has reached the flatter ground around Shotover, it is channelled by a network of ditches and permanent streams that drain away from the Hill in three different directions. Water from the southern side joins the River Thames at Sandford-on-Thames via Littlemore Brook; about half of this flow reaches Littlemore Brook via Hollow Brook and Northfield Brook south of Horspath, and the rest — from the direction of Brasenose Wood — is piped under the Cowley motor works and Blackbird Leys. Most of the northern flow from

the Hill goes to the River Cherwell at Marston via Bayswater Brook, and the strong flow from the springs to the east is piped through Wheatley and eventually reaches the Thames at Dorchester via the River Thame.

The final component in the hydrological balance is evaporation — a flow of water that is often overlooked and underappreciated. At Shotover in particular, evaporation plays a key role in the overall water balance of the Hill. With the exception of the brief periods when dew is forming (condensation), all damp surfaces return water to the atmosphere by evaporation. Also, vascular plants draw up water by their roots and return it to the atmosphere as transpiration from their leaves.

The impact of evaporation and transpiration of water from trees is particularly significant. Firstly, when wet, these large branching structures can evaporate water at a much greater rate than shorter vegetation, even during rainfall. During some light showers on woodland, all the rain can be returned to the atmosphere without reaching the soil, playing no part in the water balance at the ground. Secondly, trees reach deep into the soil for their water, and as a result of transpiration during daylight hours they extract large quantities of water from depths that many other plants cannot reach.

Measuring spring flow in Johnson's Piece

A pipe has been installed temporarily to intercept the flow of spring water and the flow-rate is measured with the aid of a jug and stopwatch.

Essential tree clearance to maintain the wetness of Long Marsh

The winter trampling of the wetland soil also benefits some of the scarcer wetland plants [see page 76].

Average monthly rainfall in Oxfordshire does not vary greatly throughout the year (plus or minus 15 per cent from the annual mean). Also, measurements of spring flow [see page 21] at the faster-flowing springs on the Hill have shown little seasonal variation, notwithstanding the relatively small area of the permeable cap of Whitchurch Sand from which they emerge. In contrast, evaporation (including plant transpiration) is by far the most widely fluctuating flow of water through the seasons: it amounts to less than half the precipitation in the winter and, at times, double the rainfall in the summer (Wright and Wright, 2000: p. 9). In wooded areas in summer, therefore, trees draw the water they need from that stored in the soil, and stream channels become dry. Typically, in the Country Park streams flow freely over their full length in the winter but as soon as leaves mature on the deciduous trees, spring flow either stops at the source or, more usually, only manages to travel a short distance before re-entering the soil [see page 20]. In earlier centuries, at times when tree cover was much patchier than today, the marshes would have been much wetter and the streams would probably have flowed off the Hill for most of the year.

An appreciation of the hydrological factors that determine the balance of water movements on the Hill is critical for understanding the conservation needs of its streams and marshes. Unlike many wetland sites, the hydrology at Shotover — restricted by a bed of impermeable clay — makes it possible to manage wetness by controlling the vegetation structure. For example, in the SSSI, marsh wetness could be increased by reducing tree cover but without due care this intervention could also compromise tree and woodland ecology. Also, water infiltration into the 400 hectares of sandy soils on the Hill is the lifeblood of all spring flow. Any development that added a substantial area of impermeable surface, such as buildings, concrete and tarmac, would reduce percolation and increase water loss by runoff.

Soils
Soil formation and classification

Soils are a product of the reduction of rock to fine particles combined with the influences of chemical metamorphosis over millennia and the organic input from animals and plants. Although their formation has been a relatively slow process, compared to their geological parent material the soils are relatively young. Almost all soils in Britain have developed since the retreat of the northern ice sheet at the end of the most recent ice age, 10,000 years ago.

The classification of soil types can be rather confusing. In reality, neighbouring soils merge smoothly into one another with no clear boundaries between them, yet it is possible to define and describe typical soils based on how the mineral structure has developed over time.

More recently, cultivation, drainage, fertilizers and quarrying have all added to the confusion but, fortunately, at Shotover these factors have generally played a rather limited role, and the Hill still retains a suite of stable soils that conform to standard classification.

The soils of Shotover

The following account is based on an extensive survey of the soils of Shotover Country Park in 1997 by Katrin Hochberg, a visiting student from Eberswalde University, Germany. The survey augered — by hand — about 200 samples to a depth of at least one metre, and recorded soil texture, colour and acidity. Shotover Wildlife has since supplemented this work with extensive measurements of acidity using a calibrated pH meter.

Considering the intricate and varied underlying geology at Shotover [see page 9] and the erosion and downhill drift of surface material over time, it might be expected that the soils of the Hill are similarly diverse. Although this is true in places, especially at the top of the Hill, mixing and merging over time have brought a measure of homogeneity rather than complexity, and it is the long-term influence of ground water and the consequent amount of aeration (specifically oxygen) that is now the defining cause of the difference between many of the soils. Nevertheless, it is the mineral origins that account for the two over-arching principal types of soil on the Hill: those that are sandy and drain freely and those that are mostly clay and relatively impermeable.

The sandy acidic soils that are typical of the upper part of Shotover Hill, along with their Cretaceous and Jurassic parent material, are not common in Oxfordshire and are the basis of the associated regionally scarce habitats. In the British classification of soils (Avery, 1980) these free-draining soils fall within two general types, Brown Sands and Brown Earths, both of which are further divided depending on whether or not the soil displays poor aeration in the form of 'gleying' [see box, page 24]. The clay soils on the flatter ground around the Hill are also divided into two types, depending upon whether they have been intermittently or more permanently saturated.

Six standard classifications of soil type can be used to describe the majority of soils on Shotover Hill. These occur approximately in descending order from the summit, as follows:

- Typical Brown Earth and Typical Brown Sand, capping most of the Hill
- Gleyic Brown Earth and Gleyic Brown Sand at mid-slope, associated with the spring lines and marshes
- Ground-water Gley and Surface-water Gley under the permanent marshes, the fields and the flatter poorly drained ground.

An example of the complexity of Shotover soils, from stony Brown Sand (left) to a fine white sand (right)

This excavation was created on Horspath Common to benefit soil-nesting invertebrates.

A deep profile of Typical Brown Sand formed on the Whitchurch Sand that caps the Hill

A more unusual profile in the Whitchurch Sand Formation, with Bracken roots protruding from a thin layer of Brown Sand overlying a fine white sand

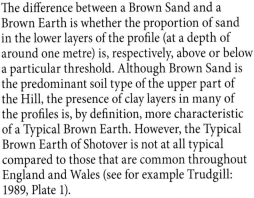

The difference between a Brown Sand and a Brown Earth is whether the proportion of sand in the lower layers of the profile (at a depth of around one metre) is, respectively, above or below a particular threshold. Although Brown Sand is the predominant soil type of the upper part of the Hill, the presence of clay layers in many of the profiles is, by definition, more characteristic of a Typical Brown Earth. However, the Typical Brown Earth of Shotover is not at all typical compared to those that are common throughout England and Wales (see for example Trudgill: 1989, Plate 1).

In general, Brown Sand covers the whole of The Plain and most of Mary Sadler Field and Horseshoe Field; it also occurs on the higher elevations of Sandpit Field, Johnson's Piece and Horspath Common, and wherever the Shotover Grit Sand outcrops in these fields. Typical Brown Sand is less extensive and tends to occur on the lower slopes of the Shotover Grit Sand, merging into Gleyic Brown Sand towards the fringes of the valley marshes. The Typical Brown Earth peculiar to the Hill — actually, as noted above, a Typical Brown Sand with a significant proportion of clay in its lower layers — can be found in all the fields where Brown Sand exists. Gleyic Brown Earth occurs at the upper spring line, in the valley marshes and at the upper end of Long Marsh in Johnson's Piece.

All the soils formed in the valleys on glacial Head are permanently waterlogged for most of their depth and all exhibit the typical blue-grey profiles for a Ground-water Gley. They are found in the lower marshy areas of The Larches and to the east of Horspath Common, as well as in Long Marsh and Holme Ground, and at both of their associated stream lines.

The soils of Brasenose Wood, Magdalen Wood and the flatter areas of poorly draining clay around the Hill — such as The Meadow and Lower Close — are Surface-water Gleys. The soil profile is usually strongly mottled orange-and-blue for the first 40–60 centimetres followed by blue clay. Some of the sample cores from Brasenose Wood also show clearly defined layers of sedimented sand, while others have beds of ironstone fragments; both sand and ironstone originate from the younger Cretaceous strata higher on the Hill.

Gley soils and gleying

Gleying is a chemical and microbial process that occurs in soils where the movement of air in the pore spaces (aeration) is restricted or eliminated by water saturation. In the resulting absence of oxygen, anaerobic bacteria multiply and mottle the soil with orange or blue blotches depending upon the iron content of the soil [see picture opposite]. In predominantly waterlogged conditions the soil becomes entirely grey or blue. The form and colour of the gleying of a soil indicate its past chemistry and bacterial activity and are used to define and describe many different types of soil.

Soil acidity

An important feature of some of the habitats at Shotover is the strong acidity of their soils, which provides a niche for certain extremophile species. This acidity is maintained naturally by a combination of soil chemistry and soil structure — the latter allowing water to pass easily through the soil. Chemical compounds that would normally balance acidity are soluble in acidic conditions and so are leached from the soil, along with plant nutrients, by the flow of percolating rain water. Therefore, the sandy soils at Shotover are both acidic and relatively infertile.

The most acidic of soils are the Typical Brown Earths, with an average pH of 4.5 (4.0–5.5) throughout most of the profile, and typically with a pH of 5.0 at a depth of one metre or more. Gleyic Brown Earths are wetter and the degree of acidity is generally lower, with an average pH greater than 5.0 at all but the shallowest depths. At about 10 centimetres in both of these soils, Shotover's soil acidity is at its most extreme. In Mary Sadler Field, a pH of less than 4.0 is fairly common and the most acidic sample ever measured was from the Horspath Common

Grassland Habitat Project [see box, page 98], with a pH of 2.8.

The Typical Brown Sands and Gleyic Brown Sands are similarly acidic to a depth of about 50 centimetres, with a typical pH of 5.5. Below this depth the acidities diverge, with the wetter gleyed soils having a pH of about 6.0 and the dryer Brown Earths a little more acidic, with a pH of 5.0–5.5. The least acidic soils that have been sampled on the upper part of the Hill are the Ground-water Gleys in the valley marshes, with a mildly acidic pH of 6.0. The near-surface samples from these profiles showed a very wide range of acidity.

Most of the Surface-water Gleys of Brasenose Wood are only mildly acidic, having a pH of between 6.0 and 6.5 at all but the shallowest depths. Some alkalinity (with pH measurements of 7.0–8.0) has been recorded in places, mostly in the southern corner of the woodland, which may be due to a calcareous influence from the nearby Coral Rag (Wheatley Limestone). Although this tendency towards an alkaline soil is not indicated in the vascular flora at this corner of Brasenose Wood, it is clearly evident in the mosses.

A profile of sandy clay in Brasenose Wood showing the orange and green of contrasting anaerobic conditions
Katrin Hochberg

The valley marshes of Johnson's Piece and Bottom Ground are perched on a mildly acidic Ground-water Gley

Jacqueline Wright, Ivan Wright and Lawrence Bee

One of the pleasures of visiting — and re-visiting — Shotover Hill is the immense variety of changing natural landscapes. The hilliness is a great asset, with fine views of the Oxfordshire countryside, but closer at hand is the intricate mosaic of shady woodland, secluded marshes, open grass and flower-rich meadows. The Hill's diverse and finely multi-layered geology [see page 9] means that no single habitat is particularly extensive and, by walking different routes throughout the changing seasons, the adventurous visitor has the pleasure of ever-changing surroundings, enjoying a different experience with every visit.

In just half an hour one can cross the open grassland at the top of the Hill, descend through the old trees of Johnson's Piece to Long Marsh, and pass by the hay meadows at Westhill Farm to reach the ancient woodland of Brasenose Wood. Then, for a further 30 minutes, one can follow the old hedges and boundary banks of the Royal Forest of Shotover to Horspath Common, ascend the Hill through open heathy areas and return to the summit along The Plain — the old road to London.

In his seminal book *The British Isles and their Vegetation* (1953), the eminent botanist Sir Arthur Tansley defined habitats as "*units*

Strolling through Brasenose Wood on the old byway from Horspath to Headington

of space, including their interacting organisms, such that discrete units may be distinguished from one another". Although the transition between neighbouring habitat units can be gradual and the boundary difficult to define,

The countryside east of Shotover, overlooking Oxfordshire and Buckinghamshire

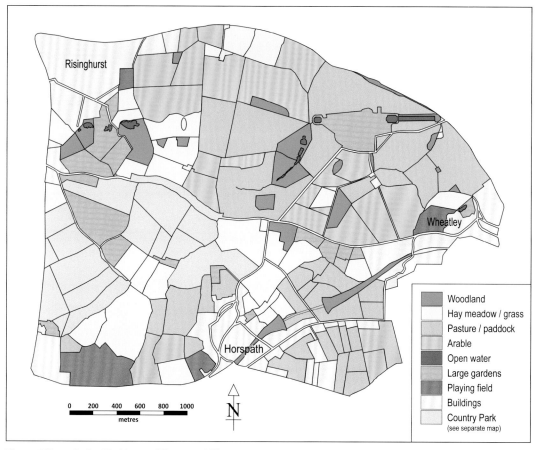

Figure 4 The principal habitats of Shotover Hill Ivan Wright/©Crown copyright 2018 OS 100057706

their classification does allow a common understanding of a number of discrete and definable habitat types. In some cases a plant species will define the structure and ecology of the habitat type, as heather defines heathland. More often the predominant vegetation will define the habitat (for example, woodland, grassland) but this is not always the case, as in marsh or parkland, and consequently a simple categorization can be inadequate.

Natural habitat types originate from a combination of relatively permanent factors such as geology, altitude or slope but may be modified by the presence of water or a particular soil type. Thereafter, the habitat reflects its land-use history, both ancient and recent. Most of Shotover Hill is still covered by distinctly definable habitats, such as woodland, pasture and arable land [see Fig. 4], which have their origins in the management for a specific product: respectively timber, livestock

and crops. The distribution of meadows, pastures and arable fields is largely attributable to the past and current agricultural preferences of the landowners. However, towards the summit of the Hill the dry and less fertile land would not have been particularly productive in past centuries, and in many places has escaped agricultural modification by, for example, ploughing or the application of fertilizer. In such places a natural diversity of flora and fauna is able to persist and flourish. In the latter half of the 20th century, species-rich habitats in Britain became better appreciated and protected (Sheail, 1998), and so it is not surprising that a substantial part of the unproductive south side of Shotover Hill became recognized in 1986 as a Site of Special Scientific Interest (SSSI).

Thus, the various habitats in the SSSI [see Fig. 5] have been able to remain in a natural state as befits their geology, hydrology and history of

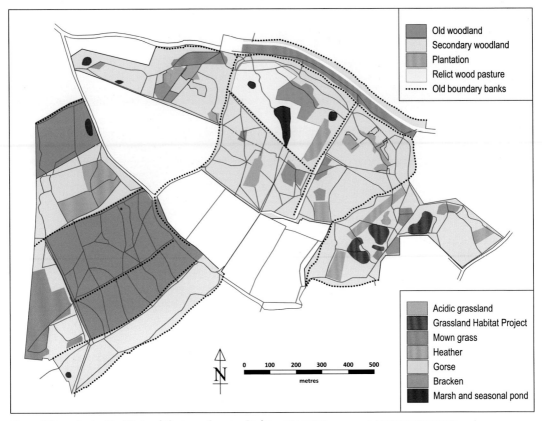

Figure 5 The principal habitats of Shotover Country Park Ivan Wright/©Crown copyright 2018 OS 100057706

land-use management. The acidic grassland is necessarily restricted to the dry sandy areas towards the top of the Hill, and the wetlands and ponds to the valleys below the spring line. The mature woodlands lie on the heavier clay soils at the foot of the Hill, interspersed with permanent hay meadows. Of these semi-natural habitats, some are stable and require little or no intervention for their wildlife conservation. Others are relatively unstable, especially where a past land-use is no longer practised, and require intervention to conserve a particular wildlife interest (for example, heath and coppice woodland).

Every habitat interacts with its neighbours, and a most important feature of an intricate patchwork — such as at Shotover — is that the ecology of the whole is much more than the sum of its individual habitats. Not only are certain plants and animals specifically associated with each habitat but there are also mobile species that utilise, or even depend upon, the juxtaposition of contrasting environments. Examples of these at Shotover are Grass Snake *Natrix natrix*,

Common Toad *Bufo bufo* and the many species of invertebrate that nest, breed and feed across a range of different habitats. On a wider scale, Shotover Hill connects to the surrounding rural landscape, at least in most directions, to the benefit of those species whose movements are not impeded by obstacles such as roads or fields of monoculture cropping.

Today in lowland Britain many richly diverse habitats are reduced and fragmented into small conservation sites set in an expansive and relatively barren landscape. Much of this landscape is dissected by wide and busy roads (some lit throughout the night) which impose an impenetrable barrier for some species. For Shotover, the conurbation of Oxford to the west and the dual-carriageway roads that border the Hill to the north and west greatly hinder the movement of wildlife, especially in Brasenose Wood which is constricted by the adjacent Oxford ring road. Even the agricultural landscape to the east and south will constrain the movement of some species. For example, there

Oak standards and coppiced Hazel in Brasenose Wood

is a real threat of local extinction for reptiles whose confined and isolated populations are particularly vulnerable. Wildlife corridors and interconnecting habitats that could link the reptile habitat of Shotover to other similar sites (Sydlings Copse four kilometres to the north and Frilford Heath 15 kilometres south-west) have been whittled down by urban development.

Woodland

The first impression that the visitor has as they wander through Shotover is of a predominantly wooded landscape. Trees seem to be growing everywhere and the name 'Royal Forest of Shotover' seems particularly apt. However, during the 500 years of Forest Law administration, from the Norman to the Tudor period, the term 'forest' meant more than woodland for hunting, and included clearings and tracts of open land where the 'chase' could take place. In more recent centuries, these great hunting forests have been dissected and reduced by agriculture to leave only small remnant

woodlands. Yet in places a few of the original trees are fortunately still standing and it is possible therefore that these ancient trees could be 1,000 years old [see also page 3].

Brasenose Wood, on the lower south-western slopes of Shotover Hill, dates back to about 1200

Ancient woodland

Ancient woodland in Britain is defined as an area of habitat where there has been a continuity of mature tree cover since before 1600. Although the trees themselves may not have reached an age of 400 years, a typical native flora develops naturally over the centuries and contributes to a characteristic ancient ecosystem. There are many plants which, having poor powers of dispersal, are only found in ancient woodland as well as a suite of fungi and invertebrates which if found in a woodland habitat are regarded as indicators of its great age. In fact, there are instances where a survey of beetles at a site has inspired further historical research, and has gone on to confirm that the woodland is much older than was first thought.

Although Magdalen Wood has a limited ground flora, the tree canopy and dead wood are rich in invertebrates

The relict wood pasture in Johnson's Piece

and is more than old enough to be classed as ancient woodland [see box, page 29]. Even though very few trees are older than 250 years the ecological value of this woodland is of particular significance. The habitat type is described as 'coppice with standards' and is a management regime dating from medieval times. For millennia, wood has been a valuable commodity for everyday life and places such as Brasenose Wood will have been intensively managed, by coppicing, to provide small-diameter timber for buildings, fences and carts, as well as fuel for heating and cooking [see also box, page 224]. Scattered throughout the coppiced hazel would be tall single-trunked trees ('standards') — predominantly Pedunculate Oak *Quercus robur* at Brasenose Wood — which were managed to produce the large timbers necessary for beams, roof trusses and ships. This management regime can still be seen in ancient woodlands today where 'conservation coppicing' occurs, even though the woodland products are no longer in such demand. By creating a range of differing light levels in the woodland ecosystem, coppice rotation can be a valuable management tool to maintain and encourage a particular biological diversity.

However, coppicing does have its shortcomings and is not necessarily desirable throughout an entire woodland. By its very nature, regular and severe cutting of the understorey, with the accompanying tree felling and 'tidying up', is clearly detrimental to those organisms that require stability and moisture, such as invertebrates and bryophytes (mosses and liverworts). Also, if wood is cleared away or

burned as part of the coppicing process, habitat for those organisms that require dead and rotting wood can be greatly reduced and species lost [see page 32].

Magdalen Wood, to the north-west of Brasenose Wood and now bisected by the Oxford ring road, has been mapped as woodland since 1780 and retains evidence of having been managed as 'coppice with standards'. Its old name of Open Magdalen suggests that it may have been a driftway or drover's track before the 18th century and therefore cannot be termed 'ancient woodland' in the strictest sense. The cessation of coppicing, probably in the early 20th century, is very evident in the eastern half of the wood and the decades of low light levels under the trees have resulted in very little ground flora. Even so, this part of the woodland has matured to a stable habitat with undisturbed standing dead wood and a rich upper-canopy insect fauna. Some of the flora and fauna would suggest a much older woodland but this may be due to the close proximity of Brasenose Wood.

On the upper slopes of Shotover Hill is one of the oldest areas of woodland to be found on the more sandy soils — Johnson's Piece. Here the infertile sloping land, with scattered springs, streams and marshes, would only have been useful as poor-quality grazing and so developed into open mixed woodland after grazing ceased in the early 20th century. In 1908, this relict of wood pasture ('rough grazing' with scattered veteran trees) was donated to the University of Oxford by the Revd. Arthur H. Johnson of All Souls College, Oxford. The name of the field was then changed from Middle Ground to Johnson's

Hawthorn succession in Horseshoe Field where, after 70 years, species diversity has become very low

Piece and an informal arboretum planted on its eastern boundary [see page 48]. The area remains remarkable for its old trees, many of which are older than those in the 'ancient' woodland of Brasenose Wood [see page 50]. Most of the oldest oaks of the SSSI can be found in Johnson's Piece, including those that mark the old boundaries.

Since most of Johnson's Piece has remained unmanaged, and consequently relatively undisturbed for about a century, it is a good example of mature 'secondary woodland' [see box below], providing opportunities for organisms to become established in a very wide range of ecological niches and providing a valuable complementary habitat to Brasenose Wood. Although the woodland flora has fewer scarce species compared with Brasenose Wood, the mosaic of marshes and different soils

contributes many alternative micro-habitats. The natural development of unmanaged older woodlands around the Hill, such as Johnson's Piece, is therefore important for their mature trees, dead wood and tranquil micro-habitats. In particular, such woodlands give a structural diversity and a greater variety of conditions for mammals, bryophytes and invertebrates.

More recent secondary woodland has also become established at Shotover where the influence of grazing declined through the 20th century. Although cattle are still grazed over quite large areas of the Hill where the grass is productive, sheep are no longer farmed commercially on the slow-growing grasslands that are characteristic of acidic soils. In addition, the arrival and spread of myxomatosis in Rabbits from 1953 to 1955 greatly reduced the semi-natural grazing by these important herbivores and has since profoundly influenced the unmanaged grasslands of the Hill [see also page 226–7]. In these areas, trees become dominant within a few decades and the grass gives way to Hawthorn *Crataegus monogyna* or Pedunculate Oak, eventually becoming young secondary woodland with little or no ground flora. This is a depauperate habitat, for although common invertebrates can be abundant, birds and mammals do not favour woodland that has minimal understorey [see also box, page 37].

However, it is fortunate that the past land-use management of Shotover has created such a mixture of woodland types, including trees of many different species, worked coppice plots and

Secondary woodland

It is generally accepted that there is no native primary woodland left in Britain and so, strictly speaking, this would suggest that all woodland in Britain is secondary. However, for convenience, the term 'secondary woodland' is used to distinguish more recent woodlands from those that have been under continuous woodland cover since before 1600 and is thus used to describe woods that have become established naturally in more recent centuries. Most typically these will have matured on neglected ground that was once used for agriculture, grazing or some other human activity, such as an abandoned settlement. Secondary woodland also includes plantation woodlands that have matured naturally through succession and become colonized by additional woodland species.

A plantation of trees developing as secondary woodland over the 1940 Slade army camp

dead wood in all stages of decay. Such areas are not common in Britain today, and the remarkable species diversity of Shotover is largely due to this mosaic of wooded and partially wooded habitats.

Dead-wood habitat

The presence of dead trees and dead wood on living trees is not a sign of poor ecological health in a nature reserve — quite the contrary. Dead and decaying wood sustains an immense diversity of associated organisms, each with their own niche and all living in balance with the woodland ecology. These organisms are described as 'saproxylic' and all in their own way contribute to the decay and reduction of organic matter, and so recycle energy and nutrients. Dead wood is in fact a living habitat, an intricate microcosm and an essential component of any woodland habitat.

Unfortunately, the increasing exploitation of woodland for fuel and recreation, especially ancient woodland, is such that although the habitat designation remains the same, the quality of the dead-wood resource within continues to decline. Consequently the saproxylic fauna is one of the most threatened species groups in Britain and beyond (Stokland *et al.*, 2012).

Dead and decaying wood takes many different forms depending on how the wood died and the 'journey' it follows thereafter. Whether twig or trunk, it may either fall to the ground while still alive or cease to live *in situ* and reach the ground at a later time. Even a tree stump will have its own journey, with saproxylic activity both above and below the ground. Moisture is a key factor for the route taken by newly deceased timber. Continuous dampness (normally at the ground) will quickly hasten decay by fungi and insects that can burrow into the softened timber, whereas sun-baked dead wood (typically a standing tree or senescence in the canopy) becomes dry and hard and takes very many years to return to the soil. Sooner or later, however, all natural dead wood crumbles, disintegrates to pulp or is processed by animal digestion and returns to the soil. Throughout these various journeys, dead material from trees provides a vast number of niches for saproxylic organisms to function [see also page 131]. An immense variety of fungi, beetles and flies as well as many moths, thrips, bugs, spiders and millipedes depends on dead wood.

Dead wood: naturally fallen, cut and stacked, and standing

Cramp-ball Fungus Weevil Paul Brock

In many cases, each saproxylic organism will fit into a sequence in which one utilises the prior activity of another and, when its own activity is completed, passes on some remainder to the next. Examples would be the wasps and bees that use holes ready-made by beetles, and by enlarging them benefit larger hole-nesting species, or insects that feed at a sap run where a tree is reacting to colonization by a fungus — and so on into deeper and deeper complexity.

A special case arises when all, or part, of a woody plant is killed by fire but not completely destroyed, creating additional saproxylic opportunities. Some species are especially adapted to the passage of a natural fire; others happen to benefit more circumstantially. Although a fire will badly damage some species, for others it can be a vital opportunity — whether provided by heat, blackened surfaces, increased access to light or even smoke-induced germination. At Shotover, where living Gorse *Ulex europaeus* has been killed by fire (accidental or deliberate), it is often colonized by the scarce fungus *Daldinia fissa* [see page 110], which is very similar to the black Cramp Ball fungus *D. concentrica* on Ash *Fraxinus excelsior*. Furthermore, the eponymous Cramp-ball Fungus Weevil *Platyrhinus resinosus*, a scarce saproxylic beetle whose larvae feed on these fungi, has been found on acidic grassland at Shotover, a few metres from fungus-colonized burnt Gorse, thus demonstrating a saproxylic sequence likely to have been induced by the fire.

Rarely is there ever too much dead wood in a woodland. Many woodlands in Britain, and the associated rare species, would benefit significantly from a greater volume of this precious resource. All too often dead and freshly cut wood is burnt on site or inappropriately removed as firewood, and the result is the depletion of a natural habitat which can take a great many years to replenish. This is especially the case within the SSSI at Shotover where a significant number of rare saproxylic beetles and flies have been recorded in recent years. And so the log on the ground should be viewed in its true context — a habitat for supporting a great richness of vulnerable species.

Heathy ground
The carpet of purple flowering heathers that appear across a heathland landscape in August is a

Heather is now an uncommon sight in Oxfordshire

Although never extensive in the county the few small areas of Heather that remain, such as at Shotover, are especially important for their associated wildlife.

most eye-catching sight. Even the small patches of Ling Heather *Calluna vulgaris* (hereafter Heather) at Shotover, now reduced to less than a hectare in total, are a delight to the visitor who may not be expecting to encounter the splash of colour.

Completely natural dry lowland heathland [see box below] does not occur in Britain and is a rare coastal habitat in Europe. Most of the current heathland habitat came about through thousands of years of continuous grazing by domesticated animals on areas with infertile soils. For example, when woodland was cleared from sandy areas, the acidic soils that developed would have been adequate for grazing but not suitable for arable agriculture — as at Shotover. The genesis of semi-natural heathland in Britain began with the clearance of woodlands for agriculture about 4,000 years ago and remained extensive on marginal soils until conversion to cropping was made possible with chemical fertilizers.

The 20th century witnessed a considerable decline in the area of grazed lowland heathland in Britain. Large areas of unproductive land in the southern counties were either converted to housing or arable crops. Unfortunately, before about 1960 the conservation status of heathland was scarcely recognized, hence the losses, but at least a level of protection has since been established. Some large areas of heath had been kept from development through alternative uses, such as for military training areas or airfields, and where such places have become disused some have become recognized as important wildlife sites. For example, Greenham Common in Berkshire was designated as an SSSI soon after its closure as an airbase. Although Oxfordshire has only ever had small areas of heathland, the memory of their locations lives on in place names such as Tackley Heath, Ipsden Heath and Eaton Heath.

Defining heathland at Shotover

The type of heathland habitat that would have developed naturally in the Oxfordshire climate is categorized as 'dry lowland heath' and is quite different from the upland heathy moorland of Scotland and Wales. Dry lowland heath is generally defined as land that is at an altitude of less than 300 metres above sea level and predominantly occupied by ericaceous species of heather.

Early evidence of an ericaceous heather at Shotover is depicted in the painting *Study of nature on Shotover Hill near Oxford* (c. 1820) by William Turner of Oxford which shows the heather intermingled with grass and taller vegetation (suggesting Gorse). The picture is of an extensive heath derived from low-grade grazing on the infertile sandy soils of the Hill. By 1908 the Oxford botanist George Druce is already lamenting the local decline of a heathland flora: *"The once celebrated district of Shotover has suffered much during the past century, at the beginning of which it was to a great extent open and uncultivated ground, in parts thickly wooded and in others showing delightful expanses of heath. … The inclosure of the heathy slopes, the cultivation of its surface, the various encroachments upon its domain, have gradually denuded the hill of its characteristic vegetation and the progress of destruction still goes on."* (Druce, 1939: p. 47)

Anecdotally, there have been varying amounts of Ling Heather at Shotover since 1900 but it is doubtful whether there has been an area large enough to qualify as a true heathland habitat.

Study of nature on Shotover Hill near Oxford (c.1820) by William Turner of Oxford, showing an early representation of an ericaceous heather on the Hill
©Private collection, with permission of the owner

Preparing the soil with a chain harrow in Mary Sadler Field in 2000 ready to receive seed collected from an adjoining stand of Heather

The new area of Heather in 2005, which six years previously had been species-poor birch woodland

In past times at Shotover, the grazing of cattle and sheep on the dry and relatively unproductive fields that cap the Hill would have created ideal conditions for the persistence of a heathland habitat. Although there appears to be no record of heath at Shotover during its years as a royal forest, grazing would have been an important part of the local economy, both before and after disafforestation in 1660 [see page 6]. Under this simple pastoral land-use, Heather is likely to have become established in various places on and around Shotover, wherever the soil was suitable. As 'rough grazing' declined with the agricultural improvement of soils, however, the unproductive local heathland also declined.

Anecdotal evidence suggests that Heather on The Plain was "*ploughed up to grow corn*" in the early 20th century (Arthur Smith, 2000, pers. comm.) [see also page 197]. A 1939 inventory of invertebrates (Salzman, 1939), in which no Heather-dependent species are listed for Shotover, also suggests there was little Heather at that time. Aerial photographs taken in the 1940s and 50s are insufficiently clear but equally suggest that the presence of extensive areas of Heather was rather unlikely. However, at least some Heather of local provenance remained on the Hill throughout (David Steel, 1999, pers. comm.), and since the 1970s various attempts have been made to establish new areas of Heather using seeds from the plants that remain.

Research by Shotover Wildlife in 2000 greatly improved the understanding and success of establishing Heather grown from collected seed, and most of the areas to be seen at Shotover today are a product of this work. In the absence of grazing, understanding the local conditions is critical for establishing sustainable new areas of Heather. For example, managing the growth of Gorse, Bracken *Pteridium aquilinum* and Bramble *Rubus fruticosus* agg. requires close monitoring as the growth-response of these species is not always the same in different locations. Unhelpfully, most of the acidic soils at Shotover have a fertility somewhat higher than is typical for other established lowland heathland, so these fast-growing 'problem' species generally flourish more readily. Nevertheless, in 2000 a substantial new area of Heather was successfully established from seed in Mary Sadler Field, which subsequently demonstrated good continuity of habitat for various scarce Heather-associated species. The area also became a source of Heather seed, only seven years after sowing, a fortuitous outcome in light of the later demise of other areas where seed could have been harvested.

In more recent years, small areas of sown Heather have been maintained in Mary Sadler Field and Horspath Common but overall the extent of Heather habitat on the Hill continues to be insufficient for an optimal heathland ecology and is vulnerable to misfortune. In Sandpit Field, the oldest remaining fragment suffered greatly from an ill-advised conservation attempt in 2007, and by 2012 very little Heather remained. Moreover, in 2009 a fire destroyed a significant area of Heather in Mary Sadler Field, which hitherto had been high-quality habitat and the main source of Heather seed for the SSSI. Fortunately, however, Heather seed can remain viable in the soil for many years and, as long as this is the case, reinstatement is always possible. Indeed, in 2016 a new initiative was begun to

The bare soil and short grasses of Horseshoe Field provide a special habitat for scarce plants and insects

Mixed scrub with flowering Blackthorn in Bottom Ground

restore the heathland habitat in the SSSI with the aim of securing a more stable long-term future for this complex and vulnerable habitat.

Acidic grassland

Wherever vegetation on the sandy areas of Shotover Hill is kept short by grazing, the natural infertility and strong acidity of the soil (pH 3–5) allow a characteristic community of grassland plants to enjoy a competitive advantage. Such acidic soils are scarce in Oxfordshire and consequently many of the plants that thrive in this habitat are similarly scarce in the county. Furthermore, the very short vegetation and sandy soils are exploited by a particular invertebrate fauna, and such acidic grassland is therefore recognized as a significant contributor to species diversity, both regionally and nationally.

Lowland acidic grassland has a similar anthropogenic origin to that of heathland but in this case heather is absent, or at least much reduced, due to a closer-cropped grazing regime. For several centuries acidic grassland was extensive at Shotover, kept short by sheep and Rabbits. However, since the mid-20th century the decline in sheep farming and the decimation of the Rabbit population by myxomatosis [see page 227] has resulted in the extent of acidic grassland now being much reduced. Before the onset of myxomatosis many areas of grass at the top of the Hill, such as The Plain, were never mown but kept short throughout the year by a sizeable Rabbit population (Arthur Smith, 2000, pers. comm.), whereas today there is enough vegetative growth by July to require

a hay cut every year. Some of Shotover's most infertile soils support a characteristic grassland on which vegetative growth is especially slow; these are some of the oldest and most stable acidic grassland ecosystems in the county. Such areas occur on both the Whitchurch Sand and Shotover Grit Sand and are characterized by large ant hills and the accompanying ant hill ecology [see page 147].

The current extent of acidic grassland is still maintained naturally by Rabbit grazing, and so remains a somewhat more stable habitat than areas with Heather. However, encroachment at the periphery by taller vegetation does require some intervention to reverse the slow overall reduction in area, especially as there is evidence that when the Rabbit population is low, the resultant increase in encroachment is not reversed when the population subsequently recovers. Indeed, the dynamics of the Rabbit population is an important consideration for all acidic grassland management and restoration on the Hill.

It may come as a surprise to learn that the wear and tear of thousands of visitors' feet has a significantly beneficial influence on the species diversity of the acidic grassland habitat in the SSSI. For small annual plants and soil-nesting insects, easy access to the soil surface due to short turf or bare soil is essential, especially where it is warmed by exposure to the sun. In fact, some of the most popular recreation areas, such as the approaches to The Sandpit, support a number of Shotover's scarce plants. Disturbance of the short turf, as well as path edges, by the action of mammals or birds, horses' hooves, runners and conservation work all readily produce additional opportunities for burrowing insects and the germination of small seeds.

Woody scrub and Bracken

In the managed fields and meadows of the countryside around Shotover, expanses of intermediate-height vegetation (other than hedgerow) are not a common habitat, yet in the SSSI and Country Park such vegetation makes a significant contribution to wildlife. These areas, often described as 'scrub', are either woody shrubs and young trees developing into the early stages of secondary woodland, or quasi-stable monocultures of Bracken, Gorse, Bramble or Blackthorn *Prunus spinosa*. All of these plants contribute to the ecology of a site, especially for invertebrates, and also their structure provides reptiles and small mammals with a place to feed and be secure from predators. Suitably managed, such vegetation can provide wildlife corridors, patches of linking habitat and a diversity of micro-climates, all of which can help species take full advantage of an area. In the SSSI, the intricate patchwork of different habitats also creates linear 'edge scrub' that occupies the vast length of transitional zone between habitat patches. This edge scrub constitutes a significant proportion of the total area of intermediate-height vegetation.

Bramble and Blackthorn are among the most valuable contributors to scrub vegetation for wildlife at Shotover, particularly for invertebrates. Both of these species are the food-plant for many insect larvae, and their flowers and fruits provide pollen, nectar and sugars for a great range of insects. The hollow stems of Bramble are also used by invertebrates for nesting and overwintering. Bracken-dominated areas, the least linear of scrub types, would seem to be rather barren of animals, yet observations at Shotover have shown that it is a valuable habitat for small mammals, reptiles, amphibians and bumblebees, and is used as a day refuge by Roe Deer. And while too much Bracken is a common problem, its positive contribution to a balanced wildlife diversity is frequently overlooked.

Sometimes the term 'scrub' is used disparagingly to mean unkempt vegetation of minimal ecological value. The scrub then becomes a target for 'conservation' effort which

Acidic grassland and secondary woodland

A remarkable feature of acidic grassland is its ability to accumulate a persistent store or 'bank' of dormant seeds. This is a key factor for the restoration of an acidic grassland habitat from secondary woodland. Using a combination of botanical surveying and 1950s aerial photography, Shotover Wildlife has observed that a diverse acidic grassland plant community can readily germinate where 60-year-old secondary woodland has been removed by conservation work.

For example, since the sheep grazing ceased on the sandy pastures above Westhill Farm, these fields have succeeded from grass pasture and scrub into either Pedunculate Oak or Hawthorn woodland. Throughout this transition the developing tree canopy has increasingly shaded the woodland floor and reduced both the diversity and abundance of the ground flora. However, when the trees were removed by conservationists between 2008 and 2010, typically with only minimal disturbance to the ground surface, there was rapid germination of acidic grasses, heathland sorrels *Rumex* spp., scarce species of St John's-wort *Hypericum* spp. and plants of the pea family (*Fabaceae*) — all strongly indicative of the previous acidic grassland habitat.

Tree clearance to restore acidic grassland in Sandpit Field

Hay-making in Lower Close below Westhill Farm in 2006

Slade Camp South in June with the typical flora of an old Shotover meadow

seeks to tidy up a habitat or eliminate a possible threat to other habitats. Reducing encroachment is often well justified but unfortunately a few non-aggressive shrubby species can become included in the scrub clearance. These are frequently removed unnecessarily to the detriment of the biological diversity of the site — for example, Elder *Sambucus nigra*, a particularly important species for mosses [see page 94].

Meadows, pasture and arable land

Hay meadows and pasture cover a substantial proportion of the area around Shotover and since the 17th century these were the dominant land-uses, supplying food and horsepower to the local villages and towns. The early 19th-century paintings by William Turner of Oxford [see pages 6 and 7] reveal an intensively grazed landscape with very little mature woodland. Although there has been no extensive sheep farming for many years, cattle and horses still graze the old pastures and paddocks around the Hill. Also, on the Shotover Estate there remains a biologically and historically important area of wood pasture, that is, an expanse of large grazed fields with scattered veteran trees [see also page 30].

Hay meadows from which the grass is cut and collected once each year occupy much of the flatter ground around the Hill as well as on the upper plateau. Some fields are very productive and continue to supply animal feed for the winter months. Here the traditional hay-making has mostly been replaced by the baling of plastic-wrapped 'haylage' which is much less dependent on dry weather. Older 'unimproved' meadows, such as at Slade Camp South and those below

Westhill Farm, are recognized for their abundant natural flora and here the application of fertilizer is not permitted where a government 'Stewardship' scheme is in place. Consequently these fields are relatively unproductive for cattle grazing by modern standards but are still cut each year to prevent the growth of trees and shrubs and to help maintain their floral diversity [see page 69].

Today, the most biologically rich grasslands are those that have been 'improved' the least, regardless of the acidity of their soils. For example, the old meadow at Monk's Farm near the summit of the Hill would not normally be associated with a rich biological diversity because of its mildly acid soil. However, after decades of light grazing and annual mowing, the flora and fauna are exceptional with invertebrate species which have not been recorded anywhere else on the Hill. Slade Camp South is a good example of 'unimproved' neutral grassland that has also benefitted from decades of annual

Wood pasture on the Shotover Estate

hay-cutting. The soil at the southern end of this field is influenced by the underlying calcareous Coral Rag (Wheatley Limestone) and the flora is consequently more diverse than is typical at Shotover [see page 70]. Many of the hay meadows that surround the SSSI play a particularly important role in providing pollen and nectar for the invertebrates that can 'commute' from their nests in the sandy soils of the SSSI [see box, page 142]; thus these meadows provide an important 'green belt' for the SSSI (Wright *et al.*, 2015).

Some of Shotover's grassland pastures are managed for agricultural productivity and their floral diversity is consequently rather limited. However, between the extremes of rich and poor diversity, there are fields grazed by cattle or horses at a variety of intensities, including the wood pasture of the Shotover Estate, and the wildlife contribution of all the pastures and paddocks is a considerable asset to the ecology of the Hill. For example, the grazing animals provide for a great many associated invertebrates such as dung beetles and flies, and the fields are a significant feeding ground for insectivorous birds such as Swallows and House Martins.

Arable land is found on the flatter ground around the periphery of the Hill as well as on the plateaux. A number of different crops have been grown over the years, including grain, brassicas, legumes and potatoes. Most, if not all, of these crops have needed the application of some form of fertilizer to counteract the acidity and the generally deficient natural fertility of the soils. In the 1980s, some of these fields were placed into 'set-aside' schemes and since then have been cut only once each year as hay meadows. After more than 20 years, these fields have developed an abundant and diverse flora, and are a particularly attractive sight when at their most colourful in May and June.

Hedgerows and boundary banks

Hedgerows are recognized as a most important habitat, not just for the plants that form their structure, or that take advantage of a warm and sheltered microclimate, but also because they form a connecting network along which birds, mammals, reptiles and invertebrates can move through the countryside. Shotover is well provided in this respect and has many high-quality hedges, some of great age. It is probable that the less fertile soils, and the consequent

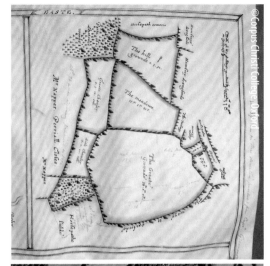

For more than 400 years, since 1605, the pattern of hedgerows west of Horspath has hardly changed

unsuitability for large-scale arable cropping, have kept Shotover mostly untouched by the 20th-century trend for the removal of hedgerows to create larger fields.

A Corpus Christi College estate map dated 1605 when compared with a more recent satellite image shows that, with the exception of the removal a few sections of old hedgerow, the field pattern to the west of Horspath village has remained unchanged for over 400 years. The map also shows "*Parte of Shotover woode*", the boundary of which was formalized *c.* 1298 by perambulation — a statutory survey of the royal

The mossy boundary bank near Ben's Bridge is over 700 years old

forest perimeter (Roberts, 1963) [see page 3] — thereby establishing the age of that particular section of hedge at more than 700 years. Although this older hedge line no longer shows any outward sign of its great age (there are no ancient trees or particular diversity of indicator species), other nearby boundaries are more notable in this respect. The southern boundary of Horspath Common (extant 1605) and the track that runs north from the summit of Shotover towards Thornhill (extant 1643) are particularly rich with woody hedgerow species such as English Elm *Ulmus procera*, Small-leaved Elm *U. minor*, Field Maple *Acer campestre*, Holly *Ilex aquifolium* and Spindle *Euonymus europaeus*.

In many ways, boundary banks are similar to hedgerows, with which they often coincide, and it is not unusual to find scarce vascular plants and bryophytes (mosses and liverworts) along these old earthworks, where the habitat has remained predominantly undisturbed for many hundreds of years. Although these banks do not form such an obvious network of wildlife corridors compared with the hedgerows, their contribution to wildlife, as a linear feature for example, can be equally important. The mature trees that often occur along ancient boundaries can be sufficiently close to one other to form interconnected 'islands' of

upper-canopy habitat for insects to extend their ranges. Recent work by Shotover Wildlife has shown that some species of 'ancient woodland' beetle can be found in the tree canopy of both Shotover Hill and Brasenose Wood, and it is likely that the older trees along the boundaries are critical for some species to migrate and find optimal habitat across the larger area (Keith Alexander, 2013, pers. comm.).

There are approximately nine kilometres of ancient boundary bank in and around Shotover Country Park alone [see Fig. 5, page 28], most of which is lined with mature trees. These boundaries include the 1298 and 1643 published limits of the royal forest, the delineation of the old road between Oxford and London, the boundaries of Magdalen and Brasenose Woods, and the bridleways from Monk's Farm to Brasenose Wood and from Headington to Horspath.

Marshes, streams and ponds

Tucked away in the wooded valleys of Shotover Hill, and just a few hundred metres from the topmost plateaux, are a great many small springs and seepages that combine to maintain the constant flow of water for the species-rich marshes and rivulets of the Hill. The water that flows out from the valleys radiates away from the Hill in a network of streams and ditches, sustaining numerous ponds along the way [see page 20]. Before the 20th century there would have been considerably more marsh and bog than there is today. For example, in the late 19th century, there were peaty marshes (Steel, 1984: p. 38) where sphagnum mosses and insectivorous bog plants once grew (Druce, 1886: p. 44). However, since

A deepened ditch on the edge of Brasenose Wood

**The pond in the
C.S. Lewis Community
Nature Reserve**

Today the reserve is a
quiet and secluded place
for wildlife yet the pit was
excavated for clay at a time
when the air was filled
with the noise and smoke
of a busy brickworks.

that time, streams on the lower slopes have been
made deeper and straighter to drain the land for
agricultural use, and evidence of this can be seen
all around the Hill.

Today, the remaining mature marshes are
quite small and are generally found towards
the top of the Hill, either where springs emerge
directly onto level Kimmeridgian clay or at
the top of the valleys on the Head deposits. It
is estimated that the total area of marsh is 14
hectares. The near-constant flow of the springs
provides sufficient water at the surface to
maintain a stable wetland habitat in numerous
places, even in the driest of years. An important
feature for wildlife is the isolated hydrology of
the Hill [see page 20] and the consequent purity
of the water. Most of the area above the springs
(the area of precipitation recharge for spring
flow) is unaffected by chemical fertilizer and the
spring water, especially on the southern slopes,
is not significantly affected by such pollution.
So although Shotover's marshes are small, their
stability, maturity and quality of water supply
make them an asset for regional biodiversity,
reflected in the richness of recorded flora and
invertebrate fauna.

The total extent of ponds and open water
on the Hill is not great, just 3.5 hectares, and
all of it created for ornamental, domestic or
commercial purposes. These bodies of water are
fed almost entirely by the ample flow of water

from the upper spring line. To the north-west of
the Hill are the water-filled pits left over from the
quarrying of brick clay in the 19th century, which
amount to about a hectare. The best-known of
these is the pond in the C.S. Lewis Community
Nature Reserve, acquired by the Berkshire,
Buckinghamshire and Oxfordshire Wildlife Trust
(BBOWT) in 1969. Here the steep sides and cool
microclimate are not ideal for a diverse marginal
flora but the pond is a tranquil habitat for water
birds and amphibians. There are two further
ponds of similar size on private land to the east.

Within the Shotover Estate, in The Spinney, is
a series of old fish ponds where the water cascades
from one to another before flowing on northwards
towards Bayswater Brook. Some of the flow is
diverted to fill The Octagon Pond to the west of
Shotover House. The fish ponds have been stocked
from time to time and have been restricted to
a rather limited vegetation on their banks. The
Octagon Pond, although somewhat turbid at
times, has a broad margin of wetland plants and
is rich in associated invertebrates, including many
damselflies and dragonflies [see page 161]. The
long ornamental pond to the east of Shotover
House — The Canal — is the largest expanse of
open water on the Hill; it is also referred to as The
Lake but at 2.5 hectares is too small to be formally
defined as such. This feature once attracted a
variety of water birds that would not otherwise
visit Shotover [see page 203] and along the

Tranquil wildlife gardens make a valuable contribution to connectivity in the countryside, providing for small mammals, nesting birds and micro-invertebrates

A well-planned floral garden increases the pollen and nectar resources for a wide range of flying insects

northern edge it is fringed with a linear margin of Common Reed *Phragmites australis*.

Small seasonal ponds can be of great value to wildlife but few of any particular age, or particular quality, are known at Shotover. Several new ponds have been excavated in the Country Park in the past few decades, mostly for public amenity but with some potential for wildlife. However, it is unusual for any wildlife diversity to develop or persist. The shallow pond to the west of Westhill Farm is an old farm pond and appears on the Ordnance Survey map of 1881 but it is adjacent to a popular public path and frequent visits from dogs have rendered it relatively barren of flora or invertebrate fauna.

Connecting all the marshes and ponds are the streams that radiate from the spring lines around the Hill. Most of these streams run in their natural valleys as they flow from the Hill, and in places there are fine examples of mature and marshy streambeds that may have undergone little change for centuries. These old and undisturbed rivulets can be particularly diverse in flora and invertebrates. On reaching the flatter ground around the Hill, most of the streams, as noted earlier, have been modified for better drainage but even these channels have remained a relatively undisturbed habitat for decades.

Buildings, grounds and gardens
Private land and buildings within the Shotover geographical area can be divided into three contrasting categories: those effectively barren of wildlife, natural gardens that complement and

enhance the ecological mosaic of habitats on the Hill, and those that make a specific additional contribution to local wildlife diversity.

Sports grounds, highly manicured lawns, tarmac, concrete and roof tiles are generally deficient in species diversity and play little part in the ecology of Shotover. Fortunately, such surfaces represent only a small proportion of the total area. In contrast to this, the environmental contribution of private gardens is considerable. Many gardens around the Hill are large and contain significant expanses that are not under intensive horticulture. Not only are these an intrinsic asset to wildlife but they also add to the natural buffer zones that surround the SSSI and other areas of specific wildlife interest. Some of the larger gardens offer more tranquil spaces for reptiles and mammals compared with the publicly accessible Country Park where dogs have free rein. The private land also provides a daytime refuge for larger mammals that hunt or scavenge at night — including inside the Country Park.

A further major contribution of private gardens, large or small, manicured or more natural, is the provision of pollen and nectar for a wide range of insects. Shotover Hill is recognized beyond doubt as an important reserve for insects, including the bees, wasps, beetles and flies that obtain their energy and protein by visiting flowers, and yet there are places within the SSSI where the flora is not wholly adequate for some insects. For example, it has been shown that some of the bees that nest inside the SSSI travel to the surrounding habitats for pollen [see box, page 142]. Although some garden plants are not used by native insects, some non-native plants provide an excellent supply of pollen or nectar, including during the winter months when most native plants are not in flower. As the British climate continues to change, perhaps with greater seasonal extremes in the future, garden plants are likely to provide an important additional resource for those creatures whose natural rhythms can become disrupted by abnormal conditions.

Finally, farmyards, gardens and most types of building — whether domestic, agricultural or industrial — support animals that are more often associated with human habitation but are nonetheless part of the biological diversity of the Hill. Apart from the much-loved Hedgehog *Erinaceus europaeus* and the much-loathed Brown Rat *Rattus norvegicus*, obvious examples are the Swallows and House Martins that nest under the eaves of buildings. Shotover is a rich hunting ground for insectivorous birds, and without old buildings or overhanging eaves these species would be seen less frequently around the Hill. At the extreme, there are a number of synanthropic species, found only in association with human activity. Many of these co-habitants are scavenging invertebrates, including the spiders, beetles and millipedes that inhabit houses, farmyards and outbuildings. It would be unusual to find any of these synanthropic species in more 'natural' habitats, yet their contribution to decomposition and nutrient recycling is no less important.

Conclusion

Within just a few square miles, Shotover Hill and its immediate surroundings encompass a remarkable diversity of habitats. The origin of this diversity is the finely layered geology of sands and clays, and the constraints that these soils impose. Then superimposed upon this foundation is a history of private and commercial activity that has formed the multi-faceted jewel of natural history that we see today. On walking the Hill, the overall impression is of an ever-changing landscape of open fields and secluded woodlands, and nowhere is this more apparent than in the Country Park. Here, in just a few metres, the soil type, the dampness underfoot and the surrounding vegetation can change markedly, providing the walker with the satisfaction of ever-changing views and atmospheres.

For the conservation of wildlife in such a relatively small and intricate area of countryside, an understanding of the component habitats is clearly needed. In the predominantly commercial landscape of Oxfordshire, a great many scarce and specialist species now depend upon the quality and continuity of habitat in isolated wildlife sites, such as Shotover, emphasizing the fragility of survival for these species. An appreciation of the interactions between component areas is vital. It is the innumerable links and natural exchanges between the habitats that make Shotover Hill so rich in species and such a fascinating and rewarding place to study.

Thornhill farmyard on the north side of Shotover has old outbuildings and undisturbed corners that add greatly to habitat diversity in the countryside

Jacqueline Wright and Ivan Wright

The present-day landscape of Shotover consists of many thousands of trees: a verdant patchwork of woodlands, copses, hedgerow trees, plantations and handsome isolated individuals. Within minutes of setting out on the Hill, it is the trees that set the scene.

For this chapter the largest of vascular plants — the trees — are artificially grouped so that they can be separated from the small shrubs and hard-stemmed flowering plants of the next chapter (Flora). Although a tall woody plant with a stout trunk and spreading canopy is self-evidently a tree, smaller woody species and multi-stemmed trees such as Hazel *Corylus avellana* are not so easily defined. Therefore, for this chapter, Hazel, Elder *Sambucus nigra*, Crab Apple *Malus sylvestris* and the larger hedgerow shrubs such as Spindle *Euonymus europaeus* and Wild Privet *Ligustrum vulgare* are included with the trees, whereas Gorse *Ulex europaeus* and

The Boundary Oak stands as a sentinel to the old royal forest

dogwood (*Cornus* spp.) are covered in the chapter on Flora. For hybrid trees, only those with common names, such as Grey Poplar *Populus* × *canescans* and Lime *Tilia* × *europaea*, have been included, although a great many other hybrids can be found, especially among the willows, oaks and birches.

The trees of Shotover

Excluding the many exotic trees and shrubs planted in private gardens, recent surveying has shown that over 70 species of tree currently grow at Shotover, including 20 large shrub species. The most dominant tree to occupy the overarching canopy of the woodlands is undoubtedly the English or Pedunculate Oak *Quercus robur*, closely followed by Ash *Fraxinus excelsior*. Where the trees are not so lofty, Hawthorn *Crataegus monogyna* and Blackthorn *Prunus spinosa* can form a dense and entangled canopy, and in the open coppiced woodlands Hazel and Aspen *Populus tremula* eventually produce a substantial under-canopy. Towards the top of the Hill where the soil is more acidic, patches of fast-growing Silver Birch *Betula pendula* can dominate — to the exclusion of other potentially tall trees.

Tree species diversity at Shotover is influenced by the varied acidity of the soils. While some trees thrive and multiply in acidic conditions, the 'calcicole' species that only grow well on a chalky or calcareous soil are particularly sparse. So although there are healthy examples of English Whitebeam *Sorbus aria*, Hornbeam *Carpinus betulus* and Beech *Fagus sylvatica*, the majority occur in close proximity to the thin seam of calcareous Portland Limestone that outcrops around the upper slopes of the Hill [see map opposite]. Furthermore and for the same reason, these calcicole species do not germinate readily at Shotover and many will have been planted. A small number of seedling Beech and varieties of whitebeam have been recorded in places on more acidic soils, and some Beech sapling trees survive quite well; however, the whitebeams all appear to be hybrids and may be the product of wind-

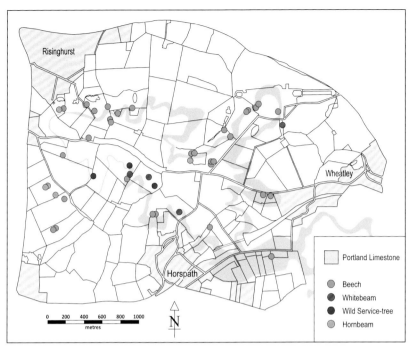

Figure 6 The proximity of mature calcicole trees to the surface limestone of the Hill
Data: ©Ivan Wright
Map: Permit Number CP16/054
British Geological Survey
©NERC 2016. All rights reserved
©Crown copyright 2018
OS 100057706

Of all the calcicole trees that have germinated or been planted on the Hill, it would seem that it is predominantly those close to the Portland Limestone that thrive and reach maturity.

blown pollen from the Swedish Whitebeams *S. intermedia* that are commonly planted along the streets of Oxford.

At the other end of the acidic soil spectrum, pines and birches thrive on the Whitchurch Sand at the top of the Hill. Although the Kimmeridgian clay on the lower slopes is mildly acidic, neither pines nor birches are particularly common on this soil, and self-seeded saplings are not often seen, especially pines.

Poplars and willows are well represented around the Hill. Although these species are important for supporting a diversity of invertebrates, they can be invasive to the detriment of some habitats. For example, willows constantly encroach upon and threaten the wetness of the marshes, and in coppice woodland Aspen can suppress ground flora if allowed to become too abundant. However, in Slade Camp North there are good examples of White Poplar *Populus alba* and Hybrid Black Poplar *P. × canadensis*, and seven Lombardy Poplars *P. nigra 'italica'* stand conspicuously high above all else. Until the severe storm of October 1987, five Grey Poplars stood tall and grand near Westhill Farm but only one managed to withstand the extreme gale. Surprisingly, the tree that survived was one of the largest of the five, and in 2018 had a chest-height girth of 4.6 metres. Fifteen years after the

storm, three of the four huge trunks that once lay on the ground had decayed away without trace: a remarkable demonstration of the rate of recycling of a relatively soft timber.

The sole remaining Grey Poplar near Westhill Farm

Wherever there are willows, water is usually nearby. At Shotover the dominant species would appear to be either Grey Willow *Salix cinerea* or Goat Willow *S. caprea* but in fact most are hybrids of the two and a pure specimen of either species can be difficult to find. Among the more uncommon species is a single specimen of Eared Willow *S. aurita* [OTP, see page 63], tucked away in a hedgerow near Wood Ground. White Willow *S. alba* is represented by a few specimens: one in the Country Park near The Ridings and several larger examples in Slade Camp North. The basket-maker's Osier *S. viminalis* with its flexible stems and long narrow leaves occurs in a small patch near Westhill Farm.

The slow-growing Wild Service-tree *Sorbus torminalis* is uncommon in Oxfordshire, especially older specimens, but the SSSI is fortunate to have three that are at least 60 years old. This species is also known as the Chequers Tree and the brown berries were commonly used to flavour beer in the days before hops became more universally adopted for this purpose. For convenience the trees were often grown in the gardens of brew-houses — giving rise to 'The Chequers' as the adopted name of the associated alehouse. As the Wild Service-tree is a calcicole species and not common in the Oxfordshire countryside, it is not easy to judge whether or not the three specimens in the SSSI were planted. Interestingly, however, their locations are all just above the outcropping of Portland Limestone [see Fig. 6, page 45] and, if they were planted, either the astute tree-planter understood the geology of the Hill or there were more and only these three survived.

The specimens of Wild Service-tree in Horseshoe Field and Sandpit Field would appear to be of a similar age to the secondary re-growth woodland in which they occur. The third and largest is in the old woodland of Johnson's Piece, on the northern edge of the informal arboretum [see page 48]. In 2013, this tree shed a major lower bough, providing an opportunity to examine the tree ring density close to the trunk and so gain a better estimate of the tree's age. At about 100–120 years its age is compatible with the hypothesis that it was planted at around the same time as the arboretum. Although this tree was known to be hollow in part (a feral colony of honeybees occupied the trunk in 2008) it was surprising to find that, for a relatively small tree of 1.5 metres in girth, its trunk was hollow down to the level of the surrounding ground and could legitimately be described as a young veteran. Hopefully it will live for many years to come, gaining extra vigour from the loss of the bough.

Among other tree species of note in the Shotover countryside are those which have most evidently been planted for a particular purpose. Pines were frequently used to mark principal roads and driveways, and a distinctive feature of The Plain at the top of the Hill is the row of Scots Pines *Pinus sylvestris* that mark the old London Road and adjoining farm tracks. Lime trees were also used in a similar way, albeit rather more grandly; on Green Lane, the southern approach to Shotover House is lined with a magnificent 750-metre arcade of Limes. With 190 of the original 200 trees still standing, their tall stature gives an imposing cathedral-like atmosphere.

The colourful autumn leaves of the Wild Service-tree in Johnson's Piece and the broken bough that revealed its hollow trunk

The avenue of Limes on Green Lane Ivan Wright

Before 1789, when the Oxford to London road passed over Shotover, Green Lane (also known as The Avenue) was the main driveway to Shotover House, and the gate-lodges and stone gateway at the southern end still remain. However, although the drive may date back to the first Shotover House of 1660, the Limes are not even as old as the current house (built in 1718 near to the older house), and it would appear from the position of the trees that the avenue track was re-laid to a more even gradient some time before the trees were planted.

Of interest on the eastern edge of the avenue of Limes is a very old Sweet Chestnut *Castanea sativa* which unfortunately has now lost its upper canopy. In 2018, it had a girth of 5.0 metres and, although supporting a great deal of dead wood, still retains some coarsely fissured bark on the eastern side with a few healthy stems rising from near the base. (Due to the curious shapes in the old gnarled trunk the tree is known to Shotover Wildlife as The Blanket Tree.) This chestnut is clearly older than the avenue of Limes and is estimated to have been about 300 years old (using White, 1998) when the upper canopy fell. It can therefore be hypothesized, albeit on the location of a single old tree, that before the

The intricately sculptured Blanket Tree
Drawing by Jacqueline Wright

The age and location of the Blanket Tree suggests it could be a survivor from an original avenue of Sweet Chestnuts that once lined Green Lane

track was re-graded Green Lane was lined with Sweet Chestnuts of which this is the sole survivor. Furthermore, the tree is approximately the same age as the current Shotover House and chestnuts were a typical avenue species at that time. Close to the western aspect of Shotover House there still stands a row of three statuesque Sweet Chestnuts, which with their strongly spiralling and deeply fissured bark present a most imposing feature.

In the early 20th century, soon after Johnson's Piece was donated to Oxford University [see page 30], a small section on the less acidic eastern boundary was planted with a variety of non-native deciduous and coniferous trees, thereby creating an informal arboretum. The specimens that survive today include a large Sweet Chestnut, a Douglas Fir *Pseudotsuga menziesii*, a Silver Maple *Acer saccharinum* of which there were previously at least two, a red-leaved variety of Norway Maple *A. rubrum*, the largest Beech in the SSSI (4.6 metres in girth), and a fine example of Austrian Pine *Pinus nigra* ssp. *nigra*. The Sweet Chestnut towers above the bracken at the southern end of the arboretum and is a stunning sight when covered in masses of pendulous creamy flowers in summer, and then later with spiny-cased fruits. A short distance from the arboretum, at the northern end of Long Marsh, stands a tall North American Paper Birch *Betula papyrifera* which may also have been planted in the early 20th century.

Although the University's original planting scheme for the arboretum is not known, some species will not have survived the intervening years. For example, a tall Silver Maple was blown down in a storm in the late 1990s, and a fine English Whitebeam died in 2001 and has now fallen.

Hedgerow trees

Hedgerows are an integral and historic part of the landscape at Shotover, providing many kilometres of species-rich wildlife corridor. Many of the hedges are very old, with some appearing in references as far back as 1298 [see page 3]. The richness of tree species within a hedge has

Ash Dieback

Ash trees are the second most abundant high-canopy tree at Shotover (after Pedunculate Oak) and the SSSI is densely scattered with Ash of all ages, forming a core component of the woodland and saproxylic ecology. Ash Dieback disease, caused by the fungus *Hymenoscyphus fraxinea,* was first discovered in Britain in February 2012 and is thought to have arrived either on imported nursery stock or on the wind from mainland Europe; it was confirmed in Oxfordshire later the same year and at Shotover in 2017. The disease causes the leaves to wilt and the treetop to atrophy, usually with fatal results within a few years.

Ash trees make up about five per cent of woodland cover in the UK and 13 per cent of broadleaved woodland. If the disease follows the same progress here as in Denmark, where only five to 10 per cent of Ash trees remain free of symptoms, Britain could lose more Ash trees than the number of English Elms that died of Dutch Elm Disease in the 1970s. Ash trees provide for many species of rare invertebrates, as well as being particularly favoured by many lichens and mosses.

A healthy Ash tree on Thornhill Farm

Leaves showing signs of Ash Dieback infection
M J Richardson

The old sinuous hedgerow and path that traverse the Hill from Thornhill to Brasenose Wood

This boundary has been shown on all local maps since 1642; its many contorted oaks and maples are typical of a very old hedge.

been demonstrated to correlate approximately with age but, due to hedge management over past centuries, there is only sparse evidence of this on the Hill. One old hedge that does demonstrate the phenomenon marks part of the southern boundary of Horspath Common. This species-rich boundary appears on the Corpus Christi estate map of 1605 [page 39], and today has Spindle, Small-leaved Elm *Ulmus minor* and several fine old specimens of Holly *Ilex aquifolium*. Also along the older hedgerows of Shotover are a number of less common species, including Midland Hawthorn *Crataegus laevigata* and Guelder-rose *Viburnum opulus*. A venerable specimen of Midland Hawthorn grows on the western edge of Rough Field on a boundary which appears on Whiting's 1643 map of the royal forest [page 5].

English Elm *U. procera* and the scarcer Small-leaved Elm once stood nobly at Shotover,

particularly in the hedgerows and field margins. Today these fine trees are all long gone, having been brought down by Dutch Elm Disease in the mid-20th century. The fatal fungal infection (*Ophiostoma* sp.) is spread by bark beetles of which three carrier species have been recorded in Oxfordshire, including the Large Elm Bark Beetle *Scolytus scolytus* at Shotover. However, as the root system is not killed by the disease and vigorous 'suckers' emerge very readily, the two species are not lost from the Hill and the locations of some of the old elms are still indicated by the shoots that proliferate in their stead. While these shoots and saplings have insufficient bark to attract the beetles, they remain healthy and free of infection and a number of young English Elms of a moderate size can be found at Shotover. Yet maturing elms continue to die and no large specimens have survived, indicating that at least one species of fungus-carrying bark beetle is still a vector for the disease on the Hill, for example, the Pinhole Borer *Platypus cylindrus* [see page 134].

The best chance for elms to build immunity to Dutch Elm Disease is by natural genetic mutation but unfortunately most trees die before they are old enough to bear seed. For this reason, flowering and fruiting elms are always of particular interest. A very large example on private land in Horspath, which was still alive in 1997, has now succumbed to the disease but good examples can still be seen on the Shotover Estate, in Brasenose Wood and on Mary Sadler Field. Small-leaved Elms can be found in hedgerows at Horspath Common, Slade Camp North and Sandpit Field; however, these are also susceptible to the disease and no tree has been found bearing mature seeds.

Seeds of English Elm on Mary Sadler Field in 2016

The Rebecca Ash is one of Shotover's 'eccentric' trees

Ancient and Veteran Trees

Following a tour of the Country Park in 2006, Ted Green of the Ancient Tree Forum was asked what he thought of Shotover's old trees, and replied, *"It's the best collection of eccentric trees I've seen!"*

Ancient trees are simply trees that are an exceptional age for their species. However, the definition of a Veteran Tree is intentionally rather vague so that trees that are culturally or ecologically important can be recognized, recorded and appreciated. A Veteran Tree

may even be relatively young but have signs of premature aging (for example, recovery from damage) and be nominated for its contribution to the landscape or its value for saproxylic species. Most of the trees nominated as Veterans by Shotover Wildlife are included for their size, age and wildlife value but also include trees that are popular landmarks, locally uncommon species and those with a particularly unusual growth habit.

Shotover Hill has very few truly ancient trees but two specimens stand out among the rest: a Pedunculate Oak and a Wild Cherry *Prunus avium*. Near to The Lake on the Shotover Estate stands a Pedunculate Oak that is 6.6 metres around the trunk. This tree would have been a fine mature specimen when the grounds were landscaped by William Kent in about 1720 and indeed, standing as it does by a main route to the house, may have influenced Kent's design. Now looking very old and gnarled, this erstwhile giant would have germinated in the 14th or 15th century and is probably the last of several to have survived into recent years; its only recent sibling, of about seven metres in girth, fell in January 2007 [see page 57] and the timber was taken away. The cracks and fractures in the structure of the remaining tree, and the uncertain state of the

The age of Shotover's oldest oak is likely to be between 550 and 650 years old (the uncertainty lies in not knowing the date of its first pollarding)

The Venerable Cherry in full blow

The huge trunk of the Venerable Cherry

trunk, leave this grand old veteran looking rather frail. Some parts may continue to leaf for another century or more — or the whole tree could be gone in a year.

Shotover's other truly ancient tree, a Wild Cherry, is very much younger than the oldest trees on the Hill but is of an exceptional size for its species. The 'Venerable Cherry', in the south-west corner of Mary Sadler Field, has a girth of 3.9 metres (2018) and is thought to be among the largest in Britain. There is no reliable estimate of its age as there appears to be no girth-age relationship published for this species. Also, the extraction of a core sample for dendrochronological analysis has been resisted for fear of introducing disease. The Venerable Cherry flowers and fruits prolifically, to the delight of visitors in the spring, the finches that enjoy the summer fruits, and finally the small mammals that feed on the cherry stones.

The register of ancient and Veteran Trees held by Shotover Wildlife was begun in 2006 as the Shotover Ancient Trees Project, with 29 different species recorded. About 300 individual trees have been mapped and measured, of which 190 are within the Country Park. The dominant species

Tree growth and age

Most trees grow exceptionally well on the upper southern slopes of Shotover Hill. This is because of the long day-length afforded by the Hill's elevation, the warmth of the sunny slopes, and easy access to water due to the high spring line. For many trees there is also little competition for resources from other surrounding vegetation. The trees that are able to take advantage of these conditions tend to be younger than their size would suggest. Any conventional relationship between tree age and trunk girth is likely to overestimate the age of such a tree, and this has been demonstrated by counting the rings of oaks on the Hill. In contrast to this, the trees of Brasenose Wood have none of these advantages, growing in strong competition on a clay soil which dries quickly in periods without rain. Consequently many of the trees in this wood, especially oaks, are very much older than their girth would suggest.

Measuring growth rings on a sample of oak from Brasenose Wood

Even though there are objective methods for calculating the age of old trees from their girth (for example White, 1998), on a varied site such as Shotover or on sites with atypical growing conditions the estimate can be particularly inaccurate. However, this can be greatly improved if the calculations are calibrated using growth-rate information from trees that had been growing in the same circumstances.

The Shotover Oak

The Shotover Oak

For many years the Shotover Oak stood at a prominent junction in the north-east corner of Johnson's Piece at the top of Gertie's Gap, and by virtue of its location, size and grandeur was probably the most iconic tree on the Hill. It has been a meeting place and a teaching space, people have exchanged lasting vows in front of it, and grandparents remember when they themselves clambered on it as youngsters. When it split and fell on Monday 13th July 2015 a feeling of sadness and disbelief permeated the community for many weeks.

Although not old enough to be truly 'ancient', the Shotover Oak was the oldest and largest Pedunculate Oak in the Country Park and was probably over 400 years old [see opposite page]. In 2010 a dendrochronological core sample showed that the tree was growing steadily and quite vigorously for its age, with healthy annual growth rings since 1930 of typically three to four millimetres. In 2014 it had a chest-height girth of 5.3 metres and a spreading canopy of 16 metres in diameter.

The underlying cause of the tree's demise was hollowing of the trunk, especially where it had been pollarded centuries before. At least twice during its long life the Shotover Oak had its upper canopy harvested for small timber and the effect of this pollarding could be most easily appreciated when viewed from the eastern side [see below]. Regular pollarding generally prolongs the life of a tree but if discontinued can lead to a weaker shape and leaves more places for rot to enter and develop. So although the Shotover Oak had been growing healthily, the new timber added each year was not enough to offset the hollowing at the top of the trunk.

The Shotover Oak
showing past pollarding

The final collapse was most probably triggered by dry weather. In the month preceding the fall, the rainfall had only been half of the regional average and the sandy soils of Shotover would have been very dry; notwithstanding the tree's easy access to deeper spring water, its vast network of surface roots would have been considerably stressed. Furthermore, oaks are among several species of tree that become brittle at times of drought and then when rain eventually arrives the sudden additional weight of dripping-wet leaves can be too much for some branches. 'Summer branch drop' is a well-known phenomenon in susceptible species.

Calculating the age of the Shotover Oak from its girth can only give a very imprecise estimate, and unfortunately when a trunk is hollow the earliest growth rings are not available for dendrochronological coring. Although the particular natural conditions under which the tree grew is an important consideration [see box, page 51], most uncertainty is introduced by the effects of pollarding or any other large-scale harvesting of branches from the canopy. Such canopy reduction significantly slows trunk expansion for several years thereafter, reducing the width of annual tree rings and making the tree appear much younger than its true age — for which an allowance must be made.

11 a.m. on 13th July 2015

Combining the best information available, and with advice from the Ancient Tree Forum, it is estimated that in 2010 the Shotover Oak was between 410 and 450 years old, suggesting that the acorn of this once mighty oak germinated in Tudor times in the reign of Queen Elizabeth 1 — in fact, not long after she travelled over Shotover in 1566.

3 p.m. on 13th July 2015

'Dick's Crab' is an unusually large Crab Apple in Johnson's Piece, shown here dwarfing the two people measuring its girth

The woodland archaeologist Dick Greenaway who first drew attention to this exceptional Crab Apple

is Pedunculate Oak with 97 individuals, followed by 32 Ash, 18 Field Maple *Acer campestre*, 15 Sycamore *A. pseudoplatanus* and 14 Beech. Together with the obviously tall and statuesque trees, there are some exceptional specimens that could easily be overlooked. These include large examples of Hawthorn, Rowan *Sorbus*

aucuparia and a particular specimen of Crab Apple — Dick's Crab — which being of modest height often escapes notice. However, it has a girth of 3.0 metres, giving Shotover a Crab Apple of an impressive size and is among the largest by girth in Britain. It flowers beautifully and bears excellent and ample fruit.

The veteran Hazel stools near Long Marsh are a relict of a centuries-old coppice landscape

An old encircling Ash stool in Brasenose Wood
Ivan Wright

Ancient coppice stools (the re-grown stumps of cut trees) are often omitted from inventories of Veteran Trees, yet they can be extremely old. With the exception of the shrubby Hazel, most coppiced tree species would have matured to a single-trunked 'maiden' if they had not been regularly cut for small timber. Although these trees have been prevented from developing into a grand tree, they have remained alive while most of their contemporaries have grown tall, aged, fallen and rotted without trace. Old coppice stools are difficult to age with any precision; however, for some species their circumference at the ground is approximately comparable to what the trunk would have been if it had grown as a maiden or pollard. On seeing a large coppice stool, especially in an area with a long history of coppice management such as Shotover [see pages 5 and 6], one can only wonder at its great age.

In Brasenose Wood there are many large and healthy stools of Ash and Field Maple, some with circumferences at the ground of up to seven

The naming of trees

Landmark trees in the countryside are often given names, sometimes several, with each tree being remembered by a family or group of friends, perhaps as a way-marker or meeting place. For some people, the process of naming is very satisfying and bonds them with their favourite tree and the surrounding landscape but this is not to everyone's taste and for some may seem somewhat sentimental or anthropogenic. However, the naming of Veteran Trees is encouraged by the Ancient Tree Forum because some names pass quickly and naturally into common usage, not only becoming part of local cultural history but also, importantly, lending a measure of protection to individual trees that are popular within the community.

The Shotover Oak had already reached this eminent status, and hopefully other named individuals will follow. Perhaps charismatic trees such as The Hairy Lime, The Sunset Oak and The Scrumpy Tree will become established landmarks — just three of the hundreds of trees that were mapped and named during Shotover Wildlife's Shotover Ancient Trees Project. Some popular and curious trees attract several names. For example, The Bendy Birch is also known by one local family as The Old Woman; they give it a hug on every visit — for *"when she's been hugged 1,000 times, she'll revert to her human form"*.

The Lollypop Snark is one of several curious 'trees' of more than one species, in this case Crack Willow, Pedunculate Oak and Rowan

The naming of trees has also proved to be a lot of fun. Jokes, puns, personal associations and memories are all tied up in the names that have flowed from surveyors' imaginations: Buddy Holly, Phoenix Ash, Baked Bean Maple and The Lollipop Snark.

The Bendy Birch
Drawing by Jacqueline Wright

The intriguing Snark Tree is a Crack Willow pollard which has trapped a stout Ash at its top and ensnared a Sycamore into its side

metres where it is possible to stand inside and be encircled by their stout regrown trunks [see page 55]. These stools are likely to be hundreds of years old and will have been cut and re-cut for timber countless times. Hazel, having a shrubby habit and being naturally multi-stemmed, is more difficult to appreciate in this way; even so, there are some very large stools, especially in Johnson's Piece, with circumferences at the ground of over six metres [see page 54]; others have developed unusually large trunks, each of a metre in circumference, since coppicing of the stool ceased.

Finally we come to some of the 'eccentric' trees that so impressed our visitors from the Ancient Tree Forum. The Bendy Birch in Johnson's Piece, with its double right-angle bends, always brings a smile. This Silver Birch seems to have partially broken when younger, with the upper part of the central stem being laid out horizontally. From this living stem a side branch has 'phoenixed' vertically to form a fine tall tree, while the original central stem has withered and rotted

away. There are also a number of Pedunculate Oaks that have recovered from breakage in years past and have gone on to provide an entertaining display of fused and contorted shapes.

Perhaps the most curious tree at Shotover is The Snark Tree. This veteran of Holme Ground began its life as a Crack Willow which, after being repeatedly pollarded, would have had the familiar club-headed shape of a riverside willow. Eventually — and typically — the trunk hollowed with age, with only part of the periphery surviving. Then at some time in the past, a Sycamore germinated at the base of the willow and grew up, partly filling the hollow trunk, while an Ash tree germinated at the top and extended its roots (now considerably thickened) downwards to occupy the rest of the hollow. The result is a composite 'tree' with three different barks around the trunk and three contrasting leaf canopies. There are also several two-species examples at Shotover, mostly based on old willow pollards and supporting a variety of 'guest' species such as Yew *Taxus baccata* and Rowan. In the case of 'The Body Snatcher', a sycamore grows concentrically within a willow [see picture, page 178].

Changes and trends

Building the inventory of Veteran Trees has also made it possible to record and appreciate the inevitable death of old trees at Shotover, some of which have already been mentioned. Trees fall and decay away, some in a relatively short space of time, and are easily forgotten: for example, the complete disintegration of the huge Grey Poplars near Westhill Farm that fell in the 1987 gales. Other notable trees that have fallen since 2000 include the once-largest Rowan which had a girth of 2.1 metres, a colossal Hawthorn of 2.2 metres girth, five significant oaks and one of the towering Ash trees of Johnson's Piece.

All trees have a finite lifetime, even though this can be 1,000 years for Yew and Pedunculate Oak. Any of our treasured trees could fall or die quite unexpectedly and this is, of course, an almost entirely natural phenomenon. However, it is the unnatural demise of trees by felling that often causes concern. Although a small number of specimen trees are protected by their iconic status, the vast majority are vulnerable to being felled for any number of reasons, ranging from the sensible to the rather more dubious. Occasionally noteworthy trees are cut down without any apparent regard for their value to the community

One of The Four Old Men, this wizened birch is a fine example of Shotover's charismatic old trees

or local ecology. However, the Shotover Ancient Trees Project has been a significant advance in raising awareness of the diversity of species on the Hill and, most importantly, the cultural and ecological role of Shotover's charismatic old trees.

This was the oldest oak at Shotover until its demise in 2007

Flora

Jacqueline Wright and Ivan Wright

This chapter encompasses wild flowers, grasses, sedges, rushes and ferns but excludes trees, which are described in the previous chapter [see page 44]. The larger plants considered here include woody species such as Heather (Ling) *Calluna vulgaris*, dogwood (*Cornus* spp.) and Gooseberry *Ribes uvo-crispa*, whereas woody shrubs, such as Elder *Sambucus nigra*, Spindle *Euonymus europaeus* and Wild Privet *Ligustrum vulgare*, have been grouped with the trees. Although Gorse *Ulex europaeus* is a substantial woody shrub, it is included here as a wild flower of the heathland habitat.

Quite apart from the beauty afforded by the colourful floral diversity of the countryside, plants are essential to all natural ecosystems — including those at Shotover. Through the miracle of photosynthetic chlorophyll, plants combine sunlight, rain and nutrients to generate the vast global blanket of terrestrial vegetation on which the majority of living organisms depend for food, energy, shelter and nesting habitat and as a structure for reproductive behaviour.

The flora of Shotover underpins the diversity of wildlife to be found and, along with the

Common Cow-wheat is a plant closely associated with ancient woodland Peter Creed

geology and soils, plays a major role in defining the habitats. Land management choices and the passage of time ultimately affect the character of the landscape. But in looking in detail at the wild flowers in a nature reserve, it becomes clear that the dispersal ability of different species also has a defining influence on habitats, especially species that have not needed to develop a strong dispersal mechanism. These plants are often

The buttercup hay meadow below Westhill Farm

This meadow and the horse paddock beyond are both surrounded by hedgerows that are ancient boundaries, and the two fields support a wide variety of associated wild flowers and grasses.

rare and may have survived in a relatively small area for millennia. Shotover Hill has many such species, and the majority are closely associated with a particular stable habitat — such as acidic grassland or ancient woodland. However, now that the wider natural landscape is greatly fragmented, species with limited dispersal ability can become imprisoned in their isolated fragment of habitat and are vulnerable to local extinction. The volume of accumulated data for Shotover's flora, representing more than a century of diversity and change, is a remarkable resource to help understand and safeguard the habitats and vulnerable species of the region.

The history of flora recording at Shotover

Not surprisingly, the first published references to a species of plant at Shotover are to oak trees, both as a source of timber and as important boundary markers in the landscape. One of the earliest is from 1513, in a petition by Thomas Wolsey to Henry VIII for a licence to cut wood at Shotover (Brewer, 1920). However, the earliest record of a herb at Shotover is in the charming 1657 herbal by William Coles (1626–62) entitled *Adam in Eden, or, Natures Paradise,* in which he summarizes the pulmonary virtues of Sundew (*Drosera* sp.). He also claims that the name

derives from the apparent beads of 'dew' on the leaves *"especially when the Sun is at the hottest"*, and continues: *"One of the sorts with round Leaves, whether it be the greater or the lesser I cannot say, groweth upon Shotover-Hill, on the side towards Heddington Quarries near Oxford, and likewise upon a Bog in Bagley Wood, betwixt Oxford and Abingdon."*

These are probably the first records of Round-leaved Sundew *Drosera rotundifolia* in Oxfordshire but it has long since disappeared from Shotover, and although it hung on for a while in the Cothill region west of Abingdon, it has not been recorded in the county since 1994 (at Parsonage Moor, Cothill).

In 1677, just 20 years after Coles' herbal was published, further important records were published by Dr Robert Plot (1640–96) in *The Natural History of Oxfordshire* [see page 13]. This fascinating and wide-ranging book summarizes the flora of the county and includes details for seven plants thought by Plot to be newly described species. Of these, Hairy Violet *Viola hirta* was noted for Shotover and *"many other places"*; however, Trailing Tormentil *Potentilla anglica* was found only on the western side of Shotover [see page 69] and according to Druce (1886: p. 101) was the first record of this species in Britain. At a time

Trailing Tormentil, shown here in Horseshoe Field in 2018, appeared as a record for Shotover in 1677 when it was recognized as a new species to Britain

Round-leaved Sundew

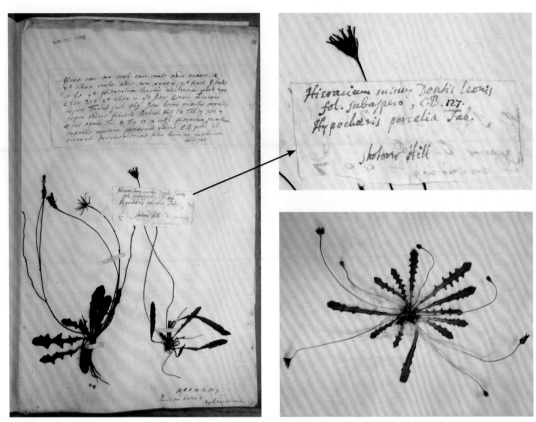

The first record of Lesser Hawkbit (c.1690) labelled 'Shotover Hill' in Bobart's own handwriting, and (below right) a prepared sample of the second Shotover record discovered in 2016 by Jacqueline Wright
©Courtesy of Oxford University Herbaria, Department of Plant Sciences

before Linaeus's binomial system of 1735, Plot knew this plant as *Pentaphyllum reptans alatum foliis profundis serratis*.

Lesser Hawkbit *Leontodon saxatilis*, or when first recorded *Hieraceum pumilum saxatile aspersum praemorsa radice*, is a similarly historic species for Shotover. It was noted for "*divers places about Oxford*" by John Ray in his *Synopsis Methodica Stirpium Britannicarum* of 1690, and this has become recognized as the first British record of the species (Druce, 1927) with creditation going to the botanist Jacob Bobart the Younger (1641–1719). The specific connection with Shotover is that a specimen of Lesser Hawkbit from that time is preserved in the Oxford University Herbarium, and labelled 'Shotover Hill' in Bobart's own handwriting. At about 300 years old this is Shotover's oldest known biological specimen. Lesser Hawkbit was rediscovered in 2016 near Bullingdon Meadow, this being only the second record at Shotover.

Following the 17th-century publications of Plot and Ray, over a century passed before John Sibthorp (1758–96) produced his *Flora Oxoniensis* in 1794. This was the first publication specific to the county's flora, and the first to give locations for scarce and less widespread species. The work added many species new to pre-1974 Oxfordshire and to Britain, and included bryophytes (mosses and liverworts), lichens, algae and fungi. This ground-breaking publication is thought to be based entirely on Sibthorp's own fieldwork, which is all the more remarkable considering that he died when just 38 years old. Much of his written work and his entire herbarium were lost — probably thrown away.

In 1886, the leading Oxfordshire botanist George Claridge Druce (1850–1932) published *The Flora of Oxfordshire,* with a second edition following in 1927. Druce's book contains a great many records for Shotover (about 470 species), much of it derived from his own visits to the Hill,

The Atlas Project and Adopt-a-sector

The Atlas Project was launched in 2010 by Shotover Wildlife as a systematic method of surveying and mapping the diversity of plant species (including trees but excluding bryophytes) across Shotover Country Park. An area including the SSSI and fields south of Westhill Farm has been divided into 600 50-by-50 metre squares, all of which have been wholly or partly surveyed. The resulting archive of over 25,000 records, for 450 plant species, is easily converted into distribution maps. These data have also proved especially useful for supporting both botanical and entomological studies associated with a particular plant species.

An unexpected bonus from the Project has been a better understanding of the spread of invasive alien species [see Fig. 7, page 81]. Furthermore, several species have been added to the known floral diversity — including Woodruff *Galium odoratum* and Lily-of-the-valley *Convallaria majalis*.

The Adopt-a-sector scheme is a coordinated method of plant recording, devised by Shotover Wildlife in 1999, in which individual surveyors, with support if required, are responsible for a sector of the SSSI for a year. The participants come from a wide range of backgrounds, from beginners to experienced botanists, with the size and habitat of the sector tailored to suit each surveyor. Since 1999,

many students have found the Adopt-a-sector scheme a most useful stepping-stone in their botanical education. In return Shotover Wildlife has received many important records for the Hill which have fed directly into conservation work — for example Wood Sage *Teucrium scorodonia* [see page 69].

Much of the Atlas Project data has been derived from the earlier years of the Adopt-a-sector scheme and since 2011 the two recording programmes have been integrated.

A Shotover Wildlife botanist recording for the Atlas Project in Brasenose Wood

but it also includes data from his predecessors and contemporaries, all of whom recorded at Shotover: William Coles, Robert Plot, Jacob Bobart the Younger, Johann Dillenius (1687–1747), John Sibthorp, William Baxter (1787–1871), Charles Daubeny (1795–1867), Rebecca Pryor (recording 1830–46), Henry Garnsey (1826–1903), Henry Boswell (1837–97), Alfred French (1839–79) and Professor Marmaduke Lawson (1840–96).

More recently, eminent 20th-century botanists who have recorded at Shotover include Eustace Jones (1909–92), John Brenan (1917–85), Humphrey Bowen (1929–2001), Richard Palmer (1935–2005) and John Killick. David Steel, himself a botanist, most notably collated the data necessary for the designation of 'Brasenose Wood and Shotover Hill' as a Site of Special Scientific Interest (SSSI), and was the first author to publish a list of vascular plants specifically for the SSSI, together with other sites within the original 1298 royal forest boundary (Steel, 1984: p. 86).

The most recent intensive period of botanical recording began in 1997 when Jacqueline Wright embarked on a survey of the wetland flora of

the SSSI. Following the founding of Shotover Wildlife in 1999, recording of flora was then extended to a systematic survey of the whole SSSI, together with surveys of private land across the Hill as opportunities arose. This has continued to the present day, with members of Shotover Wildlife learning identification skills and survey techniques under the 'Adopt-a-sector'

A grasses identification course in Mary Sadler Field

and 'Atlas Project' mapping initiatives [see box, page 61]. Since 1995 more than 450 vascular plant species have been recorded across the Hill, representing all habitats with the exception of domestic gardens. However, since records of wild flowers at Shotover began in 1657 with William Coles' Sundew, some 150 species have not been refound — suggesting a 20–25 per cent reduction in Shotover's floristic diversity [see also page 87].

The wild flowers of Shotover
Woodland flora

At the beginning of the year the first plants to flower on the woodland floor are those that can best exploit the early spring sunshine, and bloom and set seed before the trees come into leaf. The highlight of many people's year is a stroll on Shotover in April or May to see the spectacular blue haze of native Bluebells *Hyacinthoides non-scripta* and the carpets of white Wood Anemones *Anemone nemorosa*, glimpsed through the dappled shade of Hazel and oak. Fortunately, the Spanish Bluebell *H. hispanica* occurs very rarely and only around the periphery of the SSSI. Although hybridization occurs between the species, currently this common garden bluebell does not appear to pose a threat to the bulk of native Bluebells in the Country

Park. Every now and then bluebells with white flowers may be seen, and are a genetic mutation of the native species. These have given rise to a local myth that if you breathe in the aroma of a white Bluebell it will purify your soul for the coming year.

Other early flowering plants are Common Dog-violet *Viola riviniana*, Dog's Mercury *Mercurialis perennis* and the much-loved Primrose *Primula vulgaris*. Primroses were once a common sight in the countryside but underwent a major decline through the 19th and 20th centuries. Druce noted this for Oxfordshire (pre-1974) in general: "*The Primrose will probably become extirpated from many of its haunts if the raids made at present upon it continue, thousands of roots being yearly dug up to be sold in the streets.*" (Druce, 1886: p. 245) Today one can only imagine the profusion of woodland Primroses at Shotover but sadly Druce's prediction has come true; there are now very few plants to be seen.

There are still hints, however, of an admirable ancient woodland flora. Lily-of-the-valley *Convallaria majalis* was discovered on an old boundary in the SSSI in 2013. As the native form of this species is structurally indistinguishable from garden varieties, there

Native Bluebells on Shotover

A clump of mythically purifying white Bluebells in Holme Ground

Native Solomon's-seal discovered in 2015 during an Atlas Project survey

Moschatel or Town Hall Clock Peter Creed

is a possibility that it may have been planted in more recent times. However, the somewhat remote location — on a 400-year-old boundary where native Solomon's-seal *Polygonatum multiflorum* also occurs — suggests that the Lily-of-the-valley may be of native origin. Both of these ancient woodland species are included in *Oxfordshire's Threatened Plants: a register of rare and scarce species* (OTP) (Erskine *et al.*, 2018).

Johnson's Piece woodland

Johnson's Piece, a field owned by Oxford University on the upper slopes of the Country Park, is unusual among Shotover's woodlands in having remained unmanaged for over 100 years. With the exception of some usage as poor-quality grazing in the 19th century, it is likely to have remained relatively undisturbed for much longer than this, and the recent records of plants and invertebrates suggest it may be a significant relict of wood pasture (grazed land with trees)[see page 133] — a scarce habitat still to be seen on the Shotover Estate. The flora is typical of many old woodlands in Oxfordshire, yet compared with Brasenose Wood, for example, the absence of management, the different soil type and a more open tree canopy combine to produce a noticeably different woodland character. Wood-sorrel *Oxalis acetosella*, OTP, thrives in Johnson's Piece, as does Moschatel *Adoxa moschatellina*, a subtle gem known as Town Hall Clock; Wood Speedwell *Veronica montana* and Sanicle *Sanicula europaea*, OTP, appear in scattered locations. Most of these species are strong indicators of ancient woodland.

Brasenose Wood

Brasenose Wood is the largest area of homogeneous woodland habitat on the Hill. Commonly characterized as 'oak standards with coppice', this woodland was worked and valued as a source of timber and fuel for at least 500 years until demand for coppice products ceased in the 20th century. Small areas within the coppice were periodically harvested and then left to regrow, and this centuries-old industry provided the overall stability under which

Saw-wort with a Common Carder Bee in Brasenose Wood Helen Carter

a coppice-dependent ecology could become established. The outcome at Brasenose Wood is a woodland ground flora with a great many scarce and ecologically important flowering plants. Coppicing is still practised at Brasenose Wood, as in many other woodlands in Britain, with the objective of conserving this special habitat [see also box, page 224].

Several scarce plants in Brasenose Wood have not been found in any other woodlands on the Hill. Standing tall in a few open glades is Saw-wort *Serratula tinctoria*, OTP, a thistle-like plant with deep-purple flowers much visited by insects for nectar. Other plants exclusive to this woodland are Common Cow-wheat *Melampyrum pratense*, OTP, Spurge-laurel *Daphne laureola* and a number of grasses and sedges [see page 83].

Occasionally, notable plants are found after many years of apparent absence. Slender St John's-wort *Hypericum pulchrum* was rediscovered in 2002, and the regionally scarce Greater Burnet-saxifrage *Pimpinella major*, OTP, was recorded in 2013 after going unnoticed for many years. However, these discoveries are outnumbered by the overall atrophy of species — especially sedges and wood-rushes. Many plants favour the path edges in woodlands where there is usually more light but here they are particularly vulnerable to mowing; for example, Orpine *Sedum telephium* was lost in this way in 2008 [see also box, page 68].

Wood Anemone and Lesser Celandine *Ficaria verna* in the C.S. Lewis Community Nature Reserve

Magdalen Wood East

The tree canopy of this unmanaged relict of old woodland is almost entirely closed over, which greatly restricts the amount of light reaching the woodland floor. This in turn suppresses the ground flora. Plants to be found in Magdalen Wood East are mostly spring species that flower before the trees come into leaf: Bluebell, Wood Anemone, Yellow Archangel *Lamiastrum galeobdolon* and Greater Stitchwort *Stellaria holostea*. These are followed by the more shade-tolerant Lords-and-Ladies *Arum maculatum* and the delicate Enchanter's-nightshade *Circaea lutetiana*.

Slade Camp North

The plantation woodland in the northern section of Slade Camp (planted around 1980) supports a limited flora, yet retains some old hedgerows where many interesting plant species can still be found. Tutsan *Hypericum androsaemum* grows on the side of a ditch and former hedgerow [see also box, page 79], and a small patch of Woodruff *Galium odoratum* has survived, tucked away on the woodland edge. The Woodruff caused much interest when rediscovered in 2011, confirming long-standing vague anecdotal reports of its presence. Marsh Woundwort *Stachys palustris* was also found in Slade Camp North by John Killick in 1996 but has not been recorded since.

C.S. Lewis Community Nature Reserve

The area occupied by this small nature reserve was once one of the many quarries at Shotover supplying Kimmeridgian sand and clay to the local brick and tile industry. Since the quarry closed in about 1920, the clay pits have filled with water. Most of the wooded area has become dominated by Bramble *Rubus fruticosus* agg. and Nettle *Urtica dioica*, yet in the deepest shade woodland plants such as Bluebell and Wood Anemone flower in the spring, followed by Enchanter's-nightshade later in the season. A number of non-native plants have spread into the reserve from surrounding private gardens. On the path edges, where light can penetrate the tree canopy, the native flora is rather more varied, including small patches of Greater Stitchwort and Germander Speedwell *Veronica chamaedrys*. A notable diversity of wetland flora has been recorded in association with the pond margins [see page 79].

The western railway cutting viewed through the Horspath road bridge

Other woodlands

On the north side of Shotover the secluded secondary woodland of Monk's Farm, on private land, has many sandy banks and terraces creating an interesting and diverse topography. Some ground is too steep for much woodland ground flora to gain a foothold but here and there small patches of Moschatel indicate the maturity of the habitat. Where the woodland is more shaded, much of the understorey is an extensive carpet of native Bluebell.

The cuttings that form the eastern and western approaches to the railway tunnel under Sandy Lane, Horspath, have naturally succeeded to secondary woodland since the line was closed in 1963. Streams flow into both cuttings and maintain a humid micro-climate. The Horspath

section to the west has Ash, Hawthorn and Holly with an understorey of Bramble. The ground flora is now generally depauperate under the dense shade of the closed tree canopy but supports an abundance of ferns [see page 87]. By contrast, the Littleworth cutting to the east has become a relatively open woodland with Ash, willows (*Salix* spp.), a locally remarkable assemblage of mosses and liverworts [see page 96] and an extensive population of Opposite-leaved Golden-saxifrage *Chrysosplenium oppositifolium* [see also page 76].

Heathland flora

Heathland is characterized by acidic soils and the presence of associated woody shrubs such as heather and gorse. These shrubs can become over-dominant in places, to the disadvantage of other species, but when managed by cutting or grazing, more subtle heathland plants can compete and floral diversity is maintained. At Shotover this includes Heath Speedwell *Veronica officinalis*, OTP, with its soft purple flowers in spring, followed by the sparkling white of Heath Bedstraw *Galium saxatile* and the rich yellows of the hawkweeds (*Hieracium* spp.), Tormentil *Potentilla erecta*, OTP, and Trailing St John's-wort *Hypericum humifusum*.

Heath Milkwort *Polygala serpyllifolia*, OTP, is an exquisite regional rarity which Druce described in 1886 as generally distributed and *"very typical on Shotover Hill"*, and yet by 1998 the plant was considered to be rare in Oxfordshire and *"lost from Shotover and elsewhere"* (Killick *et al.*, 1998). In 2006 it was

Heath Milkwort

The reappearance of this plant from the heathland seed bank was a significant result of the targeted work to restore the heathy habitat of Mary Sadler Field.

Seeds and seed capsules of Heath Milkwort

rediscovered in Mary Sadler Field following heathland restoration work by Shotover Wildlife and has persisted in small numbers among the Heather ever since. Yet the future of the species may not be at all secure in this small and vulnerable heathy area, for although Heath Milkwort produces reasonable numbers of seeds, attempts to germinate them have so far been unsuccessful.

During Shotover Wildlife's first period of heathland restoration work and research (1999–2010), when Heather propagation trials and reseeding were under way, Shotover Hill had one of the largest expanses of Heather heathland in Oxfordshire. Also, where Heather has grown in the past an ample store of viable seed can remain in the soil even after decades, and germination can readily occur after soil disturbance. Consequently, given suitable management, heathland could develop at Shotover to at least a locally significant scale.

Acidic grassland flora

Shotover's infertile acidic grasslands provide the ideal conditions for an ecologically important community of tough, drought-resistant grassland plants to thrive, and some of the smallest and rarest of Oxfordshire's plants can be found in the patches of bare soil and short Rabbit-grazed vegetation. Acidic grassland flora is particularly evident on the slopes to both the north and south of the summit plateau, the principal areas extending from Horspath Common to Mary Sadler Field in the SSSI and

from the Ochre Pits to Sir John Miller Field on the Shotover Estate.

A defining plant of Shotover's acidic grassland is the diminutive annual Bird's-foot *Ornithopus perpusillus*, OTP, with its beautiful white two-millimetre pea-like flower, which by name is often confused with the much larger bird's-foot-trefoils (*Lotus* spp.). However, the name aptly describes these plants, as their clusters of narrow knobbly seedpods do look like the bony feet of a small bird. Because of its affinity for bare and sandy acidic soils, Bird's-foot flourishes in many places on Shotover Hill and yet is rare in pre-1974 Oxfordshire (Killick *et al.*, 1998). Similarly, Sand Spurrey *Spergularia rubra*, OTP, is a very small grassland annual with a strong population near The Sandpit. The small purple-pink flowers open and close in rapid response to changes in sunlight, making it elusive for much of the time. Although Sand Spurrey is a scarce plant elsewhere at Shotover, it has appeared in small colonies on the edges of the busier paths, suggesting that the seeds are being readily transported on the feet of people or animals.

The tiny flowers of Bird's-foot Helen Carter

Sand Spurrey

Mouse-ear-hawkweed *Pilosella officinarum* is also characteristic of acidic grasslands; as the name suggests, the rounded leaves with short soft silvery-white hairs on the underside resemble a mouse's ear. The lemon-yellow flowers are especially attractive to insects, as well as pleasing to human eyes when they flower *en masse* in Mary Sadler Field. In contrast, there is concern for the delicate and late-flowering Harebell *Campanula rotundifolia*, OTP, which has suffered a rapid decline at Shotover in recent years. In 1991 it was known at just four places in the SSSI (Bourdillon, 1991) but has now died out from three of these, and the remaining population is particularly vulnerable to mowing. When thriving, Harebell makes an important contribution to the late-summer diversity of pollen and nectar for insects.

The perennial hawkweeds (*Hieracium* spp.) are taxonomically ambiguous, with many proposed micro-species, so there is considerable uncertainty over the identity of individual plants. Over many years, eminent botanists have suggested a number of species at Shotover but there has been little recent research. Hawkweeds are not common in Oxfordshire, and it is pertinent here to describe two distinct forms that flower regularly. Narrow-leaved Hawkweed *H. umbellatum* sect. *Hieracioides,* which typically has a distinctive four-toothed leaf, is a tall plant with yellow dandelion-like flowers and is restricted to a cluster of heathy locations in the west of the SSSI. Although this form survives well enough in its leafy state, only a few individuals succeed in flowering each year, as the flower stems are readily eaten by Rabbits. Leafy Hawkweed *H. perpropinquum* sect. *Sabauda* is quite similar, although considerably more hairy, and is generally better established and more widely distributed. Trials under the Shotover Wildlife Species Recovery Programme [see box, page 68] have shown that although both species can grow well from collected seed, their different distributions suggest that Narrow-leaved Hawkweed is comparatively much less successful at self-seeding to new locations.

The mature acidic grassland south of The Sandpit, which has become established on an

Harebell is one of Shotover's many vulnerable species

Changing Forget-me-not

The Species Recovery Programme

The Shotover Wildlife Species Recovery Programme was launched in 2006 to conserve the scarcest plant species in the SSSI. The aim of the programme is to understand and safeguard the most vulnerable species, thereby encouraging more robust local populations. In the early stages of the programme, Shotover Wildlife members volunteered to become Species Champions and each investigated their species, including habitat ecology, propagation and the possibility of sustainable re-introduction should it be required.

Among the many species championed have been Harebell, OTP, Heath Milkwort, OTP, Heath Wood-rush *Luzula multiflora*, Orpine, Wood Sage, Narrow-leaved Hawkweed and Pale Sedge *Carex pallescens*, OTP.

Following the loss of Orpine from a path edge in Brasenose Wood in 2008, the only surviving plants of local provenance were those that had already been vegetatively propagated under the Species Recovery Programme. Consequently it was possible to begin re-introduction trials in 2009. Different locations were tested, using a small number of new plants at each, to determine the impact of grazing by Rabbits and deer. Then, in 2014 and 2015, 15 new plants were introduced back into the wood in the least vulnerable locations.

One of the last shoots of Orpine at Shotover, being rescued for off-site propagation

Propagated Orpine re-introduced into Brasenose Wood in 2015

area of particularly infertile and free-draining sand, is ecologically rich and important for a wide range of fauna and flora. Here the very weak vegetative growth needs no mowing, and the ant hills and Rabbit activity create an intricate diversity of micro-climates and bare-soil opportunities for annual plants and soil-nesting insects. The delightful annual Changing Forget-me-not *Myosotis discolor* appears in this habitat, along with Bird's-foot, both taking advantage

of disturbance by ants and mammals. Slender Trefoil *Trifolium micranthum* was recorded here in 2002 but has not been seen since.

In Horseshoe Field there is a further locally unique habitat, where the density of grazing Rabbits is particularly high (probably a territorially constricted population), and over much of the area the vegetation layer is seldom more than a few millimetres tall. Yet even where the vegetation is at its shortest, the diversity of

Newly liberated Wood Sage in Horseshoe Field

plants surviving these conditions is especially interesting, with Parsley-piert *Aphanes arvensis* agg., Procumbent Pearlwort *Sagina procumbens*, Heath Speedwell, Heath Bedstraw, the omnipresent Bird's-foot and the largest colony of the regionally rare Heath-grass *Danthonia decumbens*, OTP.

More importantly, around the edges of this area are two scarce plants that are not known to occur anywhere else on the Hill, Trailing Tormentil (OTP) and Wood Sage *Teucrium scorodonia*, both of which have particular regional significance. As noted earlier [page 59], Trailing Tormentil was considered by Druce (1886) to be new to Britain when first recorded at Shotover in the 17th century. Plot (1677: p. 146) gave the location as "*between Hockley [Hogley] and the woods under Shotover Hill*" which, considering the plants' preference for lighter acidic soils, was probably in the vicinity of The Ridings. Today the only known plants to remain are on the Whitchurch Sand of Horseshoe Field.

George Druce (1886: p. 224) noted that Wood Sage was growing at Shotover "*on south side, near old ochre-pits*" but, although Jean Buchanan recorded it in 1980 (the specific location not given), by 1998 Wood Sage could not be found (Killick *et al.*, 1998). However, in 2001, Shotover Wildlife discovered a small number of plants in Horseshoe Field and, furthermore, was able to demonstrate that it responds well to careful conservation. Today's location in Horseshoe Field cannot be more than a few hundred metres from the ochre pits where Wood Sage was recorded in the 19th century.

Meadows, pasture and arable land
Hay meadows
Strolling among the luxuriant flowers of an old unimproved hay meadow is one of the many pleasant sensory experiences to be had in the countryside, and there are still a few such meadows around the Hill. They are usually cut once a year, during the summer, and the vegetative material removed. This prevents woody trees and shrubs from becoming established, and until the next summer cut the field can flower freely and provide cover, pollen and predation opportunities for a wide range of animals. After many years of this management, a significant diversity of flowering plants can develop.

The traditional purpose of a hay meadow is to produce a cut of hay that can be collected and stored for feeding farm animals through the following winter. Some fields at Shotover are still used for this purpose, although the demands of modern productivity require 'improvement' by the application of at least some fertilizer, and the resulting stronger growth of grasses generally reduces floral diversity. Other fields, especially those in the SSSI or where artificial fertilizer has never been applied, are cut solely

A Bee Orchid among the developing flora of a newly established meadow

for conservation purposes. The collected material is discarded if the hay is unsuitable for animal feed or is otherwise unsaleable. Situated between these management alternatives — productivity or conservation — are a number of fields managed since the 1980s as 'set aside' [see page 71], which now contribute significantly to the diversity of wildlife habitats around the Hill.

Meadows mown for wildlife conservation

Conservation mowing is used to maintain two important types of grassland at Shotover: acidic grassland on the higher ground and the neutral grassland of Slade Camp South at the bottom. On the acidic Whitchurch Sand at the top of the Hill, particularly where the soil is more fertile, the grass grows strongly enough to require an annual cut. This is especially important now that the Rabbit population is insufficient to compete with the growth of grass [see page 36]. These areas include The Plain, Mary Sadler Field, Monk's Farm Meadow and similar nearby fields on the Shotover Estate.

Until the hay cut, The Plain is carpeted with the yellow of three different species of Buttercup: Bulbous *Ranunculus bulbosus*, Creeping *R. repens* and Meadow *R. acris*. The purples of Common Knapweed *Centaurea nigra* and Red Clover *Trifolium pratense* add further colour. Yellow-rattle *Rhinanthus minor*, also known as Hay Rattle, became established on The Plain in 2005 and has since spread extensively. This annual plant is semi-parasitic on a wide range of hosts, especially grasses and White Clover *T. repens*,

and so helps to counter the growth of some of the stronger species. Thyme-leaved Sandwort *Arenaria serpyllifolia* takes advantage of the small patches of bare soil created by Rabbits and moles but this tiny plant often goes unnoticed. The rare Annual Knawel *Scleranthus annuus*, OTP, once grew near Shotover summit but has not been recorded since David Steel saw it in the late 1970s.

Monk's Farm Meadow, near the summit of the Hill, has a character that is quite different from that of other hay fields at Shotover and is an important component of the regional ecology. It has been cut for hay every year for at least 60 years and, although lightly grazed at times, has never had an application of chemical fertilizer (Doris Stogdale, 2003, pers. comm.). The mildly acidic sandy soil is reflected in the flora such as Parsley-piert, Heath Bedstraw and abundant Sweet Vernal-grass *Anthoxanthum odoratum*. Yellow-rattle germinates prolifically in most years and its parasitic effect on the roots of grasses makes the sward thin enough to allow other flora to flourish. In spring and early summer the meadow can be awash with the yellow flowers of trefoils, buttercups and plants of the daisy family (Asteraceae), and is rich in invertebrates as a consequence.

In contrast to the acidic meadows, Slade Camp South on the flatter ground at the foot of the Hill has a neutral acidity on a heavier clay-loam soil. This field too has never had chemical fertilizer applied and is mown annually for conservation purposes. Along with Yellow-

Wild flowers along The Plain

Hay making on The Plain

Grass Vetchling Peter Creed

rattle, Agrimony *Agrimonia eupatoria* and Field Scabious *Knautia arvensis*, OTP, are a number of plants that are only rarely seen elsewhere in the SSSI, including Meadow Vetchling *Lathyrus pratensis* and Wild Carrot *Daucus carota*. The diversity is further enhanced by the calcareous influence of the Coral Rag under the southern quarter of the field. Here the regionally scarce

Oxeye Daisy in Bullingdon Meadow

Grass Vetchling *L. nissolia* grows, along with Woolly Thistle *Cirsium eriophorum*, the entirely parasitic Common Broomrape *Orobanche minor* and, in 2006, the rare 'casual' Yellow Vetchling *L. aphaca*, OTP.

Bullingdon Meadow, near Brasenose Wood, is a small mature tenanted meadow, originally quite similar to Slade Camp South. Here both Greater Knapweed *Centaurea scabiosa* and Common Knapweed have flowered among abundant Oxeye Daisy *Leucanthemum vulgare*. Locally unique to this field is the profusion of Yellow Oat-grass *Trisetum flavescens*, whose silky golden flower heads can set the field aglow in the evening sunshine. More recently the meadow has been lightly grazed by animals of various kinds.

Meadows set aside from cultivation
In 1988 a government 'set-aside' scheme was introduced to subsidize the withdrawal of selected arable land from crop production. Many fields at Shotover have remained uncropped since around that time even though the scheme closed in 2008. Fields have been maintained by annual mowing and, as a consequence, have developed naturally into young hay meadows, making a noteworthy contribution to the flora and fauna of the countryside. A good example at Shotover is the group of three meadows south of Westhill Farm that separate Brasenose Wood from the upper part of the SSSI: from west to east, Wood Ground, The Meadow and Lower Close. Although their species diversity is not outstanding, the sheer number of flowers in these fields makes a valuable overall contribution to the ecology of the adjoining SSSI, and is an important local resource of pollen and nectar [see box, page 142].

Wood Ground has a small but faithful patch of Fox-and-cubs *Pilosella aurantiaca* and for some time was the only known location at Shotover for Hemp-agrimony *Eupatorium cannabinum*. Although the latter was lost to ditching work around 1999, a few stems have since been found in Slade Camp South (first recorded in 2015). One of the more remarkable recent discoveries is Quaking-grass [see page 84]. Lower Close and in particular The Meadow are very wet for much of the year and so large patches of Cuckooflower *Cardamine pratensis* and Ragged-robin *Silene flos-cuculi*, OTP, can often be seen in flower in the late spring. Common Knapweed and Smooth Tare *Vicia tetrasperma* also grow in these fields and,

Abundant buttercups at Thornhill Farm

Common Cudweed is no longer common Peter Creed

in places, small patches of Colt's-foot *Tussilago farfara* and Scarlet Pimpernel *Anagallis arvensis*. Each May and June these meadows, along with many others on the Hill, become vibrant with the yellow of Meadow and Creeping Buttercups in great profusion.

Until 2017, the large field above Horspath, known as Rough Field, was set aside from cultivation for about 25 years, and its character is quite different from that of the damp fields below Westhill Farm. (Locally 'Rough' is pronounced to rhyme with cow, and appears as Row or Rowe Field in some publications.) The free-draining iron-rich acidic soil was improved for cropping while under earlier cultivation and retained a residual fertility throughout the following years as a hay meadow. Consequently, among the tall and strongly growing grasses in June were typical plants that could compete in these conditions: Rough Hawk's-beard *Crepis biennis*, Cat's-ear *Hypochaeris radicata* and Goat's-beard *Tragopogon pratensis*, all of which have yellow dandelion-like flowers.

Thus, over the years, the various different fields set aside from agriculture have gained their own distinctive character in keeping with their different aspect, soil and management history. A

number of these fields are on private land and one in particular, surveyed by Shotover Wildlife in 2014, was found to have an especially interesting flora. The most notable plant found was Common Cudweed *Filago vulgaris*, OTP; sadly no longer common, it is now nationally scarce. The survey counted 11 small but healthy patches of this unpretentious plant, along with Scarlet Pimpernel

Thorn-apple made a brief appearance in a Horspath pasture in 2010

Corn Marigold at Shotover in 2016

These vibrant flowers are seldom seen in the wild but where corn is grown on sandy soils this plant can be abundant and cause serious contamination of the harvested grain.

and Dame's-violet *Hesperis matronalis*, an aromatic plant which, although non-native, has been known in Oxfordshire since 1840.

Pasture

Pastures at Shotover include grassland grazed for beef cattle and fields close-cropped by horses. Even though the plants of such pastures seldom reach the flowering stage, surprises and notable records do occur. In 2010 the poisonous plant Thorn-apple *Datura stramonium*, OTP, was discovered growing in mud between two horse-grazed fields behind Manor Farm, Horspath. Several plants germinated and produced a number of handsome trumpet-shaped white flowers, followed by the spectacular thorny seedpods. This infrequent annual of the Nightshade family has not been recorded at Shotover before, although Henbane *Hyoscyamus niger*, OTP, a poisonous annual in the same family, was recorded by David Steel in Brasenose Wood in 1976–77 and by William Baxter in the 19th century.

On the Shotover Estate, pastures are predominantly nutrient-enriched for grass productivity and grazing. However, regularly waterlogged areas on the lower margins of the sloping fields make poor pasture and can support

a few interesting wetland plants, especially where trampling by livestock leaves the ground muddy. An example is Blinks *Montia fontana*, OTP, for which there is a very early record at Shotover by Sibthorp (1794) and which has also been noted more recently on wet pasture near The Spinney by David Steel and Peter Creed (2013, pers. comm.).

Arable fields

There are a number of arable fields on both the north and south side of Shotover but surveys have shown that around their margins there is scarcely any wild flora of note. The development of selective chemical herbicides in the 20th century has eliminated the great variety of colourful flora that accompanied past farming practices, and many of the plants that have not been seen at Shotover since the 19th century are of this type. However, a survey on the north side of Shotover in 1998 by the Northmoor Trust (now the Earth Trust) found Prickly Poppy *Papaver argemone*, OTP, Corn Spurrey *Spergula arvensis*, OTP, and Corn Marigold *Glebionis segetum*, OTP, three species listed as either endangered or vulnerable in England (Stroh *et al.*, 2014). Other, more common plants were recorded, such as Bugloss *Anchusa arvensis*, Common Fumitory *Fumaria officinalis*, Field Pansy *Viola arvensis*

Yellow-flowering Tansy and the silvery leaves of Mugwort on the track above Horspath

These old culinary herbs still flourish on this timeless Shotover byway.

and Parsley-piert (Kay and Gregory, 1989: unpublished report). Corn Spurrey has declined greatly in Oxfordshire as a result of agricultural intensification, as has Corn Marigold, but the latter can still be found on non-calcareous soils across the county. A single Corn Marigold plant was discovered in a muddy rut on The Plain in 2015 and thought a notable find but then the following year many thousands were found in a field of wheat on the north side of the Hill.

Tracks and byways

There are several kilometres of tracks, byways and bridleways at Shotover and their generally airy aspect can support a flora that is a most enjoyable feature of a country walk. In combination with the associated hedgerows, which often help maintain a warm and sheltered micro-climate, the track edges are an important structural and floristic component of the wildlife 'corridors' that interlace the countryside. While some of these linear features will pose a barrier to the movement of a small number of species, they are not nearly as restrictive as a pavement of concrete or a broad strip of tarmac.

Before the era of the motor vehicle when local travel was mostly on foot, people would have used the network of tracks and paths much more than they do today. It is not surprising, therefore, that at a time when people were more in touch

Lords-and-Ladies in flower

Lords-and-Ladies in fruit

The aromatic Ploughman's-spikenard Helen Carter

with the countryside, common wayside plants would be better known and attract regional names by which to remember them. Plants at Shotover that have rural names evocative of a bygone era include Traveller's-joy *Clematus vitalba*, Lady's Bedstraw *Galium verum*, Garlic Mustard also known as Jack-by-the-hedge *Alliaria petiolata* and Common Restharrow *Ononis repens*. In Britain, Lords-and-Ladies is known to have had over 100 country names including Adder's-meat, Cuckoo-pint and Parson-in-the-pulpit.

Aromatic plants too, of which there are many at Shotover, would have been well known to those who frequented country lanes, and some scarcer species can still be found. In 2014, the tall wayside Ploughman's-spikenard *Inula conyzae* was recorded at the foot of Sid's Hill on the Shotover Estate. This plant is so-called because it was used as a country substitute for spikenard, an oil extracted from a Himalayan plant and used since ancient times for expensive perfumes. On the grassy edges of the old byway that runs along the east side of Rough Field is one of the few places where the yellow flowers of Tansy *Tanacetum vulgare* can be seen in profusion. A great many benefits have been claimed for this aromatic plant; for example, the renowned 17th-century herbalist Nicholas Culpeper said, *"Let those women that desire children love this herb"*. Also nearby are the remains of an old settlement, known as Rough Barn, whose flora shows the influence of past human activity. Here may be found lingering wayside patches of Sweet Violet *Viola odorata*, culinary mints *Mentha* spp. and a species of Michaelmas-daisy *Aster* sp.. A more constant companion along the byways of Shotover is the softly scented Mugwort *Artemisia vulgaris*, which is said to relieve footsore walkers when placed in their shoes.

Marshes, ponds and streams

The marshes, ponds and streams at Shotover are mainly small and secluded but they are numerous and collectively provide a significant contribution to the ecology of the Hill. All of the damp or wet areas are fed by the many small streams that radiate from the spring line near the top of the Hill [see page 20]. Where water flows

High Triangle Marsh on the upper spring line in Johnson's Piece

Not far from the summit, the abundant marsh vegetation of this wetland flush is maintained by the constant flow of water from the spring outlet (foreground).

Marsh Valerian in Long Marsh

Shotover's most diverse marsh, supporting the highest density of different plant species on the Hill. Although most of the species are relatively common, the marsh is the only known location in the SSSI for the rather vulnerable annual, Tufted Forget-me-not *Myosotis laxa*.

Long Marsh also hosts two colonies of Marsh Valerian *Valeriana dioica*, OTP, the only known location at Shotover. This is an uncommon plant in pre-1974 Oxfordshire whose range in England has declined by 25 per cent since the early 20th century due to loss of habitat (Stroh *et al.*, 2014). Between 1995 and 2015 the number of flowering stems at Long Marsh has varied greatly, from four in 1999 to over 200 in 2001; years of greater abundance always follow the moderate disturbance of conservation work in the preceding year. So although Marsh Valerian could easily be lost if the habitat became too dry, disturbance at the right time of year promotes the spread of viable plant fragments — a process common to many wetland plants.

At any time of year Long Marsh appears lush and uniformly vegetated over its whole length, and yet on close inspection the lower two thirds has a more diverse flora, including the less common plants. The lower part of the marsh is a mature stream-head wetland that has probably lain undisturbed for centuries; however, the upper third was used for hand-grenade throwing practice during World War II. Wetland soils develop a highly stratified gaseous and mineralogical chemistry and take very many decades to mature and stabilize, and it is likely that the consequences of the deep churning of mud in the upper third of the marsh will affect

Opposite-leaved Golden-saxifrage

out at the spring line onto more level ground, or where the water is slow to drain away, a wetland 'flush' will persist throughout the year with water permanently on or just beneath the surface.

Streams at Shotover are generally less disturbed than many other habitats; indeed, some are deeply cut and overgrown, and form a dense barrier to even the most adventurous explorer. Hence, although the more ancient stream lines, generally higher on the Hill, have the most diverse flora, many of those that have been artificially deepened and straightened have remained unchanged for at least 100 years and can sustain a mature flora of some interest. Even when the flora is not particularly diverse, such streams do provide a niche habitat for some of Shotover's scarcer species, especially ferns [page 87].

Spring-line marshes

Over the 1.9 hectares of marsh surveyed in the SSSI [see box, page 77], more than 200 vascular plant species have been recorded since 1997 of which about 25 per cent are specifically wetland plants. The largest of the marshes is Long Marsh, perched on the Head deposits of Johnson's Piece and fed by several nearby springs and flushes. Surveys over many years have shown that this is the maturity of the floral diversity for decades to come.

Growing in the marshes and stream sides of the Hill is one of Shotover's early-springtime jewels, Opposite-leaved Golden-saxifrage, also known locally as Hennell's Yellow. This plant, with its small yellow flowers, is uncommon in pre-1974 Oxfordshire and not a strong competitor with other flora, and yet Shotover Hill remains a local stronghold. The abundance of the saxifrage has been mapped and monitored on the Hill by Shotover Wildlife since 1997; these surveys have revealed that this species is another that responds particularly well to soil disturbance during conservation work.

Marshes: survey and restoration

Comprehensive surveys of flora in the marshes, streams, flushes and ponds in the Country Park were undertaken by Jacqueline Wright in consecutive years from 1995 to 2000, and included four annual reports (for example, Wright and Wright, 2000) with conservation recommendations. The hydrological influences on the water balance of the marshland areas were investigated by taking regular measurements of rainfall and spring flow [see pages 21 and 22]. Since then, further botanical surveys have taken place under Shotover Wildlife's Adopt-a-sector scheme [see box, page 61]. These survey results were used as the evidence base for restoration and expansion of the marshes from 1995 to 2010. During this period the wetland extent in the SSSI, based on the presence of wetland flora, was raised by 50 per cent to 1.9 hectares.

Conservation work to raise water levels and increase the marshland area

The largest marsh on the north side of Shotover is in Sir John Miller Field and is known as Long Bog. In the past, this marsh and other nearby secluded wetlands supported a wild flora as good as any marsh on the Hill but over recent decades these wetlands have gradually lost moisture, thereby losing much of their botanical diversity (including mosses). However, Opposite-leaved Golden-saxifrage remains to some extent, along with Bog Stitchwort *Stellaria alsine*, Water Figwort *Scrophularia auriculata* and Ragged-robin.

To the north-west of Shotover, just downhill from the lower spring line, Tews Ground was once an open meadow of damp grassland. It has since succeeded to drier, patchy scrub but still retains some areas of very wet ground supporting a modest marshland flora. Tufted Vetch *Vicia cracca* and Square-stalked St John's-wort *Hypericum tetrapterum* can be found here and the field is currently the only known location at Shotover for Pepper-saxifrage *Silaum silaus*.

Ponds and open water of the Country Park

There is very little open water in the Country Park, and all the ponds are small and seasonal. The spring water that rises in Johnson's Piece collects at Long Marsh and flows through a series of three small ponds that hold at least some water for most of the year. The highest of these is impounded behind a dam that was built at the outflow from Long Marsh, probably in the 1970s. This was then repaired, raised and strengthened by Shotover Wildlife in 2001, and again in 2017 [see page 19], mainly to hold back water and ration its flow to the wetlands downstream but

Marsh-marigold Helen Carter

The Brasenose Farm Pond lies at the western end of the old driftway that once passed through Open Brasenose

The pond dates back to the 19th century and still retains a hint of its former floristic richness.

also to maintain a high water table in the southern and more mature part of the marsh. Very few plants grow on the pond margin but each spring there is a fine display of Marsh-marigold *Caltha palustris*.

The middle pond was dug in the 1980s and is surrounded by some notable flora including Brown Sedge *Carex disticha* and Opposite-leaved Golden-saxifrage. The pond itself catches the midday sun in the summer and is often covered with Floating Sweet-grass *Glyceria fluitans*. The third and lowest pond, alongside the access road to Westhill Farm, is much older and is shown on the Ordnance Survey map of 1881. As it is some distance from the spring line it is usually dry for much of the summer and covered with Fool's-water-cress *Apium nodiflorum* and yet the inflow is one of only three known locations in the SSSI for true Water-cress *Nasturtium officinale*, a species that was once fairly common at Shotover.

Four small seasonal ponds have been dug in Brasenose Wood, Slade Camp North and Magdalen Wood for amphibians but three of them are in deep shade and their flora is generally rather limited. The oldest, the Brasenose Wood newt pond, was created in the 1980s and supports Floating Sweet-grass, Common Water-starwort *Callitriche stagnalis*, Common Duckweed *Lemna minor* and Creeping Buttercup.

The Brasenose Farm Pond, which may have been created for farm animals to drink from, is fed by a small stream that rises nearby in Slade Camp South. Fortunately, the pond is isolated from the nearby deep ditch that takes the bulk of the runoff (often polluted) from north of Slade Camp and Magdalen Wood. This is the largest seasonal pond

in the SSSI and once boasted a particularly interesting flora. However, it became chemically contaminated from fly-tipping in the 1990s and its diversity has declined sharply. Nonetheless, the pond margin has False Fox-sedge *Carex otrubae*, Water Mint *Mentha aquatica* and Meadowsweet *Filipendula ulmaria*, and is the only known location on the Hill for Grey Sedge *C. divulsa* ssp. *divulsa*. Plants no longer extant include Lesser Water-parsnip *Berula erecta*, found by John Killick in 1996, and Common Spike-rush *Eleocharis palustris*.

Ponds and open water of northern Shotover

At Shotover, mostly on the northern side, there are a small number of ornamental ponds, fishponds and inundated clay pits, which are kept full by the upper spring-line hydrology of the Hill and together comprise Shotover's small area of permanent open water. Most of this habitat is on the Shotover Estate, including The Octagon Pond to the west of Shotover House, a long ornamental pond to the east (known as The Lake or Canal) and a cascade of old fishponds in The Spinney. The marginal flora of the two ornamental ponds is predominately dense pond-sedges and Common Reed *Phragmites australis*, and the narrow margin of Common Reed along the northern edge of The Lake is much used by water birds. In the 1980s, the flora recorded in and around the fishponds in The Spinney included a good range of wet-loving plants not recorded elsewhere on the Hill, such as Marsh Willowherb *Epilobium palustre*, OTP, Ivy-leaved Duckweed *Lemna trisulca*, Water Horsetail *Equisetum fluviatile*, Great Yellowcress *Rorippa amphibia* and Water Dock *Rumex hydrolapathum*.

To the north-west of Shotover Hill lies a series of three pits, filled with water, from which clay was extracted for the local brick and tile industry. The western pond dominates the C.S. Lewis Community Nature Reserve [see page 41], and many eminent naturalists have visited and recorded there. Among the historic marginal flora are the scarce Rigid Hornwort *Ceratophyllum demersum* and Marsh Horsetail *Equisetum palustre*, along with the regionally rare Spear-leaved Willowherb *Epilobium lanceolatum*, OTP. The other two ponds in the series are similar in area to the western pond, and are on private land. On the muddy margins of the eastern pond, along with some of the finest Alder trees at Shotover, grow wild Gooseberry *Ribes uva-crispa*, Red Currant *R. rubrum* and Wood-sorrel. Opposite-leaved Golden-saxifrage thrives along the stream line flushes that feed the ponds.

Stream lines and ditches

A number of small streams originate from the more copious springs around the Hill, some flowing through marshes and ponds, and all terminating in deep drainage ditches or buried pipes around the periphery of the Hill. Within Brasenose Wood and Slade Camp North is also a somewhat confusing network of ditches, cut over many years to coax the water this way and that.

The strongest flowing spring (a consequence of the eastward tilt of the geological strata [see pages 11 and 20]) issues from behind The Piggery near Horspath and creates a stream that flows towards Littleworth in a mature, classically V-shaped valley. Mature woodland has developed in the valley, with fine specimens of Ash, Pedunculate Oak and Wild Cherry, and an understorey of Hazel. Along the stream the ground flora varies with the extent of light penetration, with patches of Wild Angelica *Angelica sylvestris*, Yellow Archangel, native Bluebell, Wood Anemone,

Tutsan and Shotover Wildlife

In 1998, a year after wetland conservation work began in a small marsh in Johnson's Piece, a single plant of newly germinated Tutsan *Hypericum androsaemum* was found at the outflow of the marsh. The plant appeared to respond to the disturbance from conservation work to let more sunlight into the marsh. Coincidentally, the newly published *The Flora of Oxfordshire* by Killick *et al.* (1998) had suggested that Tutsan had become extinct at Shotover, the only record on the Hill having been published 150 years previously by Walker (1833). The appearance of Tutsan, and its probable link to carefully planned and monitored conservation work, was of seminal importance. It demonstrated that such work could produce results of historic and ecological significance, inspiring further similar efforts, and led, in part, to the founding of Shotover Wildlife in 1999.

Shotover Wildlife has since collected and stored seeds from this Tutsan plant, and trials under the Species Recovery Programme [see box, page 68] have shown that these seeds germinate readily. The stored seed is of the purest possible provenance and very unlikely to have derived from cross-pollination with a garden variety of St John's-wort. The plant discovered in 1998 was still thriving in 2018, accompanied by a second from a more recent germination. A further plant was found in 2011 in an old field boundary ditch in Slade Camp North.

The Tutsan plant that first demonstrated the true worth of monitored conservation work Ivan Wright

Tutsan berries and flowers

Gooseberry, Red Currant, Opposite-leaved Golden-saxifrage and Hart's-tongue *Asplenium scolopendrium* and, in the stream, Great Horsetail *Equisetum telmateia*, Brooklime *Veronica beccabunga* and Water-cress.

Elsewhere on the Hill, stream-line plants of particular note include Tufted Forget-me-not, Tutsan and Yellow Iris *Iris pseudacorus*. Tufted Forget-me-not, with its small blue flowers, is scarce at Shotover yet thrives in the clean water of the vigorous stream that flows north-east towards The Spinney. Tutsan is another stream-side plant of which only a few specimens are known in the Country Park [see box, page 79]. A curiosity on the royal forest boundary near Horspath is a single tuber of Yellow Iris, a plant that has declined in the wild in Oxfordshire. This rugged individual has clung on for at least 20 years under the shade of the tree canopy not far from the spring line, growing neither larger nor smaller, and throughout this time has been known to flower only once.

On the slopes above Horspath, the upper spring line gives rise to several small streams which flow south-west in secluded channels towards Hollow Brook. The damper stream sides support Bog Stitchwort, Opposite-leaved Golden-saxifrage, Water Figwort and Yellow Archangel,

Mistletoe in the Brasenose farmhouse garden in 2015

while the drier stream sides support Common Hemp-nettle *Galeopsis tetrahit* and Tansy. The marsh plants Gypsywort *Lycopus europaeus* and Lesser Spearwort *Ranunculus flammula*, OTP, grew in one of these channels until recently but neither could be found in 2013. A large flowering English Elm [see page 49] also survived in this channel for many years but died in 2000.

One of the Horspath streams flows into the western approaches to the disused railway tunnel. Before this area was cleared in 2000 for public access and pond creation, a diverse wetland flora could be found in the marshy ground in the bottom of the cutting, including Square-stalked St John's-wort, a large patch of Water-cress and the locally scarce Marsh Valerian. However, since the ponds were installed these marshland plants have given way to Fool's-water-cress, pond sedges and Floating Sweet-grass, although Opposite-leaved Golden-saxifrage still grows on a clay bank where water continually flushes out over the soil surface.

Grounds and gardens

The flora associated with human habitation is an important component of the natural environment. In addition to the many domestic gardens with their great diversity of flowering plants and micro-habitats, there is a notable contribution from areas of rough or abandoned ground, 'brownfield' sites, allotments and the environs of older buildings. In particular, churchyards and farmyards, by virtue of their longevity, can harbour uncommon species rarely seen in the wider countryside.

Within some older Shotover gardens, native plants can be found that are sufficiently scarce to occur in only a few other places on the Hill. Where these plants go underappreciated they are particularly vulnerable to local extinction. Mistletoe *Viscum album* is one such example, with its well-known translucent white berries and its strong preference for poplar, lime and apple trees. It is a rare sight at Shotover and until 2016 a large and healthy plant grew on an old domestic apple tree in the sheltered garden of Brasenose Farmhouse. The tree and Mistletoe have since been removed.

Invasive alien plants

The term 'invasive alien' is applied here to non-native plants that strongly out-compete other flora, usually undermining the diversity of native species. Occasionally, the term is also used rather

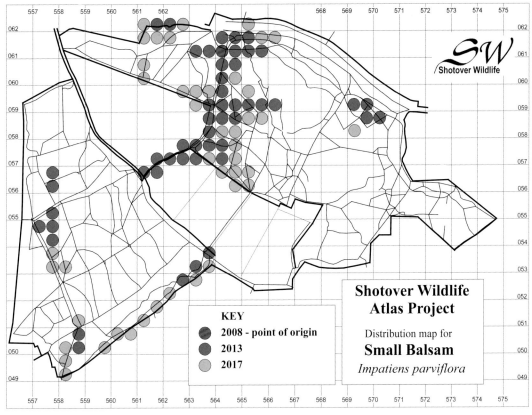

Figure 7 **The spread of Small Balsam since 2008** Ivan Wright/© Crown copyright 2018 OS 100057706

loosely for non-native plant species that are not strongly invasive but have persisted in balance with the British native flora for some years. An example of the latter at Shotover would be Wilson's Honeysuckle *Lonicera nitida* which has only spread a little from where it was planted originally in the 1950s, when Slade Camp was used for housing. A less clear example is New Zealand Pygmyweed *Crassula helmsii*, which was first recorded in pre-1974 Oxfordshire in 1973 and found by John Killick in the Brasenose Farm Pond in 1996. In the 1990s this plant was considered to be a potentially invasive species — it can be spread by animals and by human feet — but, so far at least, it has not been found in other Shotover ponds. The plant appears to require nutrient-rich conditions to thrive in this country, and remains uncommon in Oxfordshire (John Killick, 2014, pers. comm.).

In contrast, Small Balsam *Impatiens parviflora*, which was first recorded in the SSSI in 2000, has spread dramatically at Shotover,

Small Balsam

altering the woodland understorey in places. This yellow-flowered annual from East Asia has increased steadily throughout Britain and at the time of writing is the fastest spreading species on the Hill. From 2000 to 2008 it was limited to a small patch near the car park but since 2009 has rapidly extended its range in both Brasenose Wood and on Shotover Hill [see Fig. 7, page 81]. It favours unvegetated ground where the shade is at its most dense, often under a monoculture of Hawthorn, but increasingly the seed is being dispersed to other areas, transported by runoff, the movement of water-borne silt and the feet of people or animals. Himalayan Balsam *Impatiens glandulifera*, also known as Indian Balsam or Policeman's Helmet, has been established in private gardens, stream lines and woodland edges at a number of locations around Shotover for some years. However, by 2015 it had encroached upon the SSSI near the main car park and also at both Brasenose Wood and Magdalen Wood.

Japanese Knotweed *Fallopia japonica*, which is particularly difficult to eradicate, occurs in a number of places close to the SSSI and is gradually advancing. A large and invasive

Green-winged Orchid, now nationally rare, in an old Shotover meadow Eleanor Hawtree

variety of Creeping Dogwood *Cornus canadensis* was introduced to Shotover on the eastern side of Johnson's Piece — probably in the early 20th century. This 'ornamental' plant favours marshy areas and does not spread at an alarming rate; however, its dense patches and network of woody rhizomes out-compete all other flora beneath its canopy. Water Fern *Azolla filiculoides* is a tiny invasive alien which has found its way to some of the garden ponds around Shotover.

Orchids at Shotover

The highly specialized flower structures of orchids have developed to attract particular insects for pollination, and are often considered to resemble all manner of animal, insect or human forms — hence some common names such as Lizard, Bee or Man Orchid. Their exquisite and ephemeral beauty and the rarity of most species in the countryside mean that they are not only a pleasure to discover but also vulnerable to being dug up by collectors. For this reason, Shotover's orchids are described here without reference to their locations.

At Shotover the diversity of species in the orchid family (Orchidaceae) is somewhat limited by the acidity of the soils. Overall, 16 species have been found but half of these have not been recorded for many years, including Early Spider-orchid *Ophrys sphegodes*, OTP, and several marsh species. However, Common Spotted-orchids *Dactylorhiza fuchsii* are widespread and flower every year, and the Bee Orchid *O. apifera* appears in most years and in a variety of locations. The first known record at Shotover of Pyramidal Orchid *Anacamptis pyramidalis* was from the SSSI in 2009, followed by a second flowering in 2015 — possibly from the same plant. It is remarkable that the Green-winged Orchid *A. morio*, OTP, was a relatively common orchid in Oxfordshire in the 19th century, and yet in the past 100 years there have been only two records at Shotover: 2007 and 2016. Green-winged Orchid is now nationally rare and considered vulnerable to extinction (Stroh *et al.*, 2014).

Helleborines and Common Twayblade *Neottia ovata* are also in the orchid family and are rather more associated with woodland habitats. One of the scarcer species at Shotover is Violet Helleborine *Epipactis purpurata*, which is seen most years in very small numbers but often succumbs to being eaten by molluscs. Broad-leaved Helleborine *E. helleborine* is more frequent and widespread but seldom appears in the same place twice. Occasionally it produces a flowering stem of statuesque proportions (80 centimetres) and yet it has a remarkable ability to blend into the surrounding vegetation and go almost unnoticed. Common Twayblade is much smaller and also prey to molluscs but has been recorded in flower at a small number of locations.

Grasses, rushes and sedges
Grasses
To a great many people grass is simply grass: a lawn to mow, a turf for football or a park in which to stroll, play games or have a picnic. It simply serves as a hard-wearing living green carpet without any botanical or ecological relevance. And yet this remarkable group of plants, the Poaceae, includes rice, maize, wheat and sugar cane — all of which are staples of the global food supply. Literally, we could not live without them. Tall grasses, some of which can reach 30 metres, demonstrate the engineering efficiency of a simple hollow tube — including bamboo which is still used as scaffolding in many places throughout the world. Grass stems have

Early Hair-grass on Horspath Common

also been crafted into reed flutes, some of the earliest tuned musical instruments.

From a botanical perspective, grasses occur in most habitats; some appear to grow almost anywhere, while others are strictly limited to a niche habitat. Consequently, it is not surprising to find that Shotover has a rich diversity of grasses, over 60 species, from the ubiquitous Annual Meadow-grass *Poa annua* to the scarce and habitat-specific species of ancient woodland or acidic grassland.

A selection of Shotover's grasses

Wood Melick in Brasenose Wood

Unlike the rushes and sedges, which mostly favour damper places, many grasses have adapted to survive in drier locations, and the sandy soils of Shotover Hill have always supported grasses that would be hard to find elsewhere in Oxfordshire. Good examples are the diminutive Early Hair-grass *Aira praecox*, OTP, Fine-leaved Sheep's-fescue *Festuca filiformis*, OTP, and Heath-grass. Although Heath-grass is regionally scarce and only grows in a few places on the Hill, it is remarkably tough and persistent, even on well-trodden paths. The more common acid-tolerant grasses that are abundant on the Hill include Sweet Vernal-grass, Common Bent *Agrostis capillaris* and Creeping Soft-grass *Holcus mollis*. Scarce acidophile grasses which have not been recorded at Shotover for many years include Silver Hair-grass *Aira caryophyllea*, OTP, and Mat-grass *Nardus stricta*.

It is this community of drought-tolerant grasses, especially when close-grazed by Rabbits or sheep, which defines 'acidic grassland', yet this habitat is equally important for other species groups. For example, within the short sward of fine grasses grow similarly tough and scarce wild flowers [page 66] and the greater exposure of bare soil in acidic grassland, compared with tall or dense grasslands, favours lichens, mosses and soil-nesting insects.

Grasses that can survive hot dry conditions are commonly wiry, with fine leaves that conserve water, and consequently tend to be small and relatively inconspicuous. In contrast, the light-seeking grasses of shady woodlands are often tall with broad leaves. This is especially true of Brasenose Wood where many of the grasses

The attractive flowers of Quaking-grass

are indicative of ancient woodland and found in few other locations on the Hill. The tallest grasses include Wood Millet *Milium effusum* and the statuesque Hairy Brome *Bromopsis ramosa*, while along the old boundary banks are the shorter Wood Meadow-grass *P. nemoralis* and delicate lacy inflorescences of Wood Melick *Melica uniflora*. In fact, ancient woodlands in general and Brasenose Wood in particular are often overlooked as exceptional places to enjoy the diversity and beauty of grasses.

Perhaps more than any other group of plants the grasses can present some most interesting and curious discoveries, for instance, by germinating from long-dormant seed in a farmyard or field margin or as aliens from a commercial seed mixture. The most remarkable of such finds at Shotover is the nationally rare Loose Silky-bent *Apera spica-venti*, OTP, found near Brasenose Wood by Nicola Bourdillon (1991) and as a single plant in 1998 at Manor Farm, Horspath, but not seen since. This finely structured grass is nationally scarce, having declined in England by 44 per cent since the early 20th century (Stroh *et al.*, 2014), and so naturally there are very few Oxfordshire records. In 2011, Quaking-grass *Briza media*, OTP, which has also declined over recent years, appeared in the floristic margin of Wood Ground (near Westhill Farm). This discovery was particularly surprising as Quaking-Grass is more usually associated with calcareous grassland. However, it is known to reappear in old meadows and in 2015 a second, larger patch of the distinctive quivering flower heads was found on the edge of a nearby path in The Meadow.

Great Brome *Anisantha diandra* was first recorded in pre-1974 Oxfordshire as recently as 1978, and in 2000 was found in great abundance at Shotover in a privately owned field that had been recently set aside from cropping. Although the grass has become less abundant, it has persisted around the margins of the field ever since. Two examples of grasses that have almost certainly been introduced as seed with horse or game-bird feed are the handsome Yellow Bristle-grass *Setaria pumila*, seen on field margins on the Shotover Estate, and Cockspur *Echinochloa crusgalli*, a rare 'casual' also known as Barn-yard Millet, found growing in a large patch near Horspath. Although these grasses probably arrived at Shotover in only the past few years, both species have been known in Britain for at least 150 years.

Heath Wood-rush Peter Creed

Rushes and wood-rushes

Within the Juncaceae family of vascular plants, the 'true rushes' (*Juncus* spp.) are mostly distinguished by their tubular leaves and a preference for very wet soils. Wood-rushes (*Luzula* spp.) are more sedge-like with short curving leaves and have a characteristic covering of long fine white hairs; they generally prefer more acidic and drier soils compared with the rushes.

Brasenose Wood has suffered two notable losses in recent years: Blunt-flowered Rush *Juncus subnodulosus* has not been recorded since 1980 and Great Wood-rush *Luzula sylvatica*, OTP, was lost in 2004. However, Hairy Wood-rush *L. pilosa* flowers each year along some of the ancient boundaries and the uncommon Heath Wood-rush *L. multiflora*, OTP, clings on in just a few places. The future of Heath Wood-rush under the current regime of path mowing in Brasenose Wood remains somewhat uncertain and has been included within Shotover Wildlife's Species Recovery Programme [see box, page 68]. Although this declining wood-rush responds well to vegetative propagation, it has proved rather more difficult to find a suitable site for sustainable re-introduction.

In 2011 Slender Rush *Juncus tenuis* was recorded in Brasenose Wood, a relatively new arrival for Shotover. This non-native species, which does not have the hollow leaves that are characteristic of most rushes, has become naturalized in Britain since the 18th century but was not recorded in pre-1974 Oxfordshire until 1956. It is neither vigorous nor invasive and remains a rare species in the county. On the Hill, Jointed Rush *J. articulatus* was confirmed in 2000 and is quite difficult to find among the dominance of Sharp-flowered Rush *J. acutiflorus*, even though in Oxfordshire Jointed Rush is the more common. Sharp-flowered Rush is often misidentified as Jointed Rush.

Sedges

Plants of the sedge family (Cyperaceae), which include club-rushes and spike-rushes, have greatly declined in southern Britain since the 19th century — along with many other damp-

Remote Sedge

Pill Sedge is scarce in Oxfordshire but common at Shotover Helen Carter

loving species. Inevitably it is the rarer species that have been lost from Shotover, including Star Sedge *Carex echinata*, OTP, Flea Sedge *C. pulicaris*, OTP, Carnation Sedge *C. panicea* and Bristle Club-rush *Isolepis setacea*, none of which have been seen since the time of G.C. Druce. More recently, Bladder Sedge *C. vesicaria*, OTP, was last recorded in 1969 by Humphrey Bowen in the C.S. Lewis Community Nature Reserve. Spring Sedge *C. caryophyllea* was last recorded in the 1970s in Brasenose Wood, and Common Spike-rush *Eleocharis palustris* was lost from near Brasenose Farm sometime after 2002.

Currently, 16 species of *Carex* sedge are known in the Shotover area. Notable sedges in and around Brasenose Wood include Pale Sedge *C. pallescens*, OTP, Oval Sedge *C. leporina* and Grey Sedge. Pale Sedge and Oval Sedge appear never to have been particularly common in Oxfordshire, and around Shotover they occur only sparsely in areas of impeded drainage. However, both species have been shown to respond well to appropriate coppice management or similar mild disturbance. Remote Sedge *C. remota* is common at Shotover and in places provides a spectacular display of dense flowering tufts along the stream sides.

Pill Sedge *C. pilulifera* is noticeably different in preferring leached sandy soils; the densely tufted plants thrive on the dry acidic soils of Shotover. Although scarce in pre-1974 Oxfordshire, it is common on the Whitchurch Sand that caps the Hill. Pill Sedge also accumulates a healthy and durable store of seed so that when acidic soils on the Hill are disturbed, as when the topsoil was removed during Shotover Wildlife's acidic grassland restoration [see box, page 98], this species can be abundant for the first few years of succession.

Ferns and allies

The earliest vascular plants, which includes the ferns, horsetails, clubmosses and quillworts, date back to the Carboniferous period (350 to 400 million years ago). Ferns and clubmosses were the first land plants to develop a vascular system of branching veins but continued to reproduce by the more primitive production of spores — as do mosses, liverworts and fungi. However, the evolutionary development of a vascular system allowed the formation of stems and branches, and with this additional structural capability developed the rigidity for a taller and more upright growth habit. It is hard to imagine the vegetation of the Carboniferous era with its 20-metre tree ferns and 40-metre clubmosses, all taking advantage of the higher concentrations of oxygen during that period.

Before agricultural drainage began drying out the landscape around Shotover, the range of horsetails, ferns and clubmosses would have been considerable — perhaps 20 species. Of the five species of horsetail known to have been present at Shotover, three have not been recorded in recent times: Water Horsetail *Equisetum fluviatile*, Marsh Horsetail *E. palustre* and Wood Horsetail *E. sylvaticum*. Only Field Horsetail *E. arvense* and Great Horsetail *E. telmateia* are known to remain.

The same holds true for the diversity of ferns at Shotover. During the 19th century damp and sheltered places would have had Lemon-

Scaly Male-fern in Brasenose Wood

Fern crosiers in spring

scented Fern *Oreopteris limbosperma*, Lady-fern *Athyrium filix-femina*, Moonwort *Botrychium lunaria*, Black Spleenwort *Asplenium adiantum-nigrum*, Narrow Buckler-fern *Dryopteris carthusiana*, Adder's-tongue *Ophioglossum vulgatum*, Fir Clubmoss *Huperzia selago* and Stag's-horn Clubmoss *Lycopodium clavatum*. All these now appear to be locally extinct. The final record of Lady-fern was in 1987 in The Spinney, and that of Adder's-tongue in 1986 by Humphrey Bowen in the C.S. Lewis Community Nature Reserve. More recent work on buckler-ferns renders Sibthorp's early record of the rare Crested Buckler-fern *D. cristata* as uncertain.

Notwithstanding the steep decline in the diversity of ferns and horsetails at Shotover over the past 150 years, and the simplicity of their flowerless structures, these primitive plants still hold a special place in the countryside, both ecologically and aesthetically. In the spring and summer the sight of the cinnamon-coloured fern crosiers — 'fiddleheads' — unfurling in the woodland shade is a wonder of nature that can still be enjoyed on the Hill.

Perhaps the scarcest surviving species of fern are Hard Shield-fern *Polystichum aculeatum*, OTP, and Soft Shield-fern *P. setiferum*, OTP. Both of these species were present at Shotover in the 1880s and, after a long period of going unrecorded, a few solitary examples of both were discovered on ditch-sides in the SSSI in 2011. Hard Shield-fern also occurs at the Horspath railway cutting along with the delicate Wall-rue *Asplenium ruta-muraria*. The statuesque Scaly Male-ferns *D. affinis* agg. are an aggregation

Intermediate Polypody on Horspath Common

of uncommon subspecies which are difficult to separate; however, there are characteristic examples of the subspecies *D. affinis* ssp. *borreri* scattered across the Hill.

In the past, Common Polypody *Polypodium vulgare* was widely distributed in Oxfordshire but had declined in the vicinity of Shotover. However, from about 2010 this charming epiphyte appears to have increased markedly on trees and rotting stumps around the Hill, perhaps in response to the gradual improvement in air quality over recent decades, as with some bryophytes [see box, page 93]. Shotover also has a fine colony of Intermediate Polypody *P. interjectum*, OTP, recorded at a single location on the Hill. The rhizome of this fern is embedded in the cracks and crevices of an old mossy Hawthorn on Horspath Common.

Changes and trends in Shotover's flora

The floral diversity of Shotover today is much less rich compared with only a few centuries ago, a time when many plants now rare or extinct at Shotover would have been commonplace. Back in the 18th century, for example, the flower meadows of Shotover would have been host

Hard Shield-fern in the railway cutting at Horspath

to gentians and rare orchids, as well as flowers with evocative names such as Weasel's-snout *Misopates orontium*, Corncockle *Agrostemma githago* and Strawberry Clover *Trifolium fragerum*. It was once possible to explore the peat-bog valleys and discover Nodding Bur-marigold *Bidens cernua*, Bogbean *Menyanthes trifoliata*, sphagnum and many other wetland treasures. Frog Orchid *Coeloglossum viride* once grew in a local pasture but by 1822 had become extinct in pre-1974 Oxfordshire (Killick *et al.*, 1998) and the discovery of Field Gentian *Gentianella campestris* at Shotover in 1744 provided the first Oxfordshire record of a plant that is now in national decline. Around 1908, the botanist George Druce wrote the following evocative account of Shotover's declining flora: "*The once celebrated district of Shotover has suffered much during the past century ... . In some places where the water issued at the base of previous strata, bogs were formed, then the home of the sundew (*Drosera*), the wood horse-tail* Equisetum sylvaticum*, and other interesting uliginal species, while the drier spots on the sandy or peaty soil had the buck's-horn plantain* Plantago coronopus *and the clubmosses* Lycopodium clavatum *and* L. selago*; in other spots the moss* Polytrichum commune *was luxuriant, while on the turfy slopes the moonwort (*Botrychium*), the lady's-tresses* Spiranthes spiralis *and the field gentian* Gentiana campestris *delighted the wanderer, or on the heathy ground the mountain fern* Dryopteris montana* [now known as Lemon-scented Fern]

Yellow Vetchling Peter Creed

showed its fragrant fronds. But these have gone.*" (G.C. Druce, 1939: p. 47)

Shotover Hill has undoubtedly continued to lose flora diversity throughout the 20th century. However, there have also been numerous gains, and it is only when past records are compared with later survey work that the full extent of new arrivals and probable losses can be properly appreciated. It is possible to conclude from the more recent surveying by Shotover Wildlife that a number of species on David Steel's 1984 plant list have almost certainly died out, including the nationally rare Annual Knawel on The Plain, Creeping Bellflower *Campanula rapunculoides* in the Slade Camp fields, Nettle-leaved Bellflower *C. trachelium* in Brasenose Wood, and Knotted Clover *Trifolium striatum*, OTP, and Tuberous Pea *Lathyrus tuberosus* in unspecified locations.

Survey work since 1995 has added 90 species not previously recorded at Shotover but does, however, encompass a wide range of reasons for their inclusion. These are: scarce species hitherto overlooked (Fine-leaved Sheep's-fescue), species or subspecies arising from taxonomic divergence (Narrow-leaved Vetch *Vicia sativa* ssp. *nigra*, OTP), those relatively new to the British list (Slender Rush), new invasive species (Small Balsam), germinations from old seed banks (Loose Silky-bent, orchids), probable arrivals in commercial feed-seed (Yellow Bristle-grass), additions under a more inclusive policy toward introduced plants (Cotoneaster), and escapees from domestic gardens (Purple Toadflax *Linaria purpurea*). Moreover, a number of notable recent records are for species not recorded at Shotover for over a century including Marsh Valerian, Heath Milkwort and Hard Shield-fern.

The future for flora

Unable to fly, run or crawl away, plants easily fall victim to human activity and, in a general sense, most human activities are not especially concerned with wildlife conservation. The future for floral diversity depends mostly on the individual landowners' objectives and activities — including in those places that have a recognized status for wildlife. When comparing current known diversity with that of earlier decades both locally and nationally, a widespread atrophy becomes apparent. Working on the new plant Red List for England, Stroh *et al.* (2014) found that "*Almost one in five [plant] species has*

been assessed as threatened" and 17 species are thought to have gone extinct since 1930. It is therefore worth considering the flora of Shotover in this context.

For Shotover Country Park, which is a Site of Special Scientific Interest, the diversity of flora is no less vulnerable. The land is accessible to the public and is managed by the local authority as an amenity. Quite apart from any inadvertent damage by visitors, native plants have been removed, garden plants have been introduced and the management of paths and grasslands has seldom regarded the wild flowers that are present. Under these circumstances it is inevitable that species will be lost and 20 years of monitoring by Shotover Wildlife have shown this to be the case.

Nevertheless, Shotover still retains at least 12 species on the Hill whose populations in England have declined by more than 20 per cent since 1930 (Stroh *et al.*, 2014). For example, Yellow Vetchling, recorded in the SSSI in 2006, has contracted its range in England by 31 per cent and is listed as vulnerable to extinction; Marsh Valerian has contracted nationally by 25 per cent, yet is stable at Shotover. At the county

level, there are currently about 40 species of vascular plant at Shotover that are 'Register Species for Oxfordshire' in *Oxfordshire's Threatened Plants* (OTP) (Erskine *et al.*, 2018). Thus, in addition to the intrinsic value of maintaining local floral diversity and its value to the web of species interactions on the Hill, thoughtful conservation of the flora at Shotover plays an indispensable role in safeguarding the biodiversity of the county and the nation.

Although some plants have gone extinct at Shotover over the centuries, and further losses are likely, much remains to be celebrated: its rich ecology, its broad diversity, its rare species and of course such pleasures as walking among the springtime Bluebells. For the botanically inclined there is the frisson of excitement on seeing Trailing Tormentil or Lesser Hawkbit, not far from where they were found as species new to Britain over 300 years ago, or rediscovering plants thought to have gone extinct on the Hill, such as Tutsan and Wood Sage. All such experiences can serve to remind us of the remarkable toughness of some plants and their manifold strategies for survival.

Mosses and liverworts

Jacqueline Wright

Mosses thriving on an old willow in Slade Camp North

In the depths of winter, when most of Shotover's plants have died back and the colours of summer have faded, a fresh vibrant green takes centre stage. Over logs, branches and boulders, and around the bases of trees, the captivating world of mosses and liverworts is revealed. Collectively known as bryophytes, they are sometimes referred to as 'lower' plants, mostly because of their small size and relatively simple structure. Bryophyte recording in the Shotover region has a very long history and today Shotover still supports an exceptional diversity of these tiny exquisite plants.

Bryophytes are among the first land plants to have evolved from the sea flora, with their ancestral origins going back about 400 million years to the Devonian period. As primitive plants the bryophytes are non-vascular, lacking the conducting veins that developed later in the 'higher' plants, and are without flowers, seeds or fruits. They use various reproductive strategies, including vegetative propagation and the production of spores in small capsules on slender stems. The success of their spore dispersal is impressive. Due to their microscopic size, bryophyte spores can be carried great distances on air currents, enabling them to reach every corner of the planet. There are only about 20,000 species of moss and liverwort worldwide (compared with more than 400,000 vascular plants) and yet they are represented in every ecosystem except deep waters.

Although vascular plants tend to dominate wherever there is soil deep enough, bryophytes have ways to achieve a competitive advantage. They do not require soil for nutrients and, without need of roots, they extract their requirements for growth and reproduction directly from any water that contacts their leaves, stems and rhizoids (anchoring threads). In consequence they can be found not only on trees and rocks but also on tarmac, roof tiles and even metal and rubber — and almost anywhere else with suitable light and moisture. Being more tolerant of extreme conditions, many bryophytes can remain dormant through periods

Nodding capsules of Swan's-neck Thyme-moss *Mnium hornum*

Bryophytes release their spores into the atmosphere from small elevated capsules. Depending on the species, these can contain fewer than 20 spores to over 50 million.

Common Feather-moss *Kindbergia praelonga* and Rough-stalked Feather-moss *Brachythecium rutabulum* well established with mature capsules on a discarded shoe of plastic and fabric

of desiccation that would kill most vascular plants. Furthermore, many species can survive the lowest temperatures to be found naturally anywhere on Earth. It is therefore not surprising that bryophytes have survived the numerous ice ages and mass extinctions that have occurred since the Devonian period.

Quite apart from their value as a source of nesting material for birds, carder bees and mammals, bryophytes play a crucial role in the natural world by supporting the diversity of life concealed within their moist vegetative layer. Many microscopic invertebrates such as nematode worms, springtails and tardigrades feed, shelter and live out their life-cycles among bryophytes. Feeding on this well-stocked larder of micro-organisms and insect larvae are the tiny invertebrates at the bottom of the food chain of carnivorous animals. Very few animals eat bryophyte vegetation and, while a number of organisms, including molluscs, feed on the capsules, this seldom has any significant effect on bryophyte abundance.

Bryophytes are among the first colonizers of a range of bare surface types. Where they develop on newly exposed soil, the 'mat' acts as a most important stabilizer of the surface, helping to reduce soil erosion by wind or water. Having colonized an area without soil, mosses will trap dust, sediments and natural detritus, and so accumulate the beginnings of a rudimentary soil layer. Consequently, in a range of different

ways, the bryophyte structure generates a moist sheltered environment in which the seeds of vascular plants may also become trapped, then germinate and grow.

Although bryophytes only require low levels of nutrients themselves, their role in nutrient retention and recycling can be significant. For example, by absorbing and fixing nitrogen from rainwater they can influence the nitrogen budget of a habitat in both the short and longer term. Bryophytes also have a capacity, often underestimated, to retain large amounts of rainwater; their leaves and stems act *en masse* like a sponge, holding back water before returning

Silky Wall Feather-moss *Homalothecium sericeum* providing a germination opportunity for a seed of Herb-Robert *Geranium robertianum*

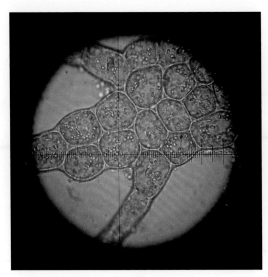

A typical bryophyte leaf is only a single layer of cells thick

it much more slowly into the environment. This buffering of rainfall can greatly reduce the impact of flood-water runoff and is a particularly important consideration in upland areas.

The leaves of most bryophytes, being just one layer of cells thick and receiving their nutrients directly through the cell walls, respond to changes in the atmospheric environment (including humidity, temperature and pollution) more rapidly than vascular plants. Also, in absorbing nutrients directly into their leaves from rainwater, bryophytes receive pollutants virtually unmodified from the atmosphere [see also box, page 93] which contrasts with the

majority of plants whose roots take up water that has been chemically modified by passage through the soil. The overall response of bryophytes to a small change in conditions may be as extreme as local extinction or, more subtly, there may be a change in vigour and the ability to produce spore-bearing capsules. Consequently, given the widespread distribution of relatively few species, bryophytes have considerable potential for study as sensitive indicators of environmental change.

The bryophytes of Shotover

The earliest known records of bryophytes in Oxfordshire date from the 17th century when Jacob Bobart the Younger (1641–1719), professor of botany at the University of Oxford, collected mosses from around Oxford — including from Shotover (Druce, 1886: p. 378). It has even been suggested that this constitutes some of the world's earliest systematic bryophyte collecting (Steel, 1984: p. 80). In 1741 Prof. Johann Dillenius published his *Historia Muscorum* in Oxford, describing over 600 mosses with 85 etched plates; some of his 'type specimens' (the specimen on which the scientific description of that species is based) are still preserved in the Oxford University Herbaria.

One hundred and sixty-six species of bryophyte were known to be listed for Shotover by the time Shotover Wildlife was founded in 1999, even though 50 of these were known to be either no longer extant or at least had gone unrecorded for over 50 years (and in some cases 150 years). Since 1995, the current diversity

Examples of mosses collected by Jacob Bobart the Younger c.1700 (with later identification labels)
©Oxford University Herbaria, Department of Plant Sciences

Surveying epiphytic mosses and liverworts in Johnson's Piece Ivan Wright

of known bryophytes is 130 species — 14 new species having been added — bringing the all-time total to over 180 species. When compared with the 400 species published for pre-1974 Oxfordshire by Killick *et al.* (1998), recent surveying results indicate that about a third of these bryophytes can be found at Shotover, reflecting the diversity of substrates on the Hill.

Most of the species known to have been lost from Shotover are those whose required substrate no longer exists. Long gone is the Cruet Collar-

Cleaner air for Shotover

Over the past few decades at Shotover, the improvement in the health of pollution-sensitive bryophytes and the increase in their distribution have been considerable. The cause is almost certainly the reduction of sulphur dioxide since the Clean Air Act of 1956 was implemented in Oxford city in 1958. Atmospheric sulphur dioxide from the burning of coal, one of the most toxic pollutants for bryophytes, reached its highest concentration over Oxford in about 1960 (Viles, 1996).

A good example of a moss that has responded well to cleaner air in recent years is Lateral Cryphaea *Cryphaea heteromalla*. David Steel suggested in his book (Steel, 1984: p. 49) that it had become extinct at Shotover. However, a single tuft was found by Sean O'Leary in Johnson's Piece in 1999, and by 2010 Lateral Cryphaea had become re-established as a fairly widely distributed species across the Hill. Another example is Lyell's Bristle-moss *Orthotrichum lyellii* found in 2008 on Horspath Common. It was discovered in sufficiently robust health to be producing spore capsules — a most unusual occurrence for this species anywhere in Britain.

Lateral Cryphaea is a moss that is particularly sensitive to air pollution

moss with the splendid Latin name *Splachnum ampullaceum*, which needs an adequate supply of wet rotting dung from drug-free livestock. However, 12 species that were noted in Steel (1984) as extinct at Shotover have been rediscovered. These include Frizzled Pincushion *Ulota phyllantha*, Bristly Haircap *Polytrichum piliferum*, Dwarf Haircap *Pogonatum nanum* and Pellucid Four-tooth Moss *Tetraphis pellucida*. The predominant reasons for these rediscoveries are likely to be: an increase in abundance through the creation of sizeable new areas of bare soil [see box, page 98], the reduction in atmospheric pollutants [see box, left] and to some extent the intensity of recent recording by Shotover Wildlife. Indeed, a bryophyte monitoring programme has been running since 2001 to record the population changes of the Hill's most vulnerable mosses and liverworts.

Squirrel-tail Moss *Leucodon sciuroides* was also thought to have gone extinct at Shotover but in 2007 an extensive colony was recorded near Brasenose Wood. Hidden on the back of a large round-topped boundary stone, this was one

Until the stone fell in 2011, Squirrel-tail Moss grew in abundance on this old boundary marker near Brasenose Farm

of only a few known locations in Oxfordshire, including a wall at Godstow Abbey. This fine moss, with bunches of tiny branchlets clustered at the shoot tips, was thriving until 2011 when the metre-tall stone was knocked over, thus irretrievably altering the microclimate and bringing about its terminal decline. Interestingly, Squirrel-tail Moss has more typically been known as an epiphyte in Britain — growing on trees — but as it is very sensitive to air pollution, and tree bark has a limited capacity to buffer the toxins, this moss has 'jumped ship' in lowland Britain and can now also be found on stone.

Bryophytes on trees

The acidity or alkalinity of the bark of a tree is predominantly related to the species, and so, together with the various degrees of bark roughness, it is to be expected that different tree species tend to host different communities of epiphytic bryophytes. Also some trees support a wide diversity of bryophytes, while others host only a few. Trees with an alkaline bark include Ash, Elder, Field Maple and willows. Elder in particular has a nutrient-rich bark which is often well exposed to light, and has a porous and coarsely fissured bark that retains a great deal of moisture. These circumstances are ideal for a luxuriant and diverse cover of bryophytes to develop. Even so, Elder is often disregarded

The boles of old coppice trees can be rich in bryophytes, and this Ash in Brasenose Wood supports a healthy colony of Blunt Feather-moss

for its contribution to wildlife and removed as a scrubland weed. The bryoflora of willow can be equally diverse due to a combination of its alkaline bark and association with wet habitats. At Shotover a Goat Willow has been host to a scarce and delicate liverwort, Tree Fringewort *Ptilidium pulcherrimum*, which grew on the tree for two years from 2006 before being outcompeted by more vigorous mosses.

Trees with an acidic bark can also be valuable and include oaks, Blackthorn and Silver Birch. Oaks on Horspath Common and Horseshoe Field support Flat-brocade Moss *Platygyrium repens*

Wood Bristle-moss *Orthotrichum affine* on Elder

and Smooth Bristle-moss *Orthotrichum striatum*, both of which were once rare in Britain. Until its discovery at Shotover in February 2009, Smooth Bristle-moss was deemed to be long extinct in the larger 'modern' Oxfordshire (Killick *et al.*, 1998; Crawley, 2005).

Some of the oldest boundary trees in Brasenose Wood support bryophytes that are either new records for the Hill or among those that David Steel regarded as locally extinct. Flat Neckera *Neckera complanata* and Blunt Feather-moss *Homalia trichomanoides* grow in sizeable patches on old tree boles, and the handsome Greater Featherwort *Plagiochila asplenioides* was found on the base of an Aspen in damp shade. Much of the rest of Brasenose Wood consists of Hazel coppice in which the bryoflora is generally sparse; however, where coppicing is undertaken sensitively [see box, page 224] a suitably moist microclimate can be preserved around existing or potentially mossy trees within the coppice.

The well-spaced parkland trees on the Shotover Estate, being more exposed to drying wind and sun, tend not to have an especially rich bryoflora. For similar reasons, any isolated veteran trees usually support only common bryophytes. However, old trees in woodland settings can have a greater diversity. In Johnson's Piece, for instance, a veteran named The Cross-bar Oak supported 19 bryophyte species in 2006, most of which occurred on a single low branch.

Rotting oak in Brasenose Wood supporting both mosses and liverworts

Bryophytes of dead wood

Dead wood is an essential component in the ecological balance of many ecosystems of which bryophytes are often a part. A number of epixylic species can be found on the surface of suitable dead wood, whether it has died recently and is at an early stage of moisture absorption, or is in a more advanced state of decay and thoroughly saturated. The size of a log has a bearing on how the wood is colonized; usually the larger the timber the better for bryophytes, as this allows the mass of woody fibres to retain moisture for longer.

It is among the liverworts — with their more flattened appearance — that some of the

Greater Featherwort is one of Shotover's largest and most distinctive liverworts

It is shown here, growing in Brasenose Wood, its broad leaves intermingled with the fine fronds of Common Feather-moss.

obligate and specialist dead-wood bryophytes are found, such as the pincerworts (*Cephalozia* spp.) and notchworts (*Lophozia* spp.). Bryophytes are not normally thought of as having a scent but Variable-leaved Crestwort *Lophocolea heterophylla* and Bifid Crestwort *L. bidentata* are two of Britain's most aromatic liverworts and can be found colonizing many of the decaying

logs at Shotover. For the mosses, the most easily recognized dead-wood colonizer at Shotover is the delicate Cape Thread-moss *Orthodontium lineare* which particularly favours rotting tree stumps. Although it is a small and fine-leaved plant, *en masse* its abundant pale capsules — all pointing downwards in a cascade — give it a distinctive appearance in spring and summer and it is often referred to as 'waterfall moss'.

Scrub woodland

Scrub woodland is a dynamic, transitional habitat occurring wherever an area is in the early stages of becoming young secondary woodland — for instance, abandoned fields and unmanaged tracts of land. A good example is the Littleworth railway cutting, which has become a valuable habitat for bryophytes since the railway was closed in the 1960s. Ideal conditions prevail due to the gradual succession of many alkaline-barked trees such as Elder, Ash, Horse-chestnut *Aesculus hippocastanum* and various willows. Many of the trees lean, enabling light to penetrate the canopy, and the numerous water seeps and springs along the embankments maintain a suitably high humidity. Among the many bryophytes to be found is the ultra-small and charming Fairy Beads *Microlejeunea ulicina*, the stems of which look like delicate strings of yellow beads when viewed under a hand lens. Interestingly, this is a strongly western and southern species, and is not often seen this far east. It is absent throughout much of the eastern side of Britain.

Heath and acidic grassland

Many ground-dwelling bryophytes thrive on the bare soil within the short vegetation of heath and acidic grassland. Although these are typically dry habitats, the bryophytes that specialize in colonizing this substrate play a key role in retaining moisture for the benefit of themselves and other organisms. They include species such as the acid-loving Red-stemmed Feather-moss *Pleurozium schreberi* among the Heather of Mary Sadler Field. Within the acidic grassland of Sandpit Field is Neat Feather-moss *Pseudoscleropodium purum*, Broom Fork-moss *Dicranum scoparium* and Juniper Haircap *Polytrichum juniperinum*, all growing in balance with the grass sward kept short by grazing Rabbits. In the more undisturbed places at Shotover where these mosses coexist with cladonia lichens, patches of 'lichen heath' develop — a habitat that is not at all common in Oxfordshire. In 2015, the robust and water-retentive Great Plait-moss *Hypnum cupressiforme* var. *lacunosum* was recorded for the first time at Shotover in Horseshoe Field. A luxuriant mat of the moss was found on an area of bare calcareous sand that had been exposed by conservation work seven years previously.

The pH of the Whitchurch Sand that caps the top of Shotover is typically between 3.0 and 4.0 but in places can be even lower (pH 2.8). When newly exposed this strong acidity is a niche opportunity that bryophytes exploit more than most other forms of plant, which explains their appearance as the first colonizers of such acidic soils. Examples are the beautiful Silky Forklet-moss *Dicranella heteromalla* with its red and yellow capsules and leaves looking like fine combed hair, and the distinctive Bristly Haircap, the latter being scarce in pre-1974 Oxfordshire due to the paucity of suitable bare acidic soil in the county. In time, Bristly Haircap gradually disappears under competition from stronger-growing mosses and vascular plants, only to re-appear when the soil is newly exposed. Also among the arrivals on bare soil is the invasive alien species Heath Star-moss *Campylopus introflexus*, which arrived in Britain from the

The beautiful capsules of Silky Forklet-moss

southern hemisphere in 1941. This vigorous moss, first recorded at Shotover in 1999 in Horseshoe Field, is gaining ground on heathy areas of the Hill, and is already beginning to affect the abundance of other heathland bryophytes in a few places. Two liverwort colonizers of this habitat are the minute Hampe's Threadwort *Cephaloziella hampeana*, first recorded at Shotover in 2008, and Common Threadwort *C. divaricata*, still

Juniper Haircap female

Juniper Haircap male

The first Grassland Habitat Project area created in 2008 on Horspath Common

Since 2000, Shotover Wildlife has embarked upon a number of initiatives in the SSSI to address the decline of acidic-soil habitats across Oxfordshire, recognizing that these areas contribute greatly to local and regional diversity. In 2007 funding was awarded to Shotover Wildlife for a Grassland Habitat Project, with the aim of creating a hectare of new acidic grassland in the SSSI over the following three years.

At Shotover the most suitable geological stratum for this work is the ferrous-orange Whitchurch Sand that caps the Hill. When the shallow topsoil is removed to expose the infertile mineral layer beneath, the area can remain almost bare of vegetation for many years and benefit a great many scarce species – including pioneer bryophytes. Areas of abundant bracken on Horspath Common were selected, and topsoil and bracken roots cleared away to expose the underlying layer and initiate a slow succession to acidic grassland [see page 36].

A year of biological surveying and related study preceded the work, and then from 2008 to 2010 an excavator was hired in the late summer of each year to scrape off about 25 centimetres of topsoil from four

Bracken and topsoil being removed to expose the mineral layer beneath

The objectives of this project have been fully met by the arrival of acidic grasses and the exceptional response by bryophytes.

separate sites amounting in all to one hectare. The excavations were planned throughout to minimize the environmental impact not only on nearby Badger activity but also on reptiles, amphibians, small mammals and bumblebees.

Felled trees resulting from the work were used to enhance habitat diversity further, with some of the trunks and branches stacked to create reptile and invertebrate habitat. Another measure to improve diversity was the selective killing of two trees as standing dead wood [see page 134] for additional saproxylic species. Perhaps the most beneficial decision, however, was to incorporate much of the timber from felled trees into the large volume of displaced topsoil, producing structured mounds that provide a labyrinthine underground habitat for innumerable creatures.

At the periphery of the cleared areas, the natural slope of the ground was exploited to create a small number of near-vertical south-facing walls of sandy soil for soil-nesting invertebrates. In 2016, Shotover Wildlife was able to cut further south-facing walls into the original mounds of sandy topsoil.

Some particularly notable invertebrates arrived to take advantage of a rare opportunity. The Adonis Ladybird *Hippodamia variegata*, never before recorded at Shotover, was found on the Project area and the handsome Green Tiger Beetle *Cicindela campestris*, which for many years was thought lost from Shotover, is now resident in the new habitat [see page 130]. The rare saproxylic beetle *Colydium elongatum* was found on one of the standing dead trees [see box, page 134] and the bare soil rapidly became home to some of the largest and densest aggregations of solitary bees and wasps in Oxfordshire [see page 141].

Moreover, the Project has demonstrated that bryophytes can remain the dominant cover for at least a decade, giving way only very gradually to acidic grasses. Bryophytes play a key role in stabilizing the soil surface, retaining soil moisture and providing a vegetative foundation for the invertebrate food chain. This exceptionally slow succession is therefore a strong indication that the Project will contribute to a rich acidic grassland ecology for many years to come.

A variety of locally scarce acidophile mosses and liverworts colonized the Project areas after the soil was exposed. Among the noteworthy arrivals was Taper-leaved Earth-moss *Pleuridium acuminatum*, a minuscule plant last recorded at Shotover by Sibthorp in the 18th century, and re-found so far in just two patches. But perhaps the most rewarding finds have been the regionally rare species Dwarf Haircap *Pogonatum nanum* and Aloe Haircap *P. aloides*. Dwarf Haircap was last recorded in the vicinity of Shotover over 200 years ago, and has declined significantly in central and south-east Britain in recent decades. Of particular importance is that all three of these species have produced mature spore capsules, thereby ensuring their likely regeneration should conditions once again prove favourable.

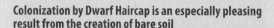

In 2018 Bristly Haircap and Juniper Haircap mosses were still dominating the slow succession from bare soil

Colonization by Dwarf Haircap is an especially pleasing result from the creation of bare soil

present in 2018. These liverworts, with their microscopically small leaves, often grow intermixed with larger mosses and their presence is usually only revealed when examining other bryophytes under a magnifier.

Marshes and streams

There are few better indicators that the valley bottoms at Shotover were once highly acidic and exceptionally boggy than the historic records of bog-mosses (*Sphagnum* ssp.) along with the carnivorous plant Round-leaved Sundew [see page 59]. The march of technology in the 19th century and agricultural land drainage quickly eliminated these 'unproductive' areas, and the bogs and their unique flora were soon lost. The last sphagna to be identified at Shotover are from the 1820s and include Spiky Bog-moss *Sphagnum squarrosum*, Blunt-leaved Bog-moss *S. palustre* and Lustrous Bog-moss *S. subnitens*. Although bog-mosses are now rare in pre-1974 Oxfordshire, in 1995 these three species were still growing at Chawley Brick Pit, Cumnor, four kilometres west of Oxford (Wright and Wright, 2006). A 20th-century report of an unidentified bog-moss on the south side of the Hill suggests that a species may have been present in the region of an old pond on the lower edge of Horseshoe Field. However, the pond and bog-moss were probably lost when a water pipeline was installed across the Hill in the 1950s.

Other historic bryophytes from the wetter habitats include the small moisture-loving liverwort Creeping Fringewort *Lepidozia reptans*, which was still at Shotover in the 1940s, and the very tall (for a moss) and noble Common Haircap *Polytrichum commune*, the loss of which particularly caught the attention of Druce (1886: p. 421), who noted, "*Formerly fine at Shotover, but destroyed by drainage about 1861.*" However, there remain a small number of bryophytes that are specifically associated with the wetter habitats at Shotover. Pellucid Four-tooth Moss is locally scarce and has only been found in very small quantities in two locations in the SSSI: on a tree at High Triangle Marsh (Johnson's Piece) and on a log in the muddy stream at Ben's Bridge. There are also a number of mosses specific to the calcareous flowing streams on the northern and eastern sides of the Hill: River Feather-moss *Brachythecium rivulare*, Fern-leaved Hook-moss *Cratoneuron filicinum* and Kneiff's Feather-moss *Leptodictyum riparium*.

Meadows and fields

The abundance and diversity of bryophytes in grassland is dependent for the most part on the degree of vigour of the flowering plants and grasses; they cannot compete if the sward is too dense, whether hay meadow or pasture. For this reason, the meadows at Slade Camp South and Westhill Farm are almost devoid of bryophytes. The private north-facing meadow at Monk's Farm, however, supports large areas of common mosses such as Neat Feather-moss,

Lustrous Bog-moss
Peter Creed

This soft-textured Sphagnum is often tinged pinky-red and has a distinctive metallic lustre, and was well established at Shotover in the 19th century.

The lower branches of trees often support a rich bryophyte ecology, such as on this graceful oak on Horspath Common

where the grasses grow more thinly and moisture is maintained in the shady sward of this very old hay meadow.

From 2002 to 2005 the British Bryological Society ran a national initiative, the Survey of Bryophytes of Arable Land (SBAL), aiming to determine the changes over time in this largely under-recorded habitat across Britain. Shotover's arable fields, which include those of the Shotover Estate, Rough Field and the pig farm fields, were surveyed as part of this initiative and found to support a variety of common bryophytes. Curiously, False Beard-moss *Didymodon fallax*, found growing in one of the fields, although a widespread moss in Britain had not been previously recorded since 1980 (Steel, 1984: p. 81).

The future for bryophytes at Shotover

One of the universal challenges in wildlife conservation today is the prevention of habitat loss and the consequent loss of species. This is not a new phenomenon, nor does it apply

only to bryophytes — most taxa and habitats are affected. Since 1999, evidence-based conservation work in the SSSI has been planned and undertaken by Shotover Wildlife integrating as many taxa as possible, including bryophytes, and species losses from the SSSI have been demonstrably minimized.

Despite their vital role in supporting the very bottom of the food chain, bryophytes are one of the most ecologically underappreciated groups of plants and the suggestion that they could be included in the management of a wildlife reserve might seem a luxury. Yet where bryological information is available it is a valuable asset for the delivery of conservation work that contributes to what is, after all, a wholly interconnected ecology. The wonderful diversity of mosses and liverworts that remains at Shotover is not something to be taken for granted. At the very least, these plants deserve a working understanding of their contribution to the natural world and the influences that affect them.

Fungi and lichens

Jacqueline Wright

Fungi

Elegant and colourful but often strangely sinister-looking, fungi are one of the most diverse and mysterious groups of organisms to be found in the natural world. Like insects and plants, fungi are very much an integral part of life on earth and the biosphere is wholly dependent on them. Without fungi the recycling of nutrients would all but collapse, and habitats would be buried under the unrotted debris of other organisms. Fungi can colonize a fallen tree with astonishing rapidity and, with the aid of saproxylic invertebrates [see page 32], can reduce the entire trunk to a crumbling heap in just a few years.

Fungi occupy their own taxonomic kingdom, distinct from both plants and animals, although this was only recognized in the 1980s; they had previously been classified as lower plants. In fact, genetically they are more closely related to the animals. Fossil evidence for fungi is limited because the soft tissue is too ephemeral but microscopic spores and some hyphae [see next page] can persist in geological strata and be preserved sufficiently for palaeontological sequencing. These analyses have been able to confirm that fungi date back 400 million years yet they have probably existed, in some form, for at least 800 million years. Fungi are a vast and complex group of organisms; in Britain alone over 12,000 species have been named and new species are frequently being discovered. Macro-fungi range in size from large brackets (Polyporaceae) measuring over a metre across to the tiny cone-shaped caps of the bonnets (Mycenaceae) and

Dryad's Saddle *Cerioporus squamosus*

the 'piggyback' species (*Asterophora* spp.) that perch on top of other fungi. In addition there are myriad unicellular fungi, including the ubiquitous white dusting of Oak Mildew *Erysiphe alphitoides* and the yeasts on which we depend for bread and beer. Pejorative names such as canker, conk, blight, scab and smut all indicate that some of the micro-fungi are also a major nuisance to farmers and horticulturalists.

As with primitive plants such as mosses, liverworts and ferns, fungi reproduce by spores which are dispersed by air currents, animals or water. Once germinated the spores extend very fine threads (hyphae) that grow into their surroundings to extract nutrients, eventually forming an extensive net-like system (the mycelium). In some fungi, the mycelial network can extend over several kilometres and has proved to be among the largest living organisms in the world. Fungi do not photosynthesize but instead obtain sustenance by breaking down the tissues of other organisms, whether living or dead. It is from the mycelium that the reproductive fruiting bodies arise — the brackets and mushrooms that attract our attention on an autumnal walk.

The fruiting bodies of fungi are an important source of food for invertebrates, especially beetles and flies which, after eating their way in, also nest and develop their larvae there. This includes the fungus gnats (Mycetophilidae flies) of which 70 species have been recorded at Shotover in recent years. In Brasenose Wood, Keroplatidae flies weave a fine web under bracket fungi and feed on the spores that become trapped there. Conversely, some fungi are able to feed on animals by invading carcass remains or even by direct capture. The common Oyster Mushroom *Pleurotus ostreatus*, which can be found at Shotover, produces small sticky projections on its hyphae which attract nematode worms; the worms then become paralysed and are consumed.

Fungi also form innumerable symbiotic relationships, including the widespread association with algae that produces the great diversity of lichens [see page 111]. However, one of the most crucial associations is the partnership between fungi and the roots of living plants. In this mycorrhizal (fungus-root) relationship the fungal mycelia, which are attached to the plant roots, extract soil nutrients and convert them

into forms that are more readily taken up by the plant. In return, the plant provides products of photosynthesis to the fungus. Most species throughout the plant kingdom have mycorrhizal associations with fungi.

Mutually advantageous relationships with invertebrates too are wide-ranging and go far beyond the combined process of reducing organic material, such as timber, for the extraction of nutrients. For example, the 'ambrosia' fungi are wholly symbiotic with the saproxylic ambrosia-beetles. The spores of the fungi, often from more than one species, are carried by the female beetles in special surface recesses (mycangia) and so are introduced into each new borehole as it is excavated. When the beetle's eggs hatch, the larvae feed on the developing fungi and in return, when the adult beetles disperse, transport the fungi to new sites for both species to continue their life cycles. Among the ambrosia-beetles at Shotover are *Xyleborinus saxesenii* and the Pinhole Borer *Platypus cylindrus* [see box, pages 134 and 135].

Oyster Mushroom Peter Creed

Flies feeding on a Stinkhorn fungus in Johnson's Piece

An example of a more straightforward exchange involves the Stinkhorn fungus *Phallus impudicus*, which provides nourishment for the flies that distribute its spores. This fungus is quite common at Shotover and emits one of the most distinctive and unpleasant odours on the Hill; in fact, its proximity is usually detected by smell long before it comes into view. As the Latin name implies, it produces an impudently phallic-shaped fruiting body. At maturity the cap, smelling like rotting flesh, is no more than a black spore-laden mass of slime which attracts flies such as greenbottles (Calliphoridae) to feed. The very fine fungal spores pass unaltered through the flies' digestive system and are thereby dispersed far and wide.

The Fungi of Shotover

The first record of any fungus at Shotover was noted in 1969 by Humphrey Bowen, who identified Mousepee Pinkgill *Entoloma incanum* in the C.S. Lewis Community Nature Reserve. Remarkably, there were no further records until Peter Creed and David Steel began recording in the 1980s and a list of 140 species found on the Hill was published by Steel (1984: p. 83). A number of specialist surveys have since been conducted and the known diversity has increased

to more than 360 species. Undoubtedly more remain to be found.

Most people notice the cap-and-stem mushrooms that suddenly appear when the weather is mild and damp, especially the deep-scarlet Fly Agaric *Amanita muscaria* — one of the signature fungi of autumn. This highly recognizable fungus, with its white-flecked cap, was claimed in medieval times to be an effective household fly killer when dried and sprinkled onto a dish of milk. Considerably more deadly is the Deathcap *A. phalloides*, which usually displays a pale olive-green cap and is fairly common in the oak woodlands of Shotover. Perhaps more impressive for sheer size is the

The poisonous Fly Agaric: a) in typical form and b) showing the subtle colours of old age

Parasol Mushroom *Macrolepiota procera*, which appears on the Hill every year and can reach a height of 30 centimetres. Closely related species include Shaggy Parasol *Chlorophyllum rhacodes* and the much less common species *M. konradii* which was recorded on the Hill in 2012.

Considering the amount of woodland in the SSSI, it is not surprising that 'bracket' and 'jelly' fungi are a common sight on the trunks, stumps and fallen branches of trees. Good examples are the smooth white disks of Birch Polypore *Fomitopsis betulina* and the impressive tiers of Chicken-of-the-Woods *Laetiporus sulphureus*, whose brackets are conspicuously orange-yellow against the bark of its host tree, usually an oak. This species is sometimes confused with Hen-of-the-Woods *Grifola frondosa*, which is much less common but has been recorded around the base of trees in Brasenose Wood. Commonest among the jelly fungi is the distinctive chocolate-brown lobes of Jelly Ear *Auricularia auricula-judae*, seen mostly on Elder; when young the translucent flesh looks and feels like fine soft velvet. Less common is the vibrantly coloured Yellow Brain *Tremella mesenterica*, which can be found on Gorse stems and the branches of a variety of trees.

Even more jelly-like are the fascinating slime moulds, grouped for convenience here with the fungi, though they are currently placed in the Amoebozoa Kingdom of organisms. Part of their life cycle includes a gelatinous stage during which they are free-living and so able to 'crawl' to a new location. When a suitable place is found the mould will switch back to a solid and more conventional fungus-like ball, which fruits and reproduces by spores as a fungus would. At Shotover there are occasional sightings of the soft white growths of False Puffball *Enteridium lycoperdon*, the pink spheres of *Lycogala epidendrum* and the bright lemon-yellow of the slime mould known as Witch's Butter *Fuligo septica*.

'Cup' fungi occur in most habitats on the Hill; although they are quite small, they tend to stand out because of their intense colours. The Green Elfcup *Chlorociboria aeruginascens* is most often seen as a turquoise stain on pieces of rotting wood but its charming jade-green cups are a much less common sight. Only a little larger, and

Green Elfcup Peter Creed

Chicken-of-the-Woods on Horspath Common

Fungi are critical for the reduction of dead wood, recycling nutrients and providing habitat for a great many invertebrates in the softened wood and fungal fruiting bodies.

Eyelash Fungus Peter Creed

scarce *Cheilymenia fibrillosa* recorded at Shotover in 2008.

Fungi of woodland

Surveys of four relatively small areas of woodland have identified over 200 species of fungi and represent 60 per cent of the total fungal diversity at Shotover; these are Brasenose Wood and Johnson's Piece in the SSSI, and The Spinney and the C.S. Lewis Community Nature Reserve on the north side of the Hill. As well as the common fungi associated with oaks and broad-leaved woodland, many scarce and notable species have been seen over recent years, including the fascinating Collared Earthstar *Geastrum triplex* [see opposite and box below].

One of the more diverse families of cap-and-stem fungi found in the woodlands on the Hill are the Tricholomataceae, many of which have characteristic names such as Blue Spot Knight *Tricholoma columbetta*, Soapy Knight *T. saponaceum*, Butter Cap *Rhodocollybia butyracea* and the aniseed-scented Fragrant Funnel *Clitocybe fragrans*. All these are common species of mixed woodland; however, Deceiving Knight *T. sejunctum*, recorded by Richard Fortey

frequently seen in the damper woods, is Eyelash Fungus *Scutellinia scutellata*, which has black 'eyelash' hairs fringing the bright orange-red cups. Also to be seen among this group of fungi are Scarlet Elfcup *Sarcoscypha austriaca*, the Orange Peel Fungus *Aleuria aurantia*, with cups up to 10 centimetres in diameter, and the very

Earthstars

For many wildlife enthusiasts, encountering an Earthstar would be the highlight of an autumnal walk in the woods. Not only are they an uncommon sight but their peculiar structure seems more fitting to an organism from another planet. On the rare occasion that anyone is lucky enough to see Collared Earthstar *Geastrum triplex* at Shotover in an early stage of development, the relatively rapid 'flowering' can be observed in the days that follow.

The fruiting body first appears by protruding through leaf litter as a pinkish-brown bulb about four centimetres across. As it expands, its tough outer layer splits radially into elongated triangular segments which arch over backwards, forcing the bulb upwards and lifting it clear of the ground. Full maturity reveals a small puffball-like inner spore sac perched on a 'stool' with up to eight curved legs.

On ripening, the apex of the spore sac ruptures to leave a small opening through which the many

Collared Earthstar with its spore sac perched on a 'stool' of curved legs
Drawing by Jacqueline Wright

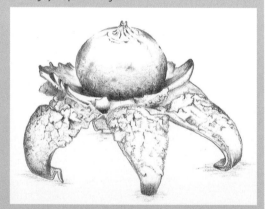

millions of spores can be released. However, rain is needed in order to complete the process. As droplets of water hit the thin springy membrane of the sac, each impact ejects a cloud of powdery spores in small puffs of air from the central hole. Ultimately, the Earthstar withers and collapses and becomes part of the soil layer once more.

This wonder of nature was first recorded at Shotover in 1987 in Brasenose Wood by Peter Creed; in September 2016 multiple fruiting bodies were discovered by Simon Anson under an old willow in Open Brasenose.

in 2014, is considerably scarcer. The uncommon Tricholomid fungus Bitter Oysterling *Panellus stipticus*, which grows on oak stumps in the SSSI, has a short lateral stem which makes it look rather like a bracket fungus. Closely related is the large and complex group of bonnet fungi, which usually appear in clusters of small neat conical caps on long slender stems. Twenty species of bonnet have been recorded at Shotover, including Rosy Bonnet *Mycena rosea* and the rare Rush Bonnet *M. bulbosa*.

Rush Bonnet
©Arne Aronsen/Natural History Museum, University of Oslo

Brittlegill fungi are a frequent sight in the woods; most of these have a monochrome cap, often red or yellow. A useful characteristic for identification includes the brittle stem and gills. One such species found in Brasenose Wood, the Geranium Brittlegill *Russula fellea*, has a distinctive fragrance yet the sap is particularly uncomfortable if tested on the tongue. In 2002 the very scarce *R. melliolens* was recorded by Marion Warland in Brasenose Wood along with Ochre Brittlegill *R. ochroleuca* and Purple Brittlegill *R. atropurpurea*. Also within the Russulaceae are the milkcaps (*Lactarius* spp.), named after their characteristically milky sap. In early October the pale-fawn cap of Fiery Milkcap *Lactarius pyrogalus* can be seen in the coppice plots, where it is specifically associated with Hazel. Unsurprisingly, its name comes from the exceptionally peppery sap which, apparently, can 'burn' the tongue for hours. The aptly named Ugly Milkcap *L. turpis*, slimy, sticky and dark olive-brown, has been recorded many times, mostly towards the top of the Hill in the birch woodland with which it is associated.

Almost all records of fibrecaps (*Inocybe* spp.) at Shotover have come from Brasenose Wood. The fungi in this large group are generally brownish in colour and often go unnoticed in their typical woodland setting. White Fibrecap *I. geophylla* var. *geophylla*, which has a silky white cap and stem, is more easily noticed than most and may be accompanied by the gently tinted variety Lilac Fibrecap *I. geophylla* var. *lilacina*. Many of the fibrecaps are uncommon, including the scarce *I. praetervisa*, which was found in Brasenose Wood in 2014.

On the north side of Shotover, two woodland areas have been surveyed for fungi: the C.S. Lewis Community Nature Reserve, by Humphrey Bowen in 1969 and by Peter Creed and David Steel in the 1980s, accumulating a total of 38 species, and The Spinney on the Shotover Estate by Creed and Steel, also in the 1980s. A number of notable species were found during these surveys, for example Red-banded Webcap *Cortinarius armillatus* and Frosty Webcap *C. hemitrichus* in association with birch trees at the C.S. Lewis Community Nature Reserve. At The Spinney, a total of 89 species were recorded, including two scarce bonnet fungi, Saffrondrop Bonnet *Mycena crocata* and the soft-brown *M. sepia*, and the more common Toothed Cup *Tarzetta cupularis* and the apricot-coloured Fishy Milkcap *Lactifluus volemus*.

Fungi of heath and acidic grassland

Fungi play an important role in Shotover's heathland and acidic grassland habitats. In an acidic soil, the nutrients needed for plant growth are not only limited but also effectively 'locked away' by the acidic chemistry of the soil. However, the hyphae of mycorrhizal fungi interact closely with the roots of the acidophile plants found in these habitats, improving the supply of nutrients and making it possible for the plants to thrive and exploit this particular habitat niche. As with the flora, many of the fungi associated with the sandy soils at Shotover also tend to be scarce in Oxfordshire.

Although several conventional cap-and-stem mushrooms appear on the dry and sandy soils of the Hill, the fruiting bodies of many acidophile fungi take the form of balls, clubs and spindles protruding from the ground. The largest of these at Shotover is the Giant Puffball *Calvatia gigantea*, which can reach 30 centimetres in diameter. Two of its much smaller close relatives are Dusky Puffball *Lycoperdon nigrescens* and the much scarcer Spiny Puffball *L. echinatum*, both of which are only three to four centimetres tall. Scaly Earthball *Scleroderma verrucosum* and Common Earthball *S. citrinum* form slightly larger ball-shaped fruiting bodies and are a frequent sight on the path edges of Horspath Common and Horseshoe Field, and along the top of Johnson's Piece.

Smoky Spindles Peter Creed

'Spindles' and other stalk-like acidophile fungi often go quite unnoticed in grass and leaf litter, and even then are not always recognized as fungi. The gruesomely named Dead Man's Fingers *Xylaria polymorpha* can poke up from buried twigs just about anywhere around the Hill. The charming spindle fungi are much less common in the county and include Smoky Spindles *Clavaria fumosa* which was found in 2014 on Horspath Common, and Golden Spindles *Clavulinopsis fusiformis* near The Sandpit in 2008. White Spindles *Clavaria fragilis* has not been seen since David Steel recorded it in the 1980s.

Waxcaps are typical of unimproved pastures and old lawns, especially those on acidic soils, and 11 species have been recorded in the fields across the top of the Hill. Only two of these species have not been recorded since the 1980s. The old pastures of the Shotover Estate have always been known for their diversity of waxcaps, and in the SSSI too the bright glossy caps of these smart little fungi are a pleasure to find among the short grasses and carpets of mosses. Crimson Waxcap *Hygrocybe punicea* is the rarest of these species, the most recent record being from Mary Sadler Field in 2012; its striking blood-red, greasy-looking cap fades to orange as it matures. The uncommon Heath Waxcap *Gliophorus laetus* var. *laetus* has a more subtle beige cap and was also recorded in the SSSI in 2012.

Following the exposure of large areas of acidic soil on Horspath Common from 2008 to 2010 under the Shotover Wildlife Grassland Habitat Project [see box, page 98], a number of waxcap fungi made a welcome appearance during the slow succession of lichens, mosses and grasses. The vibrant red cap of Vermilion

Crimson Waxcap Peter Creed

Waxcap *H. miniata* and the rich yellow Butter Waxcap *H. ceracea* both appeared in the sixth year following the work (2014). Parrot Waxcap *G. psittacinus* is well named for its unusual chromatic display. When fresh it is deep green but with age it changes unevenly to yellow, orange or red; it has been recorded once in Mary Sadler Field in 2012 as well as on one of the habitat restoration areas of Horspath Common. Occurring more widely on the Hill's grasslands is Scarlet Waxcap *H. coccinea* and Blackening Waxcap *H. conica* whose yellow-orange cap turns to black at maturity or when bruised. Golden Waxcap *H. chlorophana* has not been seen since the 1980s but there are recent records for Meadow Waxcap *Cuphopyllus pratensis* var. *pratensis*, Snowy Waxcap *C. virgineus* var. *virgineus* and Glutinous Waxcap *H. glutinipes* var. *glutinipes*.

Additional Fungi of note

In addition to the scarce species of fungi mentioned so far, there have been many further notable sightings in recent years. For example, the very scarce *Agaricus porphyrocephalus* was recorded on The Plain by David Steel in 1984 and refound by Alan Hills in 1992 on Mary Sadler Field. But perhaps the most rewarding discovery has been that of the rare Silky Rosegill *Volvariella bombycina*, a handsome fungus whose large white cap when newly emerged is covered with a luxuriantly silky pile. It is usually associated with elms, which may account for its current rarity, but when found on Horspath Common in August 2005 it was growing from a large rotting Sycamore log. As the cap matured, a number of tiny Asteiidae flies were seen to gather on its surface and a small number were collected by Shotover Wildlife for identification. Subsequent comparison with other specimens of the fly collected in southern Britain over the preceding three years revealed that it was a species new to science; it has since been named *Leiomyza birkheadi* (Gibbs and Papp, 2006) [see also page 159].

A fungus seen on less healthy branches of Ash trees is the matt-black Cramp Ball *Daldinia concentrica*, resembling spheres of charcoal and also known as King Alfred's Cakes. In common with many bracket fungi, this perennial fungus has annual growth rings which — in this species — appear as silver-grey concentric arcs when the ball is cut open. In 2009, a rare and closely related species, Gorse Cramp Ball *D. fissa*, was found

The beautiful Silky Rosegill on Horspath Common in 2005, the only record of this species at Shotover

The tiny insects that can be seen on the caps were sampled and found to include a previously unknown species of Asteiidae fly.

The discovery of Gorse Cramp Ball on Horseshoe Field in 2009 was the first record for Oxfordshire

Cobalt Crust displays an intense blue when fresh
Peter Creed

on burnt Gorse, the first record at that time in Oxfordshire. The fruiting body is superficially similar to the common Cramp Ball but the inside is more glutinous. The nationally scarce and saproxylic fruit-fly *Amiota alboguttata,* recorded at Shotover in 2013, is reported to be associated with Cramp Ball (Alexander, 2002) and in 2008 the scarce Cramp-ball Fungus Weevil *Platyrhinus resinosus* was found very close to the Gorse Cramp Ball in Horseshoe Field.

The distinctive bolete fungi (Boletaceae), with sponge-like pores under the cap, are a diverse family of predominantly scarce species, many of which are difficult to identify. Some species are unsuited to the soils of Shotover and others have associations with plants — such as Beech — that are not particularly common on the Hill. However, 11 species have been recorded at Shotover, at least four of which are very scarce: Inkstain Bolete *Cyanoboletus pulverulentus,* found by Peter Creed in the woodland of Sandpit Field in 1984; Matt Bolete *Xerocomellus pruinatus,* recorded in Johnson's Piece (2007) and Brasenose Wood (2014); Iodine Bolete *Hemileccinum impolitum* in The Spinney (1980s); and Suede Bolete *Xerocomus subtomentosus* in the SSSI (1980s). Of the common species, one of the eye-catching examples to be found under birch in Mary Sadler Field is Orange Birch Bolete *Leccinum versipelle,* with its large bright-orange cap which can reach up to 20 centimetres in diameter.

A great many fungi are easily overlooked because all that can be seen is a thin crust or layer of small warts — often only on the underside of tree branches. They usually range in colour from white through pink to red, orange or brown. An exception at Shotover, however, is the spectacular Cobalt Crust *Terana caerulea* recorded in 2012 on Horspath Common. Although it was found on the underside of a small sycamore branch, the 20-centimetre patch was visible from many metres due to the intensity of its rich cobalt blue. Cobalt Crust likes a damp mild climate and is seldom seen outside Wales and the West Country. Similarly scarce, Upright Coral *Ramaria stricta* was found in 2014 on a stump of Horse-chestnut on Horspath Common. Although patches of this fungus can be quite large, it is altogether more difficult to find, looking much like the end-grain of the rotting wood on which it grows.

Fungi for the future

The greater part of most fungi — the mycelium — lies beneath the ground or intermingled with rotting material; the conspicuous fruiting bodies form only occasionally, and then only on those species that distribute their spores in this way. Thus the constant activity of fungi is almost entirely invisible and it is particularly difficult to assess their state of health and any threats they may face. Yet, as already noted, not only is the massive volume of hyphae profoundly important to habitat ecology but also the fruiting bodies are crucial in allowing scarcer fungi to distribute themselves and the more common species to support other organisms. As with all wildlife, it is fungi's innumerable interactions with other organisms that make possible a diverse and balanced biosphere, and so the future health of Shotover as a whole depends on the pivotal role of fungi.

Lichens

At Shotover lichens are most noticeable as small, pale, bushy growths on branches of trees and as patches of colour on the boulders that line The Plain. They can withstand extremes of wet and dry, hot and cold, and are found in all terrestrial habitats. A large number of animals benefit from lichens, either directly for food, shelter and nesting material, or indirectly by feeding on other creatures within their structure. Like the fungi and bryophytes, lichens are part of the small-scale ecology that underpins wildlife diversity.

The biological riddle of the lichens was not solved until 1867 when the Swiss botanist Simon Schwendener discovered that these mysterious growths were not a single organism. Schwendener's finding was slow to gain acceptance but it is now known that all lichens comprise two or more organisms living in close mutual support, one of which is always a fungus. In the simplest terms, the fungus teams up symbiotically with a photosynthesizing partner, and the two of them construct a robust supporting structure for the survival of both. Each unique form of lichen contains a specific fungal species and consequently the Latin name given to a lichen is actually the name of its fungus. The photoactive partner is usually one of a small number of species that are common to various lichens — often an alga but in some cases a cyanobacterium. The most common algal partner is either a green alga of the genus *Trebouxia* or the orange-pigmented alga *Trentepohlia*. In wetter habitats the more common partner is a cyanobacterium of the genus *Nostoc*. *Trentepohlia* can also be found as a free-living organism (without its fungal partner) and is widespread at Shotover in the form of a distinctive bright-orange powdery coating on tree trunks, its green cells obscured by strong carotenoid pigments.

Lichens are structured as a thallus, a body of tissue that is not differentiated into leaves and stems but is layered with the alga near the outer surface to absorb light. Below the alga, the fungal hyphae absorb and process the carbohydrates produced by algal photosynthesis. Some thalli have an additional underlayer to attach the majority of thallus area to a surface, while others have an attachment point and grow more freely from the substrate such as the shrubby fruticose

Ramalina farinacea on Horspath Common

Shotover birches tinged orange by Trentepohlia

lichens. The filamentous form appears as a fine, hair-like mass, while the delicately frilly, foliose form is more leaf-like. Crustose lichens can amount to little more than a surface crust and leprose lichens to a mass of fine granules. The jelly lichens are indeed just like jelly. Although some lichen species stand out sharply on account of their bold colours, others are found in more subtle tones of grey, beige or light green and may match their substrate perfectly.

Lichens can disperse to new locations when small pieces detach and are carried away by the wind or animals. In such cases, all partners travel together for further colonization. However, when the fungus disperses by the release of spores, the lichen will not develop unless a suitable partner is present where the spores eventually germinate. Some lichens are thought to be among the slowest-growing forms of life. Circular stone-dwelling species in Britain such as *Rhizocarpon geographicum*, for instance, expand radially by only about one millimetre per year. Even this is rapid compared to certain species elsewhere whose growth is measured in millimetres per 100 years, with thalli that appear to be many thousands of years old.

While a few species of lichen can tolerate, or even utilise, some pollutants, most British species are intolerant and are, in principle at least, good indicators of the long-term impact of atmospheric pollution. In Britain, however, where air quality has improved steadily since the 1950s, lichens may prove to be less useful for monitoring the change to cleaner air (Gilbert, 2000: p. 62). Fortunately, observation of mosses, which respond relatively rapidly to changes in air quality, is now an important source of evidence [see page 92 and box, page 93].

Lichens at Shotover

Approximately 1,700 species of lichen are known in Britain, of which 71 have been recorded on Shotover Hill: 48 published by Steel (1984: p 82) and a further 23 species added by Shotover Wildlife. Perhaps the apparently meagre diversity on the Hill simply reflects the small number of visits from lichenologists; on the other hand, Shotover is a comparatively dry location and, furthermore, was downwind of industrial Cowley for many decades.

Air quality affects species diversity in several ways. Sulphurous compounds from burning

Lichen growth forms commonly found at Shotover:

fruticose

foliose

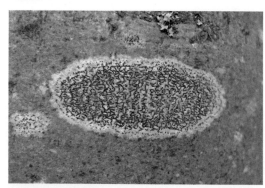

crustose Peter Creed

coal are poisonous to most organisms but fortunately sulphur-dioxide pollution around Oxford has declined markedly (Viles, 1996). However, nitrification originating from two main sources remains a widespread problem. In urban environments oxides of nitrogen are produced by the burning of fossil fuels, and in rural settings industrial agriculture releases additional nitrogen in the form of ammonia. Increased nitrogen causes harm to wildlife diversity largely as an unwelcome fertilizer, promoting the growth of common fast-growing plants at the expense of scarcer poor-soil specialists and generally reducing plant diversity.

Over time, sulphur dioxide has taken its toll on lichen diversity at Shotover, and now there is evidence that nitrification has benefitted a few species to the detriment of others. To take just three examples of lichens at Shotover that are tolerant of pollution and typical of an urban environment: *Lepraria incana* is now common on the Hill; *Xanthoria parietina* is so luxuriant on Elder bushes in Slade Camp South that it almost envelops the branches and twigs, turning them a rich bright yellow in dry sunny weather; and *Lecanora muralis*, a wall-dwelling species, can now be found on the doggers at The Sandpit (on town pavements it can be mistaken for discs of old chewing gum). On the other hand, *Collema tenax*, a species adapted to low-nitrogen environments, may eventually become a casualty of nitrogen deposition. This jelly lichen, found in Slade Camp South, is one of the few species whose photosynthetic partner is a cyanobacterium and which is therefore able to absorb nitrogen gas directly from the air. Such organisms are often a key component of nitrogen-deficient habitats and are net contributors of nutrients to other species.

Old woodlands tend to display a great variety of lichens, especially where large mature trees have plenty of space and light, and pollution levels are low. The pH of the tree bark is a major influence on the diversity of species, and Ash, with its alkaline bark, is one of the best host trees. Perhaps one of the most well-known lichens, easily noticed on the lower branches of trees, is the bushy grey growth of *Evernia prunastri*. This species is often referred to as Oak Moss, although it is not actually restricted to oaks, and in the past was used in dyeing, perfumery, flavouring and folk medicine; it is also the predominant lichen in the nests made by Long-tailed Tits. Other epiphytic lichens at Shotover include *Ramalina farinacea,* which is similar to the Oak Moss but much finer and appears as a hanging entanglement of greyish fronds, and *Parmelia sulcata*, which has frilly leaf-like lobes.

Lichens have been particularly relevant to the Heather re-seeding trials at Shotover, especially the black crustose lichens *Placynthiella uliginosa* and *P. icmalea*. Both of these species can be rapid colonizers of bare acidic soils, creating an extensive, uniform granular crust which, in a manner similar to mosses, retains soil moisture and prevents soil erosion. In fact, at Shotover the

Xanthoria parietina **with fruit cups** Eleanor Hawtree

Unlike most lichens, this urban species is resistant to atmospheric pollution and is now widespread on the Hill.

Oak Moss, a misleadingly named grey lichen sharing an Ash trunk with the green tufts of Wood Bristle-moss

Newly formed 'lichen heath' on Horspath Common (2016), with the pale cups of *Cladonia* lichen and the orange capsules of Bristly Haircap both producing spores for reproduction

lichens and mosses seem to share these roles (albeit patchily) depending on whose germinated spores eventually gain the upper hand.

In 2000, an area within Mary Sadler Field was prepared to receive Heather seed as part of Shotover Wildlife's heathland restoration trials [see page 35]. The topsoil was removed and the area sown with seed collected from mature Heather nearby. In the two years that followed, a pioneer covering of mosses and *Placynthiella* lichen developed, and it was discovered that seedlings of Heather were more abundant where the lichen had blackened the soil surface. Evidently the dark surface, which readily exchanges heat but also traps moisture beneath, favoured prompt germination, as there were far fewer seedlings among the cooler mosses and on the dry bare soil.

Lichen heaths — lichen communities associated with the infertile soils of heath and acidic grassland — are becoming increasingly rare both regionally and nationally. At Shotover this habitat has suffered a marked decline along with its associated species, although very small fragments cling on where the acidic sands are undisturbed and sufficiently nutrient-poor to support only sparse vegetation. The defining species of lichen heath belong to the genus *Cladonia* and at Shotover include *Cladonia fimbriata*, *C. furcata* and *C. ramulosa*. When in fruit, many of the *Cladonia* species are easily recognized by their charming goblet- or trumpet-shaped fruiting bodies — sometimes with bright red or orange highlights — and are aptly referred to as cup-lichens.

The future prospects for lichens at Shotover mostly depend on external factors such as air quality and climate change, neither of which can be readily controlled. Indeed, with the possibility of warmer winters, wetter summers and changes in pollution, it is far from obvious whether the condition of lichens at Shotover will improve or decline in the decades ahead. The fate of Shotover's lichen heath, however, is much more amenable to sensitive conservation work, such as initiatives to expand the extent of acidic grassland. Given time, patience and a sufficient understanding of lichens, such measures could stabilize, or even expand, this rather special habitat.

Butterflies and moths

Marc Botham

Butterflies and moths come in myriad colours and forms and are an important component of almost all well-functioning ecosystems. The extensive woodland at Shotover is a valuable habitat for these insects and, together with the more open areas, supports a wide diversity of species. For example, the sandy heath in Mary Sadler Field is one of the few places on the Hill where Grass Emerald *Pseudoterpna pruinata* has been seen regularly, Long Marsh supports species of moth preferring damper habitats, and the scrub in Slade Camp South provides the perfect habitat for Black Hairstreak *Satyrium pruni* and Brown Hairstreak *Thecla betulae* — two butterflies that are scarce in Britain.

Today, particularly in Britain, we tend to recognize and record butterflies and moths as two separate groups of insects. The former are regarded as creatures of beauty, grace and fragility, while the latter are often the object of disdain, perceived as dull-brown creatures that eat our clothes and carpets. Such negative associations go back at least as far as the Hebrew Bible, in which moths are portrayed as agents of destruction (for example, Isaiah 50.9). In fact, the closely related butterflies and moths together make a single insect order, the Lepidoptera, which have wings covered in tiny scales, hence their name (*lepis* scale + *pteron* wing).

The division between butterflies and moths is mostly a matter of convenience and therefore somewhat artificial but as a guide the majority of species can be distinguished in two basic ways. Butterflies tend to have club-ended antennae, whereas moth antennae are usually feathered, and the majority of butterflies fly only during the day whereas most moths fly at night. Unfortunately, many common species are exceptions to these criteria; for example, burnet moths (Zygaenidae) have clubbed antennae and are active during the day. The moths themselves are further split into macro-moths and micro-moths. This distinction — again somewhat artificial — separates the moth families on the general basis of size, yet within-family variation results in some micro-moth species being larger than some macro-moths, and certain macro-moths are extremely small. In addition, taxonomically, some of the larger moths are most closely related to much smaller micro-moth species — for example, the swift moths (Hepialidae) and the 40-millimetre goat moths (Cossidae). However, the division of Lepidoptera into butterflies, macro-moths and micro-moths is well established in entomological

Black Hairstreak butterfly Roger Wyatt

Cinnabar moth *Tyria jacobaeae* Peter Creed

recording and has not only simplified identification but also greatly increased the volume of data for some species by grouping those that are more easily identified. As for butterflies being more brightly coloured, this is a common misconception as shown by the stunning colours of species like the Garden Tiger moth *Arctia caja* and Elephant Hawk-moth *Deilephila elpenor*.

The life cycle and 'miraculous' metamorphosis of the butterfly are generally well known and most moths undergo much the same process. While the pupae of butterflies (also known as chrysalises) rely mostly on camouflage for protection, most moths also spin an outer protective cocoon to help protect their pupal stage. Some moth caterpillars use only their silk for the cocoon. Others incorporate pieces of vegetation or their own hairs, producing cocoons that are often extremely well camouflaged and the pupae almost perfectly concealed. For example, the Puss Moth *Cerura vinula* chews bark and other woody material to make an extremely tough cocoon that blends in perfectly with its surroundings.

The Lepidoptera are a large and diverse order with around 2,500 species in Britain. This includes 56 resident butterflies, three regular migrants (some of which are partially resident in southern parts of Britain) and a small number of rarer, more irregular, non-resident migrants. Moths in Britain differ more in size, shape and habitat usage than butterflies, ranging from the tiny leaf-miners (Gracillariidae) with wingspans of only five millimetres to the impressive Privet Hawk-moth *Sphinx ligustri* with a wingspan of 110 millimetres. Their various larvae deploy a great range of defences from predation, including

Puss Moth caterpillar Paul Brock

Lobster Moth caterpillar Peter Creed

mimicry of other creatures (for example Lobster Moth *Stauropus fagi*) or building a shell in which to live (for example case-bearer moths in the family Coleophoridae). The habitat niche of china-mark moths (Nymphulinae) is partly aquatic with the larvae living entirely underwater and feeding on water plants. All of this moth diversity is represented in the species recorded at Shotover in recent years.

Butterflies and moths perform important roles in all terrestrial ecosystems; as larvae they are herbivores and detritivores (some are even partly carnivorous), and as adults they act as pollinators. At all stages they are a significant source of food for a wide range of predators and parasites. For instance, it has been estimated that across Britain, Blue Tit chicks alone consume a total of 35 billion caterpillars each

Elephant Hawk-moth Roger Wyatt

year (Fox *et al.*, 2013). At night, moths make up a substantial part of the diet of bats, including Noctule and Brown Long-eared bats, both found at Shotover.

The food requirements of the different species are also very diverse. While the majority of larvae feed on the leaves of vascular plants, there are also species that specialize in consuming roots, fruits, mosses, fungi, dead wood and even the larvae of other Lepidoptera. At Shotover, the larvae of moths such as Dunbar *Cosmia trapezina* and Satellite *Eupsilia transerva* are perfectly capable of surviving on plant material but will also add other moth larvae to their diet. Some moths impinge upon the domestic world by consuming cloth fibres and stored food. Indeed, a number of native British species feed indoors throughout the winter, taking advantage of heated spaces such as houses. Here they can multiply to larger populations than in their natural habitats, for example as detritivores among the debris in bird's nests.

In woodlands, the larvae of some winter-active moths can be particularly abundant in early spring and cause significant, albeit short-term, defoliation of trees. This phenomenon has been seen regularly at Shotover to the point where, on the 'worst' days, an umbrella would be useful to shelter from the excrement — 'frass' — that can be heard raining down from the canopy, and it can be hard to imagine that the trees will recover from this onslaught on their first flush of palatable new leaves. The larvae eventually drop down on silken threads to start feeding on the understorey vegetation, usually because the supply of fresh leaves and buds in the canopy has become insufficient. On the Hill such species include Winter Moth *Operophtera brumata*, Pale Brindled Beauty *Phigalia pilosaria*, Scarce Umber *Agriopis aurantiaria* and the aptly named *Erannis defoliaria* or Mottled Umber.

The butterflies and moths of Shotover

Before 1995 the recording of Lepidoptera at Shotover was rather patchy, albeit with observations dating back to 1914. Most of the early work was by William Holland and Albert Hamm for macro-moths (Walker and Hobby, 1939: p. 82) and by Edwin Waters for micro-moths (Waters, 1929); altogether they noted 33 butterfly species, 71 macro-moths and 50 micro-moths. Later, David Steel reported 221 moth species for Brasenose Wood (Steel, 1984:

Night-time surveying at Shotover using a lamp to attract moths for identification

p. 104) and increased the overall records for the Hill by 161 species. Since 1995, about 4,000 Lepidoptera records have been added to these, yet only about half are for moths, reflecting the greater recording effort generally devoted to the relatively small number of butterflies.

To increase knowledge of moths at Shotover, from 2009 to 2013 the Shotover Wildlife Moth Survey Team carried out systematic recording in the SSSI, sampling different habitats at regular intervals and throughout the seasons. Six sites were chosen to cover a range of habitats: a stand of Heather, a marsh, open grassland (two locations) and mature oak woodland (two locations). The moths were collected using battery-powered actinic light traps, supplemented occasionally with higher-power mercury-vapour lamps. During the five years of the survey, 283 macro-moth and 182 micro-moth species were recorded (including 158 species previously unrecorded at Shotover), raising the overall total to 342 macro-moths (over a third of the known species in Britain) and 226 micro-moths. It must be noted, however, that many of the apparently new species for Shotover would most likely have been recorded on the Hill in earlier years but were simply noted in early 20th-century publications, such as Salzman (1939), as 'widespread' or 'common' in Oxfordshire.

Open grassland
Areas such as Mary Sadler South, The Plain, Slade Camp Field and the fields below Westhill Farm provide ideal habitat for a wide range of common species of butterfly, including Brown Argus *Aricia agestis*, Common Blue *Polyommatus icarus*, Large Skipper *Ochlodes sylvanus*, Marbled White *Melanargia galathea*, Meadow Brown *Maniola jurtina* and Small Skipper *Thymelicus sylvestris*.

Many moths also feed on grassland plants at Shotover, including Dark Arches *Apamea monoglypha* and Common Rustic *Mesapamea secalis*. Ear Moth *Amphipoea oculea* can still be found in some grassy habitats on the Hill, having probably been much more abundant in the past; it is now a species of conservation concern in Britain. The grassland traps of the 2009–13 survey were placed in open areas of Horseshoe Field and Horspath Common, and together captured 181 species of moth. Of the 43 species of micro-moths recorded in these grasslands during the five years, 17 are currently recognized

as species of conservation concern in Britain — more than in any other habitat of the survey.

Heathland
Heather provides an excellent nectar source for Lepidoptera, with many moth species feeding on this and several other heathland plants. At Shotover, however, there are no butterflies specifically associated with heathland. Emperor Moth *Saturnia pavonia*, which can be abundant on heathland, was captured in Mary Sadler Field in 2010 by means of pheromone luring [see box opposite]. Mary Sadler Field is also a stronghold for Grass Emerald, and is the only location at Shotover where this moth has been recorded.

All the heathy areas on the Hill are favourable habitats for Autumnal Rustic *Eugnorisma glareosa*, another species of conservation concern. The micro-moth *Cydia succedana* can be abundant in the SSSI, with males often seen flying in the daytime but only where there is Gorse, its larval food plant. *Grapholita internana* is another heathland micro-moth at Shotover and is consequently uncommon in Oxfordshire. Although moth diversity in the heathy areas was high during the intensive surveying period of 2009–13, actual numbers were often lower than in other habitats. Nevertheless, this habitat yielded the greatest number (47) of micro-moth species.

Autumnal Rustic Patrick Clement

Luring an Emperor Moth

The magnificent Emperor Moth *Saturnia pavonia* is widespread in Britain, particularly on heath and moorland, and has probably inhabited Shotover for many years, albeit in small numbers. But it was not recorded on the Hill until one was lured by pheromone in 2010. The males are large and fly by day, and are easily mistaken for a butterfly; the females fly at night but, being heavily laden with eggs, do not usually stray far from their natal grounds. Although the females are attracted to light-traps, a better method for surveying is to prepare an unmated female to attract a male, especially in areas where populations are low.

In a technique known as 'assembling', a female moth is reared from the pupal stage. The unmated adult female is placed in a net enclosure, in suitable habitat, where she emits a pheromone to attract the attention of a male. Adult male Emperor Moths are short-lived and do not feed; their sole function is to find a mate and so they are strongly attracted to the pheromones released by the less mobile females. In 2010 a female was assembled in the heathy area of Mary Sadler Field and within minutes a male arrived — proving that the species was present on the Hill. A short while later a second male came to the lure in the Shotover car park.

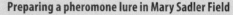

Emperor Moth Paul Brock   **Preparing a pheromone lure in Mary Sadler Field**

Marsh

As with the Lepidoptera of the heathy areas, there are no butterflies at Shotover associated specifically with the wet habitats, although the damper conditions may benefit species such as Ringlet *Aphantopus hyperantus* and Green-veined White *Pieris napi*. Willows grow well in this habitat, serving as the food plant for numerous moths, including species of conservation concern such as Minor Shoulder-knot *Brachylomia viminalis*, which has been recorded regularly as both adult and larvae in the marshes of Shotover.

Light-trapping at the edge of Long Marsh attracted the most species during the moth survey, and the abundance of moths at this location was also the highest. However, most of those caught were woodland species. The marsh is relatively small in area compared with the surrounding woodland and it is likely that Long Marsh is providing a sheltered clearing for moths with a valuable mixture of habitat structure, including woodland edge, mature trees and a diverse marshland flora.

Scrub

The scrub habitat around Slade Camp South and Brasenose Farm is especially important for two of Shotover's rarer butterflies: the Brown Hairstreak and Black Hairstreak, both of which use the dense Blackthorn in these areas. While Brown Hairstreaks tend to lay their eggs on young Blackthorn suckers, Black Hairstreaks prefer the more mature thickets. Black Hairstreak is a particularly rare species in Britain, found in only a small number of localities across the Midlands from Cambridgeshire to Oxfordshire.

Brown Hairstreak populations suffered so greatly through the 20th century that the species was locally extinct around Shotover for many years. However, in the 1990s a population centred on Otmoor — seven kilometres to the north — began to spread outwards, eventually reaching Shotover in 2004. Its increasing range

Mature Blackthorn in Slade Camp South

species. Such places often have a rapidly changing vegetative structure and a range of different microclimates. At Brasenose Farm an actively worked gravel pile was colonized by a number of ruderal plants, including Great Mullein *Verbascum thapsis*, the food plant of Mullein moth *Cucullia verbasci*, and is the only place this moth has been recorded at Shotover to date.

Mature woodland

The woodlands of Shotover can be rewarding at any time of year for anyone with an interest in butterflies and moths. Some species are abundant on warm summer days while others are active only in winter. The structure and composition of Shotover's woodlands are a major influence on Lepidoptera diversity, with the open tracks, glades, coppiced blocks of different ages and mature trees all providing the appropriate food plants and micro-climates.

Several uncommon woodland butterflies are resident at Shotover. White Admiral *Limenitis camilla*, whose larvae feed on Honeysuckle *Lonicera periclymenum*, is seen every year in Brasenose Wood and very occasionally in Johnson's Piece. Purple Emperor *Apatura iris*, which feeds on willow leaves, is also seen most frequently in Brasenose Wood, while Purple Hairstreak *Favonius quercus* has been seen on oaks in all parts of the SSSI. Since 2009 Silver-washed Fritillary *Argynnis paphia* has colonized Slade Camp South

was monitored by the Upper Thames Branch of Butterfly Conservation by searching for the small eggs during the winter months. Eggs were found in the hedgerows below Westhill Farm, at Slade Camp South, in Horseshoe Field and along The Plain, with the annual count rising from seven to 93 in the first five years of surveying (2005–09). Monitoring has continued at Slade Camp, where eggs are found annually, although numbers fluctuate greatly. Adult Brown Hairstreaks are known to be especially elusive and so it has proved at Shotover, with only two sightings in the scrub just east of Brasenose Farm (2008 and 2009).

Scrub vegetation on disturbed (ruderal) ground can also host a wide diversity of moth

Brown Hairstreak in Slade Camp South
Sandra Standbridge

Adults are seldom seen but breeding is confirmed each winter by finding their eggs on Blackthorn.

and Brasenose Wood [see page 123] and should remain a species of Shotover woodland wherever violets, its food plant, continue to grow.

For moths, the light-trapping of recent years has revealed a number of species typical of mature deciduous woodland: for example, Leopard Moth *Zeuzera pyrina*, Lobster Moth, Great Prominent *Peridea anceps*, Blotched Emerald *Comibaena bajularia* and Oak Nycteoline *Nycteola revayana*. The woodland has also been found to host saproxylic moth species, including Lesser Tawny

Tubic *Batia lunaris*, whose larvae feed under dead bark, and Pale Corn Clothes *Nemapogon variatella*, whose larvae develop in dead-wood fungi. By using a torch at night to search for the wingless females, it is also possible to see some of the winter-active species in abundance — for example, Winter Moth, Mottled Umber and Scarce Umber in early winter and later, towards spring, Dotted Border *Agriopis marginaria*, Small Brindled Beauty *Apocheima hispidaria* and March Moth *Alsophila aescularia*.

Leopard Moth has a wingspan of up to seven centimetres
Ilia Ustyantsev/Flickr

The adult moth emerges to breed during July having spent two to three years in larval development.

Changes in butterfly and moth diversity at Shotover

Of the 33 butterfly species recorded on the Hill before 1995, 26 are resident in Britain, including Red Admiral *Vanessa atalanta*, which is no longer a migrant to Oxfordshire. One species is a regular migrant to Britain — Painted Lady *V. cardui* — and six species have not been seen on the Hill in recent times. All but one of these 33 species could be found at Shotover in the early 20th century. Only Essex Skipper *Thymelicus lineola* is a more recent arrival, in the course of a westward expansion of its range in the 1980s; it was first recorded on the Hill by David Redhead in 1990. Since 1995 three further species have been added: two British residents, Small Blue *Cupido minimus* and Silver-washed Fritillary, and one migrant, Clouded Yellow *Colias croceus*.

Butterfly diversity at Shotover has remained high — 36 species overall — with six species no longer seen: Large Tortoiseshell *Nymphalis polychloros*, Wall Brown *Lasiommata megera*, Small Heath *Coenonympha pamphilus*, Duke of Burgundy *Hamearis lucina*, Dark Green Fritillary *Argynnis aglaja* and Green Hairstreak. Although Large Tortoiseshell has become a more regular visitor to the southern shores of Britain, perhaps even establishing itself on the Isle of Wight (Botham *et al.*, 2013), it became extinct as a resident species in Britain in the 1950s and is now considered a rare migrant. Records for this species at Shotover in 1962 and 1976 may be misidentifications or possible migrants.

Small Heath Roger Wyatt

Wall Brown has declined sharply from inland habitats in Britain and, though once common in gardens and parks, it is now rarely encountered away from coastal sites. It has not been seen at Shotover since the 1970s and is probably now lost from Oxfordshire. The last confirmed record of Small Heath at Shotover was in 1990; it was once abundant in the grasslands but has suffered a steep decline nationally in recent decades, becoming largely restricted to unimproved semi-natural grasslands. Duke of Burgundy has also suffered a major decline in recent years, particularly in woodland, where it is thought to depend on Primrose in open coppice.

Considering the ideal Gorse and scrub habitat afforded by Shotover and the amount of recording effort in recent years, it is surprising that Green Hairstreak has not been sighted for over 40 years. Similarly, Dark Green Fritillary has increased its range and abundance in Britain over the last three decades, yet it has not been recorded at Shotover since a single sighting near Brasenose Wood in 1979. Although Dark Green Fritillary shares the same food plant — Common Dog-violet — as Silver-washed Fritillary, the former is a species of open sunny habitats, while the latter prefers woodland. At Shotover, Common Dog-violet is more frequent in wooded areas than in open habitats, and may account for the presence of Silver-washed Fritillary on the Hill [see page 123] and the absence of Dark Green Fritillary.

Of the butterflies that have only recently been added to the records at Shotover, Small Blue is the most unexpected, as the food plant, Kidney Vetch, is not suited to acidic soils and has not been noted on the Hill. However, a small number of vagrant Small Blues have been recorded since 2003, which may be associated with a known colony three kilometres north of Shotover (David Redhead, 2014, pers. comm.). The only records of the migrant species Clouded Yellow are from Sandpit Field in 2002 and the fields below Westhill Farm in 2016. There has been a general increase in migrant species to Britain over the last three decades in response to the warmer climate (Botham *et al.*, 2013) and it is possible that Clouded Yellow will become a more regular visitor to Shotover.

Silver-washed Fritillary — a woodland species — has had a fairly wide distribution in Oxfordshire throughout the 20th century

Clouded Yellow Roger Wyatt

not been recorded since 1995 include Forester *Adscita statices*, Broad-bordered Bee Hawk-moth *Hemaris fuciformis*, Lappet *Gastropacha quercifolia*, Dotted Rustic *Rhyacia simulans*, Beautiful Brocade *Lacanobia contigua* and Puss Moth, all of which have declined substantially throughout Britain.

Nationally declining macro-moth species not recorded at Shotover since 1995

Common name	Scientific name	Decline in Britain, 1968–2007
V-Moth	*Macaria wauaria*	99%
Garden Dart	*Euxoa nigricans*	98%
Spinach	*Eulithis mellinata*	96%
Flounced Chestnut	*Agrochola helvola*	94%
Garden Tiger	*Arctia caja*	92%
Broom Moth	*Melanchra pisi*	84%
Grey Chi	*Antitype chi*	80%

(Walker and Hobby, 1939: p. 84; Fox *et al.*, 2011) but until recently had not been recorded at Shotover. Its range has increased since about 2000, however, and a new colony had become established in Brasenose Wood and Slade Camp South by 2009, with individuals seen every year since. Woodland ground flora is especially important for Fritillary butterflies, particularly the various species of violet that are the larval food plants. Consequently, sensitive coppice work and an increase in violets could see Dark Green Fritillary also return to Brasenose Wood, although the increasing numbers of deer and their impact on the ground flora [see pages 224–225] could threaten the viability of any future colonies of both species of Fritillary.

It is more difficult to examine trends for moths at Shotover because of the increased recording effort since 1995. Apparent gains will mostly consist of previously undetected species, for example Emperor Moth [see box, page 119], whereas losses of species are more likely to be genuine. Of the 342 species of macro-moth recorded at Shotover, 46 are of conservation concern in England but of these only 27 species have been seen since 1995. The table [see above] lists those species which seem to have disappeared from Shotover in recent years and which have also declined by at least 80 per cent throughout Britain since 1968 (Fox *et al.*, 2013). Other species of note that have

On a more optimistic note, a number of species of conservation concern in England still thrive at Shotover and 21 nationally declining species were recorded during the period of intensive surveying from 2009 to 2013. For example, Autumnal Rustic, despite a 94-per-cent decline nationwide, is relatively common in the SSSI, with records from three different sites during the period of recording, and Sprawler *Asteroscopus sphinx* and Green-brindled Crescent *Allophyes oxyacanthae* are still abundant throughout the woodlands of Shotover notwithstanding declines of 80 per cent across Britain. Dusky Thorn

Dusky Thorn is in severe national decline Paul Brock

Lepidoptera as indicators of biodiversity

Butterflies and moths are frequently used as representative taxa to indicate how biodiversity is faring in the face of environmental change. Several key aspects of these insects make them valuable bioindicators in Britain.

Firstly, the records for butterflies and moths are unusually comprehensive; the recording of these taxa has been a popular activity for decades. An exceptional volume of distribution data on Lepidoptera has been collated by the charity Butterfly Conservation through two of its projects — Butterflies for the New Millennium and the National Moth Recording Scheme. In parallel with these initiatives, standardized monitoring programmes have been established to assess population changes. For butterflies, the UK Butterfly Monitoring Scheme is operated by a partnership between Butterfly Conservation, the Centre for Ecology and Hydrology and the British Trust for Ornithology; and for moths, the Rothamsted Insect Survey has conducted systematic light-trap recording since the 1960s. The combined data demonstrate a great decline in moths and butterflies since recording began (Fox *et al.*, 2011 and 2013).

Secondly, as their activities are strongly temperature-dependent, Lepidoptera are among the most sensitive to climatic change (Thomas *et al.*, 2004). For instance, increasing temperatures have caused a northward spread of Orange-tip *Anthocharis cardamines*, which has recently colonized Scotland. Conversely, species of colder regions, such as Mountain Ringlet *Erebia epiphron*, may be declining as the climate becomes warmer; it is a species found only at high altitudes in Britain and is restricted to a few localities in northern England and Scotland.

In addition, many Lepidoptera have specialized ecological requirements which render them highly sensitive to changes in their habitat brought about by management, pollution or other factors. A reduction in traditional management practices such as coppicing has contributed to the decline of many species in woodland for example, while other habitats are threatened by inappropriate levels of grazing. Development and agricultural expansion have directly removed much of the required habitat, while intensification of agriculture has had a significant negative impact on Lepidoptera diversity and abundance. The classic studies on Peppered Moth *Biston betularia*, for example, have neatly demonstrated the impact of pollution. A previously rare dark (melanic) form of the species became much more common in industrial areas of Britain where trees were predominantly blackened with soot, making this form better camouflaged from predators. With improvements in air quality the melanic form has once again become much rarer. Similarly, research on moths that feed on lichens has shown that where air quality has improved, both lichens and moths have recovered (Pescott *et al.*, 2015).

Peppered Moth Paul Brock

Ennomos fuscantaria, one of the worst cases in Britain (98-per-cent decline), has been recorded several times in Brasenose Wood and once in Mary Sadler Field (2006). It is not possible to say whether the abundance of any of these species has declined at Shotover in recent years, nor how they will fare on the Hill in the future. The larval food plant of Dusky Thorn is the foliage of Ash trees and so the threat of Ash Dieback disease [see box, page 48] heralds a very uncertain future for this already declining moth species.

Conservation of butterflies and moths at Shotover

Most of the changes in the Lepidoptera fauna at Shotover in recent years are in accordance with national trends. Despite governmental conservation targets, butterflies and moths have undergone significant declines over the last few decades (Fox *et al.,* 2011 and 2013). Woodland butterflies have decreased more than those of any other habitat, and recent reports show a similar trend for woodland moths. While agricultural intensification has been one of the main agents of decline in the wider countryside, in woodland one of the greatest problems is inappropriate management. Since traditional practices such as coppicing are no longer economic, woodlands throughout England have lost structural diversity and have become generally less suitable for the associated Lepidoptera.

Many woodlands, even when managed well, can suffer a dramatic loss of ground flora and sapling trees (due to the browsing of deer), greatly reducing moth and butterfly diversity. The loss of ground flora not only removes food plants and their associated species but also depletes the supply of nectar. In Brasenose Wood, it is hoped that the recent experimental coppicing [see box, page 224], with high-cut stools and imaginative brash distribution, will help to conserve ground flora and the woodland ecology.

Maintaining open habitat at Shotover is also clearly important, exemplified by the great diversity of moths on the grassland and heath. The sandy areas, which are rare in Oxfordshire, are particularly diverse in the butterflies and moths associated with this habitat. However, the heathy areas will only continue to be suitable if the Gorse, Bracken and Silver Birch are prevented from dominating the heath and acidic grassland.

Clearing Gorse and Silver Birch from the acidic grassland in Mary Sadler Field

Beetles

Tim Newton and Ivan Wright

Most people will be familiar with beetles. Indeed, it is often a beetle — a ladybird — that first attracts a child's close attention to the world of insects. At Shotover it is more likely to be the ponderous Bloody-nosed Beetle *Timarcha tenebricosa* that catches the eye, as it crawls unhurriedly across a path. Yet this audacious behaviour is unusual in beetles; most prefer to remain concealed and are seldom seen without a hunt. In the early 20th century entomologists from Oxford University recorded nearly 400 beetles at Shotover, of which many are now considered scarce. However, since 2008 the known diversity has been raised to over 1,000 species through targeted survey work by Shotover Wildlife, including many rare species, leading to a growing awareness and recognition of the importance of Shotover for its beetle fauna.

There are over 4,000 species of beetle (Coleoptera) in Britain. One of the most obvious features that set them apart from other insects

The Wasp Beetle's *Clytis arietis* vibrant markings are formed by scale-like hairs Paul Brock

is their front pair of wings, the elytra, which are hard and thick in order to encase and protect the hind wings. Usually the rear half of the body (the abdomen) is completely covered by the elytra but there are numerous exceptions, particularly the rove-beetles (Staphylinidae) [for example, see box, page 134–135]. Although most beetles can fly, they are generally more at home on the ground, and flightless species have no hind wings under their elytra. Their jaws — which are typically strong and pointed for biting — are another key defining feature, in contrast, for example, to the sucking mouthparts of 'true bugs' [see page 164], some of which look very similar to beetles.

Toughness, the ability to fly and adaptability are the foremost factors in the evolutionary success of beetles. Considering the vast number of micro-habitats that beetles exploit, and their tendency to specialize, it is not surprising that they have evolved into a great diversity of species and a wide range of colours, shapes and sizes. Some beetles are intricately patterned with colours or patches of dense hair while others are spectacularly shiny. The patterns and colours often serve as protection from predators, either as camouflage or deterrent, discouraging a predator which might have learned to associate a colour or pattern with harm or discomfort. More persistent attackers may be actively repulsed by poisons, obnoxious secretions or blistering agents. When under threat, even the seemingly harmless ladybirds (Coccinelidae) can exude a distasteful chemical which 'bleeds' from their leg joints.

The beetle family contains the largest living insects in the world, with some up to 20 centimetres in length and with grandiose names to match, such as the Elephant, Hercules and Goliath beetles. The largest ever recorded at Shotover is the Stag Beetle *Lucanus cervus* but this grand creature has not been reported on the Hill since the early 20th century [see page 136]. At six centimetres long the Stag Beetle is as large as the Hill's smallest mammal, the Pygmy Shrew; however, beetles are generally much smaller than this, with most species measuring between three and 10 millimetres.

Beetle recording at Shotover

The first invertebrates from Shotover to be identified to species level were three beetles: Bloody-nosed Beetle, Black Oil-beetle *Meloe proscarabaeus* and Dor Beetle *Anoplotrupes stercorosus* (Walker, 1907). As an undergraduate in 1819 the Revd. F.W. Hope — later the eminent Oxford University entomologist — noticed both the Bloody-nosed Beetle and the Black Oil-beetle while *"going up Shotover Hill"*. It was only by chance and good fortune that Hope made this incidental note in the margin of his copy of *Entomologia Brittanica* (published in 1802 by Thomas Marsham), possibly because the Bloody-nosed Beetle had been reclassified from the genus *Chrysomela* to *Timarcha* [see below]. Bloody-nosed Beetle and Dor Beetle are still to be found on the Hill, whereas the Black Oil-beetle is now

A specimen of Black Oil-beetle *Meloe proscarabeus* collected by Hope from around the time of his Shotover record ©Katherine Child, OUMNH, University of Oxford

Shotover's first invertebrate records appear as a hand-written note in Hope's copy of *Entomologia Brittanica*: '1. Now in the genus *Timarcha*, taken in company with *Meloe proscarabeus* in 1819 in going up Shotover Hill' ©OUMNH, University of Oxford

The fourth line of records for Shotover begins 'moguntiacus' and refers to *Ceutorhynchus thomsoni* which has since become scarce in Britain [see page 136].

nationally scarce and has not been recorded at Shotover since Hope's sighting in 1819.

Much of what we know of the early beetle fauna around Oxford was collated in 1907 by Commander J.J. Walker, who catalogued the known species within seven miles (11 kilometres) of the centre of Oxford, "*being about the limit one can effectively work a district by the aid of one's legs unassisted by a bicycle*" (Walker, 1907: p. 52).

Glow-worm Paul Brock

He also noted in 1907 that 42.5 per cent of British beetles had been found within this radius — a remarkable feat of recording. Walker's diaries show that he continued to visit Shotover in most years until 1933 and it was largely on the basis of his work over these years that by 1939 213 species had been recorded for Shotover, most of which are published by Aubrook (1939: p. 107).

It has been estimated that the total number of beetle species currently at Shotover could be well over 1,000 (Darren Mann, 2014, pers. comm.). It is therefore surprising that so few species had been recorded for the Hill, including only 10 species from Brasenose Wood. This may be due partly to a tendency at that time to publish only the less common species. A resurgence of recording in the 1980s by David Steel and Pond Action (now the Freshwater Habitats Trust) raised the total to 516 species. More recently Shotover Wildlife has found a further 565, taking the all-time recorded diversity in 2018 to 1,081 species. Of these, 144 have not been found since before 1939 and may no longer be extant on the Hill. The current recorded beetle fauna — that is, records since 1995 — is 811 species.

Of the 565 species newly added by Shotover Wildlife, 35 are new county records: that is, species not previously recorded for 'modern' (post-1974) Oxfordshire. A further 30 species are new to the officially recognized recording area of pre-1974 Oxfordshire (Vice County 23), which excludes the part that was once within Berkshire.

Habitat-specific beetles at Shotover

As with other taxa, the impressive diversity of beetles at Shotover is due to the wide range of habitats on the Hill. For example, the dry sandy soils accommodate burrowing species that are not normally found elsewhere in the county. The many different species of tree and the woodland habitats, both ancient and secondary, are especially rich in beetles. Even the Glow-worm *Lampyris noctiluca*, which many older people will remember as more common in their childhood, still emits its curious green light in Shotover's grasslands and mature hedgerows. Among all the beetles, only the water-beetles are comparatively low in diversity because of the relatively small scale of the wetland habitats across the Hill.

Sandy soils

No chapter on the beetles of Shotover would be complete without a description of the Bloody-nosed Beetle: not only a sandy soil specialist but also an insect that excites more curiosity than almost any other on the Hill. Furthermore, it seems entirely fitting that Hope's observation of it "*in 1819 in going up Shotover Hill*" should herald nearly 200 years of continuous recorded occupancy by this locally iconic and popular creature.

The Bloody-nosed Beetle is a handsome insect (11–18 millimetres long), and is the largest of the leaf beetles (Chrysomelidae) in Britain. It can be seen all year round, and especially from April to September when it is most active. At first glance it appears to be black but under a bright sky an iridescent deep blue or green is revealed. It cannot fly; indeed, it has no wings and the two elytra are fused together into a single domed covering for the abdomen. The larvae are large, plump and dark green. Both adults and larvae feed on the leaves and stems of bedstraws (*Gallium* spp.), of which Shotover has several species, including Cleavers *G. aparine* and Heath Bedstraw in abundance. The beetle gets its common name from its reflex of 'bleeding' a red fluid from its mouthparts when threatened. Picking one up

Bloody-nosed Beetle

'Blood' dripping from the eponymous beetle Eleanor Hawtree

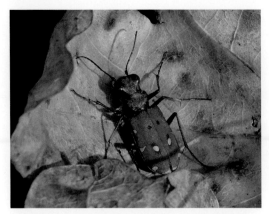

One of many Green Tiger Beetles seen on Horspath Common following the grassland habitat restoration
Ivan Wright

often results in a blob of red 'blood' on the hand. Although the adults have been known to live for up to 14 months, they move laboriously on huge feet and, being flightless, are readily predated by animals such as birds and foxes — in fact, anything that is not put off by the foul-tasting 'blood'.

In contrast to the Bloody-nosed Beetle, one of Shotover's fastest beetles, running or flying, is the viciously predatory Green Tiger Beetle *Cicindela campestris*. This 10–14 millimetre member of the ground beetle family (Carabidae) has matt-green upper parts with buff-yellow spots, and under parts that reflect lustrous metallic reds and greens. The adults can be seen in late spring and summer in sandy places, and it is here that their larvae dig their traps. The trap is a hole in the soil with a funnel-shaped entrance of loose sand, where few insects can land without tumbling towards the bottom. Any unfortunate visitor that suffers this fate is grabbed by the powerful jaws of the waiting larva, and drawn down into the hole to be eaten.

The Green Tiger Beetle was recorded on and around Shotover in the early 20th century and seen frequently until around 1984 (David Steel, 2001, pers. comm.). Then this conspicuous beetle went unrecorded for more than 20 years and was feared lost from the Hill. However, it reappeared in some abundance in April 2011, mostly on the large areas of bare soil newly created at Horspath Common by Shotover Wildlife's Grassland Habitat Project [see box, page 98]. It is thought most likely that this new colony is derived from an existing population from somewhere else on the Hill (Darren Mann, 2011, pers. comm.) rather than pioneer individuals that have flown three to four kilometres from other sandy places such as Garsington to the south or Beckley to the north. The nearest known colony is at Tubney Wood, 14 kilometres to the south-west of Shotover — an unlikely distance for a colonizer to have flown.

A common sight on the sandy soils of Shotover are the large and distinctive holes made by the Minotaur Beetle *Typhaeus typhoeus* of the Geotrupidae family. This large (11–18 millimetres) shiny black dung beetle can burrow to a depth of 1.5 metres — deeper than any other beetle in Britain. The beetle digs a central hole with side chambers in which its eggs are laid. Rabbit droppings are then drawn down the hole and rolled into the chambers for the hatched beetle larvae to feed on. The adult males are very

Minotaur Beetle Peter Creed

Burrows of the Minotaur Beetle are a much more common sight than the nocturnal insect itself

striking, with three spiked horns behind the head, but being nocturnal are seldom seen and only very rarely spotted rolling a dung-ball. Yet the unusually high density of holes at Shotover suggests that after dark a crowd of Minotaur Beetles bustle about, rolling Rabbit droppings in all directions. Since this beetle is dependent on deep sandy soil, it is a good example of a species that is common at Shotover and yet scarce in the rest of Oxfordshire.

Woodland

Beetles are especially plentiful in old woodlands and although many of these species depend on dead or decaying wood [see below], there are numerous others with quite different requirements. Leaf litter, fungi and fallen timber form a multi-layered gradation of decaying matter on the woodland floor, providing a continuity and diversity of niches for the small creatures that contribute to this critical ecosystem. Beetles are an integral part of the forest underlayer, especially rove- and ground-beetles which consume and reduce plant material, and prey on the cohabiting fauna. For example, 82 ground beetle species have been recorded in Brasenose Wood alone, including *Pterostichus oblongopunctatus* which although nationally scarce is found in any ground survey of Shotover's woodlands.

Many beetles also inhabit the tree canopy. Some of these seldom come to the ground and consequently may not be as scarce as national records might suggest. The niches exploited by these beetles include cracks, crevices, loose bark

The scarab-beetle *Trox scaber* with several mites using a transport opportunity for dispersal Trevor Pendleton

0.5 mm

The very rare ladybird *Clitostethus arcuatus*
©Katherine Child, OUMNH, University of Oxford

and, for the detritivores, the nests of wasps, mammals and birds. At Shotover these include: a longhorn beetle, *Callidium violaceum,* on pine trees, the scarab-beetle *Trox scaber* which is frequently found in owls' nests, and the nationally scarce *Gnathoncus buyssoni* of the Histeridae family, which is thought to exploit the nests of raptors.

Although ladybirds are not specifically woodland beetles, two particularly scarce species were recorded in the upper canopy of oak trees in 2012. *Clitostethus arcuatus* is listed as a very rare beetle, with only 32 records in Britain since 1872. This tiny insect (1.5 millimetres) is generally found on old Ivy *Hedera helix*, where it feeds on aphids, and has a distinctive horseshoe-shaped mark across its wing cases. *Stethorus punctillum* is scarce in Britain, yet was found in Brasenose Wood and near Westhill Farm. Across all its habitats, Shotover supports a rich diversity of ladybirds; of the 47 species in Britain, 21 have been recorded at Shotover since 1995.

Beetles of dead wood

An especially important group of beetles at Shotover are the saproxylic species — those which depend on dead or decaying wood for at least part of their life cycle. Of all the taxonomic groups in the wider countryside, the saproxylic

A vane trap in use on an oak tree in Johnson's Piece

The scarce longhorn beetle *Anaglyptus mysticus*
Paul Brock

species are among the most vulnerable [see page 32], and some of the rarest insects in the SSSI are saproxylic beetles. For example, since 1995, of the 35 species of beetle that have been recorded as new to Oxfordshire, 10 are saproxylic and nationally scarce or rare.

In his 1984 book, David Steel considers the status of dead-wood beetles at Shotover, an unusually progressive step at that time as the importance of the conservation of saproxylic invertebrates was only just beginning to be more widely recognized. Unfortunately — or so it seemed — Steel was only able to report that: "*One disappointment is the shortage of noteworthy dead wood beetles at Shotover. The dead wood species are mostly common … whereas Oxfordshire's other Royal Forests (Wychwood and Woodstock Chase) boast a range of rarities.*" (Steel, 1984: p. 96)

This observation, however, tells us more about the relative paucity of specialist invertebrate surveying at Shotover prior to 1984, and the methods used, than about the beetle fauna itself. In recent years, flight interception traps (vane traps) hung in the canopy of mature trees have shown that Shotover in fact has a great variety of notable and rare saproxylic invertebrates.

For example, since 2010 the number of longhorn beetles (Cerambycidae) recorded at Shotover has risen from six to 21; of these, 16 are dead-wood specialists, representing a third of the British saproxylic longhorn beetle fauna. Many of these handsome beetles are relatively

large and some are strikingly coloured, while others are remarkably well camouflaged. As their name suggests, most have long antennae; in a few species these can be up to four times their body length. Nationally scarce saproxylic longhorn beetles at Shotover include *Poecilium alni*, *Anaglyptus mysticus* and *Grammoptera abdominalis*.

To assess the quality of the woodland habitats and saproxylic beetle fauna in the SSSI, the Species Quality Index (SQI) and the Index of Ecological Continuity (IEC) [see box, page 133] were calculated separately for Brasenose Wood and the 'upper Shotover' part of the SSSI, as well as for the combined area. The indices are specifically for broad-leaved woodland and exclude beetles associated with coniferous trees. The table [page 133] shows that, overall, 155 species qualify for inclusion in the SQI and 53 species in the IEC. Both of these figures amount to over 25 per cent of qualifying species in Britain for each index. The data in the table are for species recorded since 1995; in fact, inclusion of earlier data would add only eight species and change the SQI scores by less than three per cent.

The rankings in the table [page 133] of saproxylic indices are based on 203 qualifying woodlands in Britain (Fowles, 2017) and take no account of the differing survey circumstances at each site, nor does the analysis take into account the size of the site; thus the results from the SSSI at Shotover (130 hectares) are not adjusted relative to much more extensive sites such as Windsor Great Park (4,800 hectares). Consequently, a ranking of 37th in Britain for SQI and 24th for IEC suggests that the saproxylic habitats at Shotover are of considerable importance. Indeed, the IEC of 71 for the entire SSSI is of high national significance and only nine points below qualification for European significance (Alexander, 2004).

Particularly informative, and rather surprising, is a comparison of the ancient woodland of Brasenose Wood with the ex-pasture fields of 'upper Shotover', each of which has been surveyed to the same extent. More qualifying species of saproxylic beetle, for both the SQI and IEC, have been recorded in 'upper Shotover', and the IEC here is markedly higher. This may be due to timber extraction from Brasenose Wood in past centuries, resulting in few trees in the woodland of today being older than 250 years. In comparison, the relict wood pasture of 'upper Shotover', particularly Johnson's Piece, is relatively unmanaged woodland with several oaks older than 250 years, and with mature trees of species not normally tolerated among the oak standards of managed coppice woodland. The significantly higher SQI for Brasenose Wood (527) is partly due to the presence of three rare and strongly saproxylic species: *Lymexylon navale*, *Plectophoeus nitidus* and *Platydema violaceum*.

The rare saproxylic darkling beetle *Platydema violaceum* of which there have been very few records in Britain in the last 100 years
©Katherine Child, OUMNH, University of Oxford

Beetles lost and found
Most beetles have to be hunted for, and therefore it cannot be assumed that a species is lost just because it has not been seen for many decades.

Quality indices for saproxylic beetles
The diversity of saproxylic beetles can be used as an indicator of both the ecological quality and the antiquity of a woodland habitat, not only for beetles and other saproxylic organisms but for the woodland ecology overall. By applying standardized numerical criteria, sites may be compared and placed in a national context. Unfortunately, the procedure described here is somewhat limited by making no adjustment for site size or survey circumstances but is useful at least in providing comparable indices while so few sites have sufficient data. However, Shotover is sufficiently large to compare subsites that have been surveyed simultaneously with identical methods (for example, 'upper Shotover' versus Brasenose Wood), in which case comparison can be very instructive.

Two saproxylic indices are used in Britain: the saproxylic Species Quality Index (SQI) (Fowles *et al.*, 1999) and the Index of Ecological Continuity (IEC) (Alexander, 2004). Both indices give a higher numerical score to saproxylic species that are both rare in Britain and more strongly dependent on the dead-wood habitat. The SQI is an estimate of the average species rarity and is therefore independent of the number of qualifying species found. The IEC is an accumulative measure of beetle species that are associated with long-established woodlands, and rises with the addition of newly found qualifying species.

Saproxylic indices at Shotover

	Species Quality Index (SQI)		
	whole SSSI	upper Shotover	Brasenose Wood
Qualifying species	115	123	115
Score	519	455	527
National ranking	37th	63rd	35th

	Index of Ecological Continuity (IEC)		
	whole SSSI	upper Shotover	Brasenose Wood
Qualifying species	53	44	36
Score	71	57	46
National ranking	24th	35th	49th

Shotover: a saproxylic stronghold

Of particular relevance to a proper appreciation of Shotover are those saproxylic beetle species that are not only rare but have also been recorded more than once and at different places in the SSSI. The rarity of the scarcer beetles found at Shotover suggests that only a small number of British woodlands support these species. However, their distribution in the SSSI shows that they are able to disperse and breed without being vulnerable to a small area, or perhaps a single tree. The presence of such insects emphasizes the quality and importance of Shotover's saproxylic habitat.

Colydium elongatum (Colydiidae) is a slender 6-millimetre beetle with shiny, intricately sculptured elytra and strawberry-like punctures on its thorax and head; it is rare in Britain and strongly associated with ancient woodlands. Before the work of Shotover Wildlife it had not been recorded in Oxfordshire; the nearest record was from Windsor Great Park in southern Berkshire in 2000.

The Mug Tree has been a successful example of dead-wood habitat creation

The first record of *C. elongatum* in the SSSI was in 2006 when it was found among leaf litter in Brasenose Wood; more recently it was recorded high in the canopy of tall oaks in Open Brasenose Wood and Johnson's Piece. Most notably, however, it was found under the bark of a small oak known as The Mug Tree, which was specifically chosen to be trimmed, killed and then retained as standing dead wood on Horspath Common, as part of the Shotover Wildlife Grassland Habitat Project [see box, page 98]. Therefore, notwithstanding its rarity, *C. elongatum* appears to be well distributed and mobile at Shotover, and has demonstrated that it can respond to conservation work which specifically creates standing dead wood.

Euplectus tholini is a very rare and strongly saproxylic rove-beetle. It is a rich golden-amber and very small — just 1.5 millimetres long. *E. tholini* has only been recognized as a distinct species since 1994, when it was separated from *E. punctatus*, and since then only a small number have been found and identified in Britain. However, two specimens of *E. tholini* have been recorded in separate locations in Brasenose Wood: the first in May 2010 from a rot-hole in a large dead oak, and the second in a well-rotted log on the ground in April 2013.

The Pinhole Borer *Platypus cylindrus* is also associated with long-established woodlands and is a small (five millimetres) cylindrical ambrosia beetle. Its larvae feed on the ambrosia fungi that the beetle carries with it [see page 103]. Taxonomically it is closely related to the weevils (Curculionidae), and especially to the bark-beetles (Scolytinae) that spread Dutch Elm disease [see page 49]. Although the Pinhole Borer has been recorded in Berkshire in recent years, the first record for Oxfordshire was in 2000 in Brasenose Wood. It has since been found in the tree canopy of Holme Ground and for a second time in Brasenose Wood. These results further demonstrate that the old woodland habitats across Shotover make a vital contribution to local and regional saproxylic diversity.

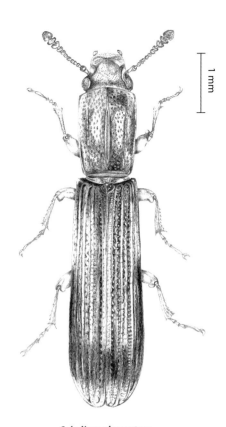

Colydium elongatum

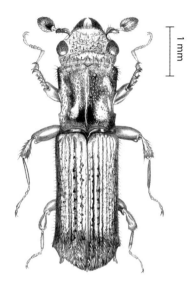

Pinhole Borer
Platypus cylindrus

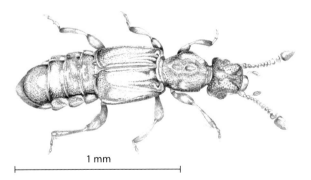

1 mm

Euplectus tholini

Drawings by
Jacqueline Wright

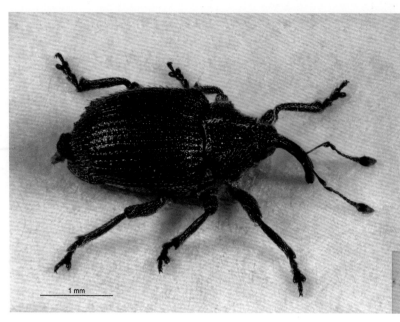

One of J.J. Walker's specimens of *Ceutorhynchus thomsoni* and its pin label [below]
©Katherine Child, OUMNH, University of Oxford

Walker's local records were simply labelled 'Oxford district'; his more detailed diary entries were important therefore in confirming a number of beetle species at Shotover [see page 128].

1 mm

Oxford district J.J. Walker.

Where a species is known to have been in general decline for decades, however, its local extinction is more probable. For instance, the leaf beetle *Chrysomela tremula,* which was last recorded in Brasenose Wood in 1946 and might still live there on the abundant Aspen, has declined across Britain from 'very local' to 'critically endangered (possibly extinct)'. Another example is the small weevil *Ceutorhynchus thomsoni,* which was found at Shotover by Walker on four occasions between 1919 and 1929, yet now is seldom recorded in Britain.

The Stag Beetle was recorded at Shotover some time before 1939, and it may still linger on in private woodland on the Hill. This large and charismatic beetle, however, has probably disappeared from the SSSI, where once the habitat would have been most suitable. To reach adulthood, the larvae need to spend at least five years feeding and growing in undisturbed rotting logs or tree stumps, so the species has suffered greatly, both in the Country Park and more generally across Britain, from years of woodland 'tidying up' and the removal of timber for firewood.

A most welcome re-discovery — like that of the Green Tiger Beetle [see page 130] — was of the nationally scarce Rugged Oil-beetle *Meloe rugosus* in 2014. The British oil-beetles have an intricate parasitic relationship with solitary bees and were once a frequent sight in flower-rich meadows and coastal grasslands but they are now rare in Britain. A single sighting of the Rugged Oil-beetle was reported by J.W. Munro near the summit of Shotover in October 1927, and the lack of any further records had been especially disappointing considering the suitability of the habitat on the Hill. However, in March 2014, while searching after dusk, Richard Comont found and photographed a specimen in Mary Sadler Field in the same general area

Rugged Oil-beetle photographed in Mary Sadler Field in 2014 Richard Comont

as the 1927 record. It is thought most likely that a small population had survived in the region throughout this period (Darren Mann, 2014, pers. comm.) but which, due to its generally nocturnal activity, had gone entirely unnoticed.

The future for beetles at Shotover

In the 1986 assessment which established Shotover's status as an SSSI [see page 242], beetles were without doubt the largest group of insects (for which data were available) to be overlooked by the public authorities. This is all the more astonishing given the age and quality of the habitats, the history of recording, and the number of rare and scarce species known on the Hill at that time. In recent years, through the work of Shotover Wildlife, the importance of Shotover for beetles has been proven beyond doubt. It remains a pity that public authority regard for entomology still does not extend much beyond butterflies.

Fortunately, many beetles are tough and adaptable, and a large proportion will survive at Shotover for many years to come. However, it is the beetles with more complex life cycles, or those less well understood, which require care and caution in the conservation of their habitats. For example, the dependence of oil-beetles on solitary bees is only partially understood, and so while measures to improve the flora and nesting habitats for the solitary bees are fairly straightforward, the effect of conservation work on oil-beetle ecology is much less predictable.

The high point of the recent focus on beetles has been the discovery that Shotover is a nationally important site for saproxylic species and that some of the rarest and most vulnerable insects in the SSSI are to be found among the dead-wood beetles. Saproxylic species of all kinds are reported to be among the most internationally threatened of any habitat (Stokland *et al.*, 2012), mainly through a lack of understanding of their role in woodland ecosystems. Shotover has suffered greatly from many years of dead-wood attrition, whether by tidying up, removal for firewood and timber, or the disposal of felled trees by burning [see pages 231–232]. Perhaps the most worrisome threat at present is the view that ancient woodland is a legitimate source of firewood for the community. Simply on economic grounds this exploitation is indefensible — the income from any truly benign and sustainable extraction would be negligible; it is even less defensible when such woodland work is claimed to promote biodiversity, often sanctioning the collection of firewood under the disingenuous guise of wildlife conservation.

With recognition of Shotover's importance for beetles now beginning to permeate the wider natural history community, it can only be hoped that this will move the public authorities to take Shotover's beetles — and invertebrates in general — much more seriously. The beetle fauna at Shotover is a national asset that should be guaranteed a secure future.

Shotover is now widely recognized as a special place for beetles

In 2015 Shotover Wildlife hosted the inaugural meeting of the British Entomological and Natural History Society's Saproxylic Special Interest Group.

Ivan Wright

On a warm summer's day, the flower-rich grassland along The Plain will be astir with the movement of bumblebees. A closer look reveals countless other insects visiting the flowers, among them tiny wasps and smaller bees all gathering pollen or finding nectar for their diverse purposes. Some of these smaller bees and wasps will then fly the short distance to the nearby bare soil of the old London road, where neat little piles of sandy soil mark their individual nesting holes. The bumblebees and all the burrowing bees and wasps belong to the Hymenoptera, and for over 100 years Shotover Hill has been recognized as a major site for this immensely diverse group of insects.

The Hymenoptera is a particularly large insect order which, in addition to bees and wasps, also includes ants (Formicidae), sawflies (Symphyta) and the gall-causing wasps.

Bumblebees (*Bombus* sp.), common social wasps (*Vespula* sp.) and the Honeybee *Apis mellifera* are all well known for their fascinating behaviour or their painful sting, yet the vast majority of Hymenoptera go quite unnoticed, even though they play a very important role in nature and commerce. For example, the parasitic wasps (Parasitica) are a crucial natural predator of other insects, and bees are by far the most efficient pollinators of flowers. Indeed, the beauty of the flowers in which we may delight is due to their co-evolution with bees and the primitive wasps that preceded them.

The most primitive surviving form of Hymenoptera is that of a sawfly. These plant-feeding ancestors of the bees and wasps appear in fossils from the later Triassic period (200 million years ago) and so were flying around long before any association between bees and flowers became

Early Bumblebee *Bombus pratorum* is one of the 26 species currently found in Britain
Steven Falk

Bumblebees are charming and photogenic insects but their appeal often diverts attention from the 220 other species of bee in Britain.

Bee and wasp nesting holes in newly exposed sandy soil at Shotover

The solitary wasp *Oxybelus uniglumis* dragging a fly to its nest hole Jeremy Early

established. Throughout the Jurassic period that followed, Hymenopteran diversity increased dramatically, especially with the evolution of the parasitic wasps and their predation and exploitation of other insects. It was not until the middle Cretaceous period (100 million years ago) that the stinging Hymenoptera began to evolve through a modification of the female's ovipositor — an appendage for the precise placement of eggs. As eggs are laid, their passage through the ovipositor can be facilitated by a basic lubricant which, in some species, contains more complex compounds that modify plant growth or the behaviour of an injected insect. However, it would seem that the egg-placing function of the ovipositor eventually became of secondary importance to, or even incompatible with, the potential to deliver toxic fluids, and thus the ovipositor evolved into a formidable and versatile weapon — the sting. Bees developed from wasps by adopting a vegetarian diet in the form of pollen, so heralding the remarkable co-evolution towards colourful and scented flowers. The ants also developed from the Parasitica, and together with the stinging bees and wasps are grouped together to form the aculeate Hymenoptera, often referred to as the aculeates.

In Britain about a quarter of aculeates are 'cuckoos'. These are bees, wasps and ants that do not follow the typical life-cycle associated with these insects but, as their name suggests, lay their eggs in the nests of other aculeates. Cuckoo bees and wasps do little or no nest building, do not forage for food and contribute very little as pollinators but can be seen on flowers while

The cuckoo bee *Sphecodes rubicundus* Steven Falk

feeding on nectar. In most cases the cuckoo lays an egg in a brood cell of the host and the cuckoo's egg hatches before that of the host. The ultimately successful cuckoo larva in each cell will either eat or destroy all other eggs and larvae in the cell before eating the host's food store to complete its own development.

The Hymenoptera of Shotover
Shotover has long played a leading role in the history of Hymenopteran study due to its proximity to the University of Oxford [see also page 153]. The great diversity of bees and wasps on the sandy sunlit slopes of the Hill has attracted eminent entomologists since Victorian times, and many 19th-century specimens from Shotover may be seen in the national collections of both the Oxford and London Natural History

Museums. Among these entomologists were the prolific collector A.H. Hamm, and R.C.L. Perkins of Oxford University who in 1919 began publishing the first comprehensive identification guides to British bees.

Hymenopterist Chris O'Toole listed 166 bee and wasp species for Shotover in 1984, including many early 20th-century records (Richards, 1939: p. 147), and on this basis asserted that Shotover Hill should be attributed *"Class 1 in status"* for Hymenoptera in Britain (Steel, 1984: p. 108). Indeed, had O'Toole included early records of locally ubiquitous species the total would have risen to about 195 (Wright and Gregory, 2006). Yet, by 1984, 96 of the species listed by O'Toole had not been recorded on the Hill since before 1939. Consequently, Shotover Wildlife embarked on a thorough re-survey — including the use of yellow water-pans and a Malaise Trap [see below] — and from 2000 to 2010, 205 species of bee and wasp were recorded. This is an exceptional diversity for an inland location in Britain, confirming the continued status of Shotover as an important site for aculeate Hymenoptera. Although the number of species in the two survey periods is similar (195 and 205), Wright and Gregory (2006) found a significant difference in species composition. This was, however, consistent with the overall change in habitat since the early 20th century — from short-turf pasture to woodland.

It is the sandy geology and light soils that make Shotover Hill particularly suitable for a broad diversity of soil-nesting invertebrates.

Ornate-tailed Digger-wasp

The Ornate-tailed Digger-wasp *Cerceris rybyensis* is a good example of an aculeate with a specific nesting requirement. The nest holes are easily found along the paths and tracks at the top of the Hill where the orange Whitchurch Sand is exposed. This brightly coloured solitary wasp requires a site with a plentiful supply of solitary bees of a suitable size and has a preference for nesting in hard-packed level soil that is completely bare of vegetation. In particular it nests, among other places, along the vehicle track of the old London road, seemingly oblivious to the passage of car tyres and walking boots over its nesting hole.

On a warm summer's day, its yellow face can be seen at the hole entrance waiting for the 'all-clear' and a safe departure. On its return from hunting, the wasp will fly in clutching a paralysed bee, which is then dragged underground for the wasp's larvae to feed on.

An Ornate-tailed Digger-wasp approaching its nest with a freshly paralyzed solitary bee Jeremy Early

A Malaise Trap intercepts flying insects which are collected in the bottle at the trap's apex

A particularly dense aggregation of bee nesting holes in the fine sand of Horspath Common Ivan Wright

The leafcutter bee
Megachile centuncularis
on Greater Knapweed
Steven Falk

Leafcutter bees are
particularly efficient
pollinators and are among
the largest of solitary
bees in Britain — up to
18 millimetres long.

These include the bees and wasps that create the many small heaps of excavated soil to be seen along the sandy paths in spring and summer. Some species prefer the unvegetated loose sand typical of The Sandpit, while others will favour the hard-packed sand or denser vegetation along The Plain. Sometimes just one or two isolated holes indicate nesting activity but where conservation work has exposed an area of suitable soil, remarkably dense and extensive nesting aggregations can develop.

In terms of overall distribution, there is a strong tendency towards a greater diversity of species on the south side of the Hill where it is generally warmer. However, species with a dependence on a limited flora will have a distribution that is also influenced by the location of their food plant. For example, the tiny Harebell Carpenter Bee *Chelostoma campanularum*, which has limited flight capabilities, must nest relatively close to the Campanula flowers that it requires for pollen.

Bees

Bees (Apidae) are among the most biologically advanced of insects, and all species feed their larvae on vegetable protein in the form of pollen foraged from flowers. Depending upon the species of bee, the pollen may need to be collected from a particular group of plants, such as willows, or in a few cases from a single species of flower. The pollen is then carried back to a pre-constructed nest.

It is usual to divide all British bees into two groups, the bumblebees and the remainder — often termed the solitary bees. The bumblebees are fully social, where a queen originates a colony and is then assisted by large numbers of worker-daughters in feeding and rearing further larvae. In comparison, truly solitary bees have no colony and do not live to see the emergence of their offspring. However, many 'solitary' bees are not truly solitary and exhibit some aspects of social behaviour. For example, overwintering female sweat-bees (Halictidae), of which there are many species at Shotover, produce a small group of worker females to establish a nest in the spring but are not fully social because their larvae are not tended or fed by the adults as they grow.

Solitary bees

In most cases the truly solitary female bee builds a series of cells in a small nest, lays one egg in each cell together with a complete provision of pollen, and then seals it up without any further attention. This contrasts with the queen

Mason bee cells in the tubes of an observation nest showing the dividing walls, pollen stores and developing larvae

bumblebee who is surrounded by her numerous and attendant offspring. However, there are several advantages to the simple solitary life-cycle. For example, the short time needed to complete a nest simplifies the search for flowers and pollen, and since each nest can be small — containing only a few offspring — the female can exploit a number of suitable niches and complete several nests. Some solitary bee larvae are fed on pollen from a very limited range of flora and so enjoy the advantage of an unsophisticated

digestive system. The Ivy Bee *Colletes hederae*, which was new to Britain in 2001 and to Shotover in 2011, usually feeds its larvae entirely on the pollen of Ivy, while *Andrena fuscipes* is restricted to an ericaceous flora, and at Shotover is only found on the Heather.

Over the past 100 years more than half of the 220 British solitary bee species have been recorded on Shotover Hill. Of the 103 species recorded in recent years, 55 are soil-nesters and 29 are cuckoo bees of soil-nesting species. The relatively high proportion of cuckoo bee species (28 per cent) is a further indicator of the quality and maturity of the site for these insects (Wright and Gregory, 2006).

Among the soil-nesting bees, there is a considerable range of preconditions for a suitable nesting hole, be it the type of soil, local gradient or the sparseness of the surrounding vegetation. For example, at Shotover *Andrena humilis* is only found nesting in the coarse-grained Whitchurch Sands that cap the Hill and is seldom recorded at other sites in Oxfordshire. Although nationally scarce it is frequently recorded in the grasslands and hay meadows of Shotover, and visits the flowers of yellow Asteraceae such as hawk's-beards. In balance with the population

The Shotover landscape and solitary bees

Research by Shotover Wildlife has demonstrated that the hay meadows adjoining the SSSI, for example at Westhill Farm and Monk's Farm, provide a significant amount of pollen for the solitary bees that nest in the bare soils within the SSSI. This is partly due to the abundance of flowers in the hay meadows compared with the SSSI. However, it has been shown that the smallest bees (some only four millimetres in length) are not capable of flying far enough to utilise the full extent of the surrounding meadows (Wright *et al.*, 2015).

These findings demonstrate the key role of closely adjoining meadows for the flying invertebrates of the SSSI. If the national policy towards hay meadows were altered and enhanced by the addition of flower-rich margins (such as those supported by government incentive schemes), this would make a significant contribution to local wildlife. More importantly, if the abundance of suitable flora in the SSSI continues to be limiting, the placement of these margins close to the SSSI boundary would be particulary advantageous for smaller species of soil-nesting bee. However, research at Shotover has also shown that the meadows do not necessarily meet all the pollen and nectar requirements for the smallest of soil-nesting solitary bees (Wright *et al.*, 2015) and therefore management for the abundance and diversity of flora within the SSSI is similarly important.

Pollen-rich meadows at Shotover are crucial to the invertebrates of the SSSI

The mining bee *Andrena humilis* **(above) and its cuckoo bee** *Nomada integra* **(below)** Steven Falk

Hylaeus cornutus

Among the aerial nesters are the tiny 'yellow-faced' bees of the primitive genus *Hylaeus*. Unlike other bees, the *Hylaeus* ingest pollen at the flower for regurgitation for their larvae at the nest, and so have no external structures for carrying pollen. In fact these bees are among the least hairy and only make a minor contribution to pollination. A possible exception is *H. cornutus*, a nationally scarce bee recorded at Shotover in 1900 and 2004. Although similarly hairless, some reports have claimed that the female is unique in carrying its pollen in a three-lobed bowl-like structure on its face.

The unusual facial structure of the bee
Hylaeus cornutus Drawing by Jacqueline Wright

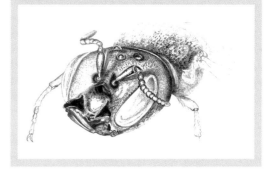

of *A. humilis* at Shotover is its specific 'cuckoo' *Nomada integra*, which is a small black-and-red bee, and much less hairy than its host. In Britain, *N. integra* is considerably more scarce than *A. humilis,* with recent records from just two other sites in Oxfordshire.

The smaller proportion of Shotover's solitary bee species (18 per cent) that nest above ground — 'aerial nesters' — use cavities such as old beetle burrows in dead wood or the hollow stems of suitable plants such as Bramble or Elder. These bees include the 'leafcutter' and 'mason' bees for which the popular 'bee homes' are often placed in domestic gardens. A curious development of aerial nesting behaviour is exhibited by the mason bees *Osmia spinulosa* and *O. bicolor,* both of which can be found at Shotover, which nest in empty snail shells.

Bumblebees

Thirteen species of social bee — the bumblebees — have been recorded at Shotover in recent years including eight colony-forming species and five species of 'cuckoo'. In the case of these social bees the female 'cuckoo' enters and lays her eggs in the host species' nest, and the host queen's daughters raise the cuckoo's offspring. The Tree Bumblebee *Bombus hypnorum* (a host species), was first recorded in Britain in 2001 and within a decade had spread from the south coast to most parts of England and Wales. It arrived at Shotover in 2009 and is now a common sight

Tree Bumblebee Steven Falk

in gardens around the Hill, frequently nesting under eaves or in bird boxes. The Red-shanked Carder Bee *B. ruderarius* (a host species), is the least common bumblebee at Shotover but sometimes appears in unusually high numbers on flower-rich grasslands.

The nests of bumblebees, with their behaviourally sophisticated social colonies, are mostly associated with the hedgerows, woodlands and gardens that make up the general mosaic of the countryside of the Hill. Often the nests are located in abandoned rodent holes and at Shotover old Rabbit burrows are often used. Areas of Bracken provide excellent habitat, especially where mammal activity has networked the underlying soil or soil surface with channels, both for nesting colonies in the summer and for overwintering queens. Bumblebee queens establish their summer nests in carefully chosen locations from which the workers will need to fly far and wide for suitable pollen. Consequently these bees are somewhat less dependent on a particular soil or habitat niche compared with the solitary bees, and can be seen visiting their preferred flowers almost anywhere on the Hill.

Badger predation: a lone bumblebee flies into the gaping hole where once its colony resided

A common vertebrate predator of bumblebee nests at Shotover is the Badger, which can dig out an entire nest from the ground or from under a tree stump and consume it with remarkable alacrity. When a freshly excavated nest is found, the cause of the disturbance is not always obvious but closer inspection usually reveals a few bewildered bees left wandering around in a cavity that had recently contained their home.

The Honeybee

The Honeybee is a domesticated animal with colonies kept in hives for the production of honey and as a commercial pollinator of some crops. When no hives are being maintained in the vicinity of Shotover, the Honeybee can become an infrequent sight, yet it is not uncommon for a vagrant swarm to adopt a suitable woodland location, usually a hollow tree, and persist for some years as a feral colony.

Since 2004, five feral Honeybee colonies have been known to become established at Shotover, mostly in oaks but Wild Cherry and Wild Service-tree have also been used. The longevity of the colony has depended on the health of the swarm and the security of the location from predators. Regular and frequent observations of these feral nests have shown that the colonies can sustain continuous occupation for at least seven years and survive a number of very hard frosts. Typical predators are woodpeckers, Hornet *Vespa crabro*, Wax Moth *Galleria mellonella* and Bee Moth *Aphomia sociella*.

Wasps

Like the bees, the various types of wasp can be partitioned into three basic forms of biology: social, solitary and cuckoo. The colony life of the social wasp differs little from that of the bumblebee, with a large number of female workers attending a single egg-laying queen. The principal dissimilarities are that the social wasp's nest is made of wood pulp, including an enveloping outer wall of 'paper', and the larvae are fed on regurgitated animal protein. In Britain there are only 10 species of social wasp, of which seven have been recorded at Shotover. These include the Common Wasp *Vespula vulgaris*, the Hornet and a number of 'tree wasps' (*Dolichovespula* spp.), all generally recognizable by their distinctive yellow and black patterning.

A magnificent Hornet on Ivy Roger Wyatt

The ruby-tail wasp *Hedychrum niemelai* from Shotover
©Katherine Child, OUMNH, University of Oxford

Solitary wasps

The sandy soils of Shotover provide ideal habitat for a large number of solitary wasps and over the past century 110 species have been found on the Hill. During the 2000–2010 period of surveying, 91 species were recorded, with nearly equal numbers of soil-nesting and aerial-nesting species. Most solitary wasps do not emerge from overwintering until the latter half of the year,

The spider-hunting wasp *Priocnemis perturbator*
Steven Falk

the exception being the elusive and fast-moving spider-hunting wasps (Pompilidae), which lay their eggs on or in spiders. Of the 40 British species of spider-hunting wasp, 17 have been recorded at Shotover, of which six are listed as nationally scarce. This exceptional diversity appears to be associated with the hay meadows around the Hill, especially the old meadow at Monk's Farm.

Solitary wasps are less hairy compared with most bees and are often strikingly tinted with yellow or red. They generally nest in similar places to the solitary bees: in hollow stems and old beetle holes and, at Shotover, among the aggregations of holes along the sandy paths where they can be seen returning with captured insects [see box, page 140]. The article of prey, for example a fly, beetle or small bee, is first either killed or paralysed by stinging and then dragged into the nest where the wasp lays an egg on it and seals it in.

A curious variation to this behaviour is displayed by *Oxybelus uniglumis* [see page 139] which can be seen nesting in the fine-grained sand at The Sandpit. This small (six to seven millimetres) black-and-white wasp preys on small flies but, after stinging, the wasp leaves the fly impaled on its sting, where it remains throughout the return flight to the nest. *O. uniglumis* is also one of several wasps that covers its nest entrance with sand every time it goes out to hunt — leading to the fascinating spectacle of the wasp returning, with impaled fly, and seemingly vanishing into the ground as it rapidly re-opens its hidden burrow and scuttles in.

Scarce bees and wasps at Shotover

Of the 228 species of aculeates recorded at Shotover since 1995, five are listed as rare, according to the most recent review of threatened species, and 37 as nationally scarce (Falk, 1991). Although this review is a useful guide to rarity, the 1991 statuses for some species are now in need of revision. Aculeates can be very responsive to circumstances and several species have been seen much more frequently in recent years; conversely, some are likely to have declined since. Perhaps a better indicator of the current status of the aculeates at Shotover is to consider the species that have been recorded on the Hill recently, yet have not been found elsewhere in Oxfordshire.

In recent years, eight species of aculeates have been recorded nowhere in Oxfordshire other than at Shotover, including two tiny rare wasps, *Spilomena enslini* and *Crossocerus congener,* and the cuckoo bee *Nomada flavopicta.*

Further significant indicators of the quality of the aculeate ecology found at Shotover are the obligate host-and-parasite pairs such as the scarce ruby-tail wasp *Hedychridium roseum,* which is a nest parasite of the solitary wasp *Astata boops.* The host bee *Colletes succinctus* and its cuckoo *Epeolus cruciger* have only been recorded together in Oxfordshire at Shotover. As both of these species depend on the pollen of ericaceous heathers, they could easily be lost from the county if the heathland resource degrades.

The heather-specialist bee *Colletes succinctus* (left) and its cuckoo bee *Epeolus cruciger* (right) Steven Falk

The sizes and colours of aculeate wasps at Shotover are rather more diverse than those of the bees. The smallest (*Spilomena* spp.) are only three millimetres long, whereas a queen Hornet can be 31 millimetres — excluding the antennae and sting. Of the solitary wasps, *Ectemnius cephalotes* and the Bee-wolf *Philanthus triangulum* can be up to 17 millimetres long; the latter is a muscular wasp capable of flying with a captured Honeybee. Without doubt the most brightly coloured aculeates on the Hill are the 'ruby-tail' cuckoo wasps (Chrysididae). These wasps are nest parasites of other solitary aculeates and have two formidable defences — a very hard and highly polished outer surface which is impenetrable by any sting, and an ability to roll into a defensive ball. Their rich and beautiful colours are stunning, with shiny metallic reds, greens and blues [see page 145].

Ants

Ants are most closely related to primitive wasps, yet have developed a sophisticated social biology that is far removed from their solitary carnivorous ancestors. Although ants, bumblebees, Honeybees and the social wasps all form colonies, their apparently similar modes of social biology have all evolved independently of each other. Each group has advanced towards a biology in which the survival of the colony (and its genes) takes priority over the survival of the individual.

Of the 54 species of ant found in Britain, seven common species and four less common

The common Small Black Ant *Lasius niger* on a seed-pod stalk of Garlic Mustard Rosemary Winnall

species have been recorded at Shotover. The most numerous species form large colonies, and are particularly noticeable when their nests are disturbed, exposing the vast numbers of industrious workers. Some species build conspicuous ant hills, while others live in smaller colonies in hollow trees or within the nests of other species of ant. The species that are less frequently seen at Shotover are: the large black Negro Ant *Formica fusca* with workers up to seven millimetres long; Jet Black Ant *Lasius fuliginosus* which is one of the few species in Britain whose individuals travel to and fro in a purposeful column; thirdly, *Stenamma debile* which typically has small colonies of fewer than 100 individuals and requires undisturbed woodland leaf litter; and, finally, Brown Ant *L. brunneus* which often nests in rotting tree stumps. A particularly large colony of Brown Ants was found in the hollow

trunk of the Shotover Oak when it fell in July 2015 [see box, page 52].

Notwithstanding the low number of ant species in Britain and at Shotover, their contribution *en masse* is of vital importance to the ecology of all but the wettest habitats. Despite their small size, the total volume of ants can be a significant fraction of the living biomass of a habitat, and their great abundance, ubiquity and ceaseless activity make indispensable contributions to many species of flora and fauna. At a basic level they serve as food for birds and other insects but, more interactively, their nests provide protection for 'guest' invertebrates as well as creating beneficial soil conditions for plant germination and growth. There are also particularly complex interactions through which plants or animals benefit from offering a nutritional 'reward' to lure the ants, and which may or may not be of net benefit to the ant.

Good examples of a non-specific benefit at Shotover are the ant hills of Yellow Meadow Ant *L. flavus* which develop a specific soil structure and microclimate that can be exploited by other species. The mounds frequently accommodate the scarcer annual plants associated with acidic grassland (for example, Changing Forget-me-not and Bird's-foot) and it is not unusual to see warmth-loving animals basking where an ant hill is catching the sunlight. Also, when the sides of the mounds are disturbed by Rabbits, birds or other animals, further opportunities are created for seed germination and burrowing insects. Green Woodpeckers feed almost entirely on ants in the winter months, their exceptionally long

A large ant hill created by Yellow Meadow Ants in Mary Sadler Field

Taking advantage of the bare soil on the side of the mound is Neat Feather-moss, a species characteristic of heathy soils.

tongues allowing them to probe deeply into an ant nest for food.

In addition to these non-specific interactions, many plants and invertebrates have a more specialized or symbiotic relationship with ants. It is well known that ants 'manage' and 'milk' aphids for the sugary honeydew that they excrete, and will enslave or deceive other insects for their own purposes. Three further examples are known at Shotover.

The first is the relationship between ants and the 'blue' butterflies (Lycaenidae), which has been known for some years. In its simplest form, ants are attracted to nutritious secretions on the caterpillar, which is then taken into the ants' nest where it can safely overwinter. More recently this symbiosis has been confirmed for many more species of ant and butterfly with some expressing a deeply complex relationship more akin to the duplicities of a cold war. Among such species of Lycaenidae butterfly at Shotover are the hairstreaks, Brown Argus, Small Copper, Holly Blue and Common Blue.

The second example is quite different and involves a 2.5-millimetre rove-beetle, *Claviger longicornis*. This tiny beetle spends its entire life in the total darkness of ant nests so that it has no need for eyes, and indeed has none. In return for beneficial secretions the ants feed and tend the beetles, even carrying them deeper into the nest when the colony is threatened. It is thought that the particularly stout antennae of *C. longicornis* serve not only as 'feelers' but also as handles by which the ants may carry them around.

Thirdly, and perhaps the most important and intriguing contribution of ants at Shotover, is the strategic translocation of the seeds of certain plants by the process of myrmecochory. The seeds of these plants have a gland at one end — an eliaosome — which exudes a substance to which the ants are strongly attracted. Ants collect the seeds and move them closer to their nest, thereby transporting the seeds some distance from the plant. Also, the seeds are moved to where they are less likely to be eaten and, in some cases, to an environment that is more conducive to dormancy or germination.

Some common plants such as Gorse and violets produce seeds with an eliaosome but at Shotover myrmecochory is also the seed dispersal strategy used by several of the rarest plants in the SSSI, including Heath Milkwort [see page 65]

Claviger longicornis **is a tiny rove-beetle with no wings and no eyes** ©Katherine Child, OUMNH, University of Oxford

and Heath Wood-rush. It has been shown (Oostermeijer, 1989) that low-density plants such as Heath Milkwort manage to compete for the attention of ants by offering an appreciably more delicious reward at the eliaosome compared with that of much more abundant seeds such as Gorse. The size, shininess and hairiness of the seed are all further factors in determining which ant species are more likely to carry the seed away.

Parasitic wasps

The large and somewhat artificial group of insects termed the Parasitica has seven superfamilies of non-aculeate wasps and includes over 5,000 known species in Britain. This is nearly four times the total diversity of all other British Hymenoptera, with many species yet to be named or described. Unfortunately, since only a few entomologists are able to tackle the identification of this large and difficult group of insects, Parasitica are seldom included in surveys or taxonomic lists. Only 120 species have been listed for Shotover from the early 20th century (Salzman, 1939: p. 139–146) and since then little work has been attempted on the group, and very few species added.

The parasitic wasp *Rhyssa persuasoria* ovipositing
Paul Brock

Even so, in 1994 Clive Hambler found the parasitoid wasp *Gnypetomorpha tubertae* in Brasenose Wood, and in 2012 it was named as a species new to science (Horstmann, 2012). The specimen from Shotover is the holotype from

which the species was described, and Brasenose Wood is, therefore, the 'type' habitat for the species. The wasp is a parasite of the rare spider *Tuberta maerens* [see page 183].

Although many different organisms cause galls to form on plants, including a modest number of flies, fungi, bacteria and nematode worms, the largest group of gall-causers are within the Cynipidae family of parasitic wasps. Each species of gall-wasp induces a unique form of gall, and finding the gall is usually an easier route to naming the wasp than finding the wasp itself [see page 168].

Sawflies

The sawflies are a primitively structured insect and are the very first Hymenopterans to appear in the fossil records of invertebrates [see page 138]. Compared with bees and wasps they have many more wing veins and no 'wasp waist', and are placed in a separate suborder, the Symphyta. The common name 'sawfly' is derived from the specialized dual-function ovipositor of the female, which has serrated lower edges for sawing a slot into the larval food plant, thereby facilitating the placing of eggs.

Although some adult sawflies are carnivorous with strong piercing jaws, in Britain their larvae are all vegetarian and most species are specifically associated with a single plant group such as grasses or birch trees. Indeed — as befits

***Tenthredopsis litterata* showing typical sawfly wing veination and the ovipositor saw protruding from under the tip of the abdomen**
©Katherine Child, OUMNH, University of Oxford

This specimen was collected at Shotover by Albert Hamm in June 1904.

The nationally scarce sawfly *Apethymus serotinus*
©Katherine Child, OUMNH, University of Oxford

an order which originated before flowering plants — some sawflies are associated with plants that were prevalent during the first half of the Jurassic period, such as horsetails and ferns.

About 540 species of sawfly are listed for Britain but, even though some species are serious economic pests, they are not commonly recorded in biological surveys. No species were recorded at Shotover through the later 60 years of the 20th century. Prior to 1939, 72 species were listed for the Hill by Benson (1939: p. 136) and since 2000 Shotover Wildlife has increased the overall total to 143 species. However, only 33 of the pre-1939 species have been found more recently, leaving a substantial number unaccounted for. No clear pattern or trend has emerged to suggest a cause for these apparent losses and gains.

Even though many sawflies are common, including some that are large and colourful, they receive much less attention from entomologists compared with many other groups of insects. In fact, there are insufficient records of most species

Hand-netting for soil-nesting bees and wasps following conservation clearance in Mary Sadler Field

in Britain to suggest or publish their national statuses. Currently it is only possible to infer scarcity by the paucity of records compared with other species of sawfly. Whereas several species are seen every year across Oxfordshire, many Shotover species currently have fewer than 100 records nationally. Examples of such sawflies are the two British species of *Apethymus* — *A. serotinus* and *A. filiformis* — both of which have been recorded at Shotover in recent years and yet in 2016 were represented by only 15 records on the central national database (National Biodiversity Network Atlas Partnership, 2017).

The future

In Britain, the general decline of wild bees and other invertebrates during the 20th century has been brought about by the use of chemical insecticides and a dramatic reduction in the extent of flower-rich meadows. Perhaps some pollen-dependent species of insect can gain a measure of security in designated conservation areas, especially where a nature reserve, as at Shotover, is surrounded by flower-rich gardens and unimproved meadows that can buffer the harmful effects of intensive agriculture.

Most Hymenoptera are adaptable insects whose demands on the environment for nesting, pollen and nectar are sufficiently flexible to ensure their continuance. At Shotover, as long as the sandy soils remain reasonably well exposed across the Hill, the soil-nesting species will find a niche in which to thrive (see for example Gregory and Wright, 2005), and the exceptional diversity of the Hill will be maintained. The main threats to Hymenopteran diversity at Shotover are to the scarce species that have more exacting habitat requirements, such as bees that require a sufficient abundance of a particular species or family of flowers.

Of particular relevance at Shotover is that the Hill is located at the north-western limit of the European range of a number of aculeate species. As the climate continues to change in the coming decades, the aculeate fauna of Shotover could change as species' ranges expand or contract. Now that the diversity of Hymenoptera on the Hill has been thoroughly surveyed, any losses or gains have the potential to be combined with biological indicators from other sites or taxa to demonstrate the future effects of climate change across Britain.

Ivan Wright

Flies seem to get everywhere, and into everything; apart from the open ocean, no habitat is without them. Often massing in vast numbers, some are carriers of serious diseases such as malaria, some have a painful 'bite', and some are just infuriating. No wonder that so many people consider flies, along with the Common Wasp, to be among the most insufferable of insects, worthy only of eradication devices such as fly spray, fly paper and the fly swat. But do they deserve that reputation?

A mating pair of the gallfly *Urophora cardui* on Creeping Thistle Paul Brock

Over 30 species of big-headed fly (Pipunculidae) have been recorded at Shotover Peter Creed

Like fungi and bacteria, flies derive most of their protein from the products of decay, often living and feeding in places that most other creatures would avoid [see also page 104]. Furthermore, few organisms are faster than flies at finding and utilising the decay and waste products of other species. One striking example is the use of maggots (fly larvae) to clean infected wounds — an application where pharmaceutical drugs cannot match their simple efficiency. So although many claims are justly made about the importance of other insects such as pollinating bees for human survival, we would soon find the world intolerable without the Diptera — that is, true flies [see box, page 152] — and their universal contribution to cleaning up and recycling.

In Britain the Diptera include over 7,000 different species, from large 50-millimetre robber-flies to the gall-midges of less than a millimetre. Apart from their role in breaking down and recycling organic material, the billions of individual adult flies and their multitudes of larvae are a major source of food for other animals such as bats, birds and other insects (and a few British carnivorous plants). A great many flies are important predators and parasites of other insects, and many are significant

Fleshflies and blowflies recycling a disintegrating fungus on Horspath Common

pollinators, especially for wild flowers. In fact, flies are collectively the second most important pollinators after bees.

All species of fly have two habitat requirements, one for each of the two main stages of development, larva and adult. Most adult flies require a range of habitats which they can explore widely and effectively for the purposes of feeding, breeding and egg laying. The larvae, on the other hand, are much more confined to a particular micro-habitat, not least because they will have hatched from eggs that were laid on or near their specific source of food. Understanding the habitat requirements of the larvae — and not just those of the adults — is fundamental to an appreciation of dipteran biology and conservation.

The history of Diptera recording at Shotover

The recording of flies at Shotover has a fascinating history. By 1939 over 700 species had been noted specifically for Shotover Hill and 200 species for Brasenose Wood and 'Open Brasenose Common' (now known as Open Brasenose Wood). Although these two lists overlap to a certain extent, they still amount to 770 species overall (Hamm, 1939: p. 156), which is a remarkable number for such a small area at that time. Also, the early records included only those

Albert Harry Hamm (1861–1951)
©OUMNH, University of Oxford

What are Diptera?

Most people know that the household bluebottle is a fly and that butterflies and dragonflies are not true flies — but then neither are sawflies, whiteflies, caddis-flies or damselflies. However, hoverflies, craneflies, blowflies, soldierflies, fruit-flies and horseflies are all Diptera, as are many organisms without a hint of 'fly' in their name, such as midges, gnats, mosquitoes and bee lice.

Many flying insects use two pairs of wings for flight (as is clear, for instance, in butterflies and dragonflies) and most other insects in their adult form, whether capable of flight or not, show a least a relict of two pairs of wings. However, some major groups of insects use only one pair of wings for flight and these include the flies, terrestrial bugs and beetles. Bugs and beetles fly using the rear

A thick-headed fly *Conops vesicularis* showing two wings and the halteres Paul Brock

pair of wings, the front pair having evolved into a hard covering to protect the flying wings when not in use. The Diptera (*di* two + *ptera* wings) use only the front pair of wings to fly; the rear pair appear as two tiny, club-ended stumps, called halteres, that act as stabilizers. In flight the halteres vibrate in sympathy with the front wings, and without them effective flight is impossible. There are a small number of wingless Diptera, including several that are parasites of bees and birds, and others that live in vegetable detritus such as woodland leaf litter or the matted grass ground-layer of old meadows.

species thought worthy of mention, and excluded those listed by Hamm that were widespread and common in Oxfordshire at that time — perhaps a further 120 species.

This total is even more remarkable for being due almost entirely to the work of one man, Albert Hamm. Shotover was only one of several sites around Oxford that attracted the attention of this exceptionally prolific amateur entomologist. Hamm also assembled important collections of Diptera specimens as predator-prey pairs; his observational research into the courtship behaviour of Empid flies was a major advance in entomological understanding; and he made significant contributions to the recording of many other insect orders [see page 140]. His work was recognized by an honorary degree from Oxford University and election as an Associate of the Linnean Society.

Albert Hamm began recording Diptera at Shotover around 1897; his first known specimen dates from 7th September of that year and is Shotover's first and only record of *Physocephala rufipes* (Conopidae). He continued visiting the Hill until he retired from the Oxford University Museum in 1931. In Hamm's obituary, O.W. Richards remarked that: "[Hamm] *never, unfortunately, acquired much facility in recording his discoveries in print and a good deal of his unique information is only preserved in the form of carefully labelled specimens.*" (Richards, 1951)

This statement was borne out by a search of the British Collections at Oxford under Shotover Wildlife's 'Then & Now' project, which yielded nearly 700 specimens of Diptera collected by Hamm from Shotover including 400 different species, of which 174 were hitherto unknown in the historic records for the Hill. The dates on Hamm's specimens showed that he collected mostly at weekends, probably walking to most survey sites from his house in Southfield Road, East Oxford, four kilometres from Shotover summit. Weekdays were spent at the museum where he was employed as an assistant, not so much as an entomologist but as a printer, his original trade (Smith, 1986: p. 56).

When Hamm finally ceased collecting insects in the Oxford area around 1930, no further Diptera were recorded at Shotover for over 50 years. Recording resumed with *ad hoc* visits by dipterists during the 1980s and '90s, adding about 50 species, and was probably part of David Steel's initiative to obtain SSSI status for the Country Park. Surveyors at this time included eminent entomologists such as Michael Ackland, Peter Chandler, Keith Porter and Alan Stubbs.

The recent work of Shotover Wildlife, particularly the use of Malaise Traps and upper-

Shotover's first recorded fly was collected in 1897
© Katherine Child, OUMNH, University of Oxford

Hamm's well-preserved and characteristically labelled specimen of *Physocephala rufipes* which is kept at the Oxford University Museum of Natural History. This is the only record of the species for Shotover.

Shotover Natural Heritage

canopy vane traps [see page 132], has greatly increased the known diversity of Diptera for both Shotover Hill and Brasenose Wood. During the period 2000 to 2014, a further 380 species were added, bringing the all-time total to over 1,300 species — nearly a fifth of the British dipteran fauna. However, although Shotover Wildlife has accumulated records for over 750 species in recent times, there remain 550 species of fly that have not been re-recorded since Albert Hamm walked the Hill between 1897 and 1925.

Methodological problems beset any attempt to draw conclusions from a comparison of the Shotover Diptera records up to the end of Hamm's work with the records since then — for instance, whether a species not recorded since 1930 has truly gone from the Hill and, furthermore, whether it has disappeared due to habitat or climate change. Firstly, at least 130 species found by Hamm cannot be identified at present as they are in taxonomic groups that require specialist skills that are unavailable or unaffordable (for example, the tiny midges Ceratopogonidae and Chironomidae). Conversely, the number of fungus gnats (Mycetophilidae) and big-headed flies (Pipunculidae) identified in recent years has greatly increased through access to taxon specialists such as Peter Chandler and David Gibbs respectively. New and improved identification keys have allowed many more specimens to be identified without recourse to such specialists. And, finally, productive new survey techniques, such as powerful suction samplers, gather up many species that would previously have been particularly elusive. For all these reasons, generally the rest of this chapter does not offer explanations regarding the apparent gains or losses over the past century.

The Diptera of Shotover
Saproxylic flies
In Britain the great diversity of saproxylic flies (those that depend on dead and rotting wood) [see page 32] is similar to that of the saproxylic beetles [see page 131], and together these two invertebrate orders make up 80 per cent of all British saproxylic insects. In contrast to beetles, however, adult flies are particularly fragile and even the saproxylic species are not adapted for burrowing into rotten timber or crawling beneath flaking bark. It is the larvae that burrow

and develop in association with fungi or dead wood, with the adult female of some species specially adapted for laying eggs into a suitable substrate. Consequently, the free-living adults of saproxylic flies can be found in a range of habitats, including those without dead wood, and can be recorded using most of the common sampling methods.

At Shotover 196 species of saproxylic fly have been recorded — over a quarter of the British saproxylic Diptera. The number of species from the upper sandy part of the Hill differs little from that of the surrounding woodland on clay soils, probably because of the wide-ranging mobility of the adult flies. Yet, unlike the high proportion of saproxylic beetle species recorded exclusively from the upper-canopy vane traps, only 25 species of saproxylic fly have been added by this survey method.

Woodland flies
Perhaps it is not surprising that the majority of fly species recorded at Shotover are associated with the various types of woodland, shady marshes and woodland streams. This includes all 72 species of fungus gnat, a large proportion (40 per

A veteran Field Maple in Brasenose Wood: rot holes in old trees are an important habitat for flies

The saproxylic cranefly *Tanyptera nigricornis* Paul Brock

cent) of the extensive diversity of hoverflies (Syrphidae), and many specialized woodland flies such as Heleomyzidae on fungi and Lauxaniidae in rotting leaf litter. The Lauxaniid fly *Homoneura interstincta*, though a rare species, has been found widely distributed in the SSSI in recent years. Similarly, the nationally scarce fungus gnat *Sciophila thoracica* has been recorded twice since 2013 and yet there are few British records.

The woodland habitats at Shotover harbour the greatest number of the scarcer Diptera, probably due to the long-term stability of this habitat and the diversity of undisturbed substrates such as rot-holes, leaf mould, decaying wood and fungi. Nearly all of these scarcer flies pass their larval stage in dead wood and include the handsome craneflies *Tanyptera nigricornis* [above] in Brasenose Wood and *T. atrata* in Johnson's Piece. The *Tanyptera* are large glossy red-and-black flies up to two centimetres long but are seldom seen as they spend most of their life high in the tree canopy. The woodlands of Shotover are a critical habitat for these scarce craneflies, which have been recorded several times in recent years; their populations are probably secure as long as the saproxylic habitat is maintained.

Flies of wet habitats

In the early 20th century much survey work was done on the small midges and gnats of open water and marsh, including the biting midges, non-biting midges, mosquitoes (Culicidae), shoreflies (Ephydridae) and sub-families of the dance-flies (Empididae). Unfortunately, identification within these groups requires

specialist knowledge and although 120 species have been noted, these are mostly old records, with only about 20 wetland dance-flies identified in recent years. This is a pity, as Shotover is much less wet than it was 100 years ago and it would be interesting to see a reappraisal of the local wetland Diptera.

Among the wetland flies for which recent data are available, however, is the highly diverse Limoniidae family of small craneflies [see box below]. By 1939, 29 species had been recorded for the Shotover area and, although only 12 of these have been noted since, a further 19 species have

Craneflies

After the Hoverflies, the next most diverse group of Diptera recorded at Shotover is in the super-family Tipuloidea, the biggest of which are the well-known craneflies or 'daddy-long-legs'. Although most people are familiar with these insects, notable for their long gangly legs and narrow wings, some species in the group are surprisingly small (only three millimetres long).

These flies belong mostly to one of two types: the larger long-palped craneflies (Tipulidae), which are typically grassland or woodland species, and the smaller short-palped craneflies (Limoniidae) of wetlands, marshes and streams. Although the larvae of some Tipulidae (Leatherjackets) can be a significant pest of crops and gardens, this family includes some of Shotover's scarcest and most handsome woodland species.

Nearly 100 species of cranefly have been recorded at Shotover, equally divided between the Tipulids and Limoniids; only 17 of the former and four of the latter have gone unrecorded since first collected in the early 20th century by Albert Hamm.

A short-palped cranefly (Limoniidae) Peter Creed

Black-legged Horsefly James K. Lindsey

been added. The 23 species of snail-killing flies (Sciomyzidae) — whose larvae feed on slugs and snails represent nearly half the British fauna of these mainly wetland flies.

Although over 200 wetland-associated fly species have been recorded at Shotover, very few are rated as rare or scarce, and none among the more recent records. However, there are three particularly scarce species recorded in earlier years for which new records would be greatly valued. *Ormosia bicornis* (a short-palped cranefly), which is now considered a vulnerable and declining species, was caught by Hamm in Open Brasenose Common (now Open Brasenose Wood) in September 1915, and the rare fungus gnat *Sceptonia concolor* was also caught by Hamm in Open Brasenose Common (no date). Both of these species are associated with boggy ground near old trees and with decaying wood. Black-legged Horsefly *Hybomitra micans* (Tabanidae) [above] may now be rare in England, yet it was recorded on Shotover Hill in about 1898 (Hamm, 1933 and 1941), and "*another on the pavement outside Pembroke College, May 1921*" (Walker, 1926: p. 259) at a time when horse-drawn vehicles were more common in Oxford city.

Flies of dry habitats and heathland

Flies, especially their larvae, are generally found in wetter places and damp rotting material, and therefore it is not surprising that dry acidic grasslands and heath have fewer associated species. Many of the adult flies of such habitats are predatory, preying on other species of invertebrate, with the predator's larvae exploiting the host species for their development.

A good example of this advanced development is the Dark-edged Bee-fly *Bombylius major* (Bombyliidae) [below], more often referred to simply as the Bee-fly. This creature is well named; not only does it mimic a bumblebee in appearance but its larvae are parasitic on the solitary bees. It is frequently seen at Shotover on warm spring days, and its flight is unmistakable — like a hummingbird, it hovers at a flower and inserts its proboscis to suck up nectar. The wings are marked along the front edge with a distinctive dark-grey undulating pattern. For a long time it was thought that the Bee-fly could be seen laying its eggs directly into fine sandy soil but this was a misinterpretation of the action of the female collecting sand in a special cavity under its tail. When eggs are produced, they are coated with sand from the cavity and flicked at anything that looks to her like the nest of a mining bee. After hatching, the larvae go in search of a bee's nest, and those that succeed in finding one enter and eat the bee larvae to complete their own life-cycle underground.

On Shotover's dry soils, where the diversity and abundance of soil-nesting bees and wasps are particularly high, the fleshflies (Sarcophagidae) are especially interesting for, as with the Bee-fly, many specialize in exploiting the nests of burrowing bees and wasps. For example, the females of certain species in the genera *Metopia* and *Miltogramma* are able to catch the soil-nesting aculeates off guard in various ways and then, with lightning speed, lay their eggs in the aculeate's burrow. In the case of mining bees, the fly lays its eggs on the underground pollen

Dark-edged Bee-fly Peter Creed

Metopia fleshflies are among the many insects that benefit from Shotover's abundant bees and wasps
Peter Creed

A specimen of *Oxyna nebulosa* collected by Hamm in 1919; the species is a rare gallfly of Oxeye Daisy
©Katherine Child, OUMNH, University of Oxford

store, in the same manner as a cleptoparasite bee [see page 139], and the fly larvae hatch and out-compete the bee's larvae in consuming the food-store. The fly then completes its life-cycle in the nest of the bee.

Flies of open habitats and grassland
Many fly species are specific to grassland, such as meadow or pasture, and even more species frequent the generally open and sunny habitats of parks and large gardens, and along hedgerows and woodland edges. At Shotover a great many species of these types of fly have been recorded, including houseflies (Muscidae), gallflies (Tephritidae), a third of the national fauna of big-headed flies [see page 151], and the majority of hoverflies. However, apart from the hoverflies, species in these families of fly can be particularly difficult to identify, and a high proportion of grassland species have not been recorded at Shotover since the early 20th century.

Open grassy habitat is widespread in Oxfordshire — in contrast, for example, with flower-rich hay meadows or old woodland — and the majority of grassland Diptera at Shotover are common. An exception is the rare big-headed fly *Cephalops perspicuus*, previously seen only in marshes in East Anglia, which was recorded on Shotover Hill in 2013. Several specimens of the finely mottled *Oxyna nebulosa* [above right] were netted by Hamm in 1919 but this grassland gallfly is now rare in Britain. The larvae are known to induce root galls in Oxeye Daisy and, although the host plant is not scarce, the fly may

have declined through the loss of unimproved meadows; there are only a few British records of *O. nebulosa* from the past 50 years.

Flies without specific habitat associations
A large proportion of flies at Shotover, by their very nature, are not strongly linked to a particular habitat but benefit from the diversity of habitats, niches and microclimates. Apart from the common and widespread generalists, including flies whose larvae mine the stems and leaves of ubiquitous plants, most flies in this category are adult predators of other invertebrates, larval parasites of other animals, or sometimes both.

The Conopidae are specialist predators of Hymenoptera, particularly bumblebees, and 10 of the 24 British species have been recorded at Shotover, including Hamm's *Physocephala rufipes* of 1897 [see page 153]. The adult females of these remarkable flies do not prey directly on the bee but catch it and lay an egg into its abdomen — sometimes while still in flight. In the case of the Tachinidae flies, the adults attack and feed on other invertebrates and also deposit their eggs on or in specifically targeted types of insect. Among the Tachinidae at Shotover is the rare fly *Meigenia majuscula*, a parasite of beetles, which has been recorded twice in Brasenose Wood since upper-canopy samplers were set up by Shotover Wildlife.

Three scarce species of robber-fly (Asilidae) at Shotover demonstrate the diverse habitat requirements of these relatively large and

Hoverflies

The hoverflies (Syrphidae) are among the more easily recognized Diptera, especially those with striking yellow markings, and although some are small and darkly coloured, their capacity to hover with pinpoint precision is a familiar indicator. Others are large and hairy and remarkably convincing imitators of honeybees or bumblebees. Only a very few species have been given English names but the common Marmalade Hoverfly *Episyrphus balteatus* is easily recognized by the narrow orange bands on its abdomen.

Hoverflies are by far the largest family of Diptera recorded at Shotover. There are early records of over 90 species and, although 24 of these have not been seen since before 1939, 45 species have been added recently, bringing the recorded total to 136 — over half the national fauna. The habitat preferences of the various species are fairly evenly distributed across the habitat types but at Shotover there are slightly more woodland species.

Although about a tenth of Shotover's hoverflies are uncommon in Britain, none of the species recorded since 1939 are nationally rare. There is, however, an unconfirmed early record of the very rare *Pipizella maculipennis* (undated), and in 1904 Hamm netted the large and handsome yellow-and-black wasp mimic, *Chrysotoxum elegans*. This latter species is thought to have declined in the north and west of Britain in recent decades but could yet be seen again at Shotover.

Marmalade Hoverfly Peter Creed

Chrysotoxum elegans Peter Creed

aggressive flies. The female Spring Heath Robber-fly *Lasiopogon cinctus*, first found in 1992, lays her eggs into unconsolidated sand with the aid of an abdomen adapted for digging. In contrast, Golden-haired Robber-fly *Choerades marginatus*, recorded at Long Marsh by Shotover Wildlife in 2013, is a saproxylic species of old woodland whose larvae have been found in beetle burrows. Shotover meets all the requirements for the very large and impressive Hornet Robber-fly *Asilus crabroniformis* — open ground, abundant dung-beetle burrows and grazing animals — and yet it has not been seen since the 1920s and then only "*at rare intervals at Shotover Hill*" (Walker, 1926: p. 260). It may well have disappeared from the region, perhaps due to reduced cattle grazing on the Hill, but is more likely a casualty of the widespread use of agro-veterinary products which persist in manure.

The closely related families of Dolichopodidae, Empididae and Hybotidae, which include the dance-flies and long-legged flies, are similar to the robber-flies in that both adults and larvae are carnivorous. These small predatory flies are well represented at Shotover and evenly distributed across all habitats. Of the 670 British species, 200 have been recorded

The Hornet Robber-fly can be 28 millimetres long
Paul Brock

Small flies attracted to the fungus Silky Rosegill on Horspath Common, 2005

overall, with 130 species recorded in recent years. Since upper-canopy sampling began in 2010, the scarce saproxylic fly *Oedalea tibialis* (Hybotidae) has been recorded in numerous woodland locations across the SSSI.

The leaf and stem miners of the families Agromyzidae and Anthomyiidae are found in both open and woodland settings. Of particular relevance to Shotover is *Ophiomyia skanensis* (Agromyzidae); Shotover Wildlife's discovery of this species in 2013 was the first record in Britain (Wright and Gibbs, 2015) and it has since been added to the list of British Diptera. The host plant for the fly is unknown, although closely allied species are known to mine leaves of Goldenrod and other related Asteraceae. The specimen was caught in a Malaise Trap at the north end of Long Marsh and identified by David Gibbs, and is now kept at the Oxford University Museum of Natural History. *O. skanensis* was first described in 1957 (a specimen from southern Sweden) and since then has also been recorded in Lithuania and Ukraine.

The rare flies of Shotover

Two fly species recently recorded at Shotover could hardly be rarer. Firstly, as noted above, *O. skanensis* was new to Britain. Secondly, in

August 2005 four tiny flies were collected from the cap of a fungus, Silky Rosegill *Volvariella bombycina* [see also page 109], growing on a large rotting Sycamore log at the edge of secondary woodland on Horspath Common. When the flies were compared with other examples in Hungary and recent specimens from southern Britain, they were found to belong to a species not previously described — in other words, new to science (Gibbs and Papp, 2006). The species has since been named *Leiomyza birkheadi* (Asteiidae)

Ophiomyia skanensis: the first British record of this species was from Shotover in 2013
Drawing by Jacqueline Wright

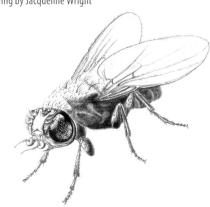

Variegated Fruit-flies Peter Creed

and the four Shotover examples are now held at various museums around Britain as paratypes (verified reference specimens) for the species.

Of the other species of fly recorded at Shotover that are particularly rare, most of these have not been recorded since before 1939; however, two rare fruit-flies are an exception. Variegated Fruit-fly *Phortica variegata* was caught in Mary Sadler Field in 2013 and is of national conservation concern, having declined by 66 per cent in the UK between 1980 and 2004 (JNCC, 2010). It is thought to be associated with sap runs on oaks caused by the burrowing larvae of Goat Moth *Cossus cossus*. However, as Goat Moth has so far not been recorded at Shotover, it is unclear what might be done to promote the survival of the fly. The second fruit-fly, *Amiota basdeni*, was caught

in Brasenose Wood in 2013, and is also associated with tree sap runs. This rare fly currently has Red Data Book status 'RDB2 — Vulnerable' and has been recorded at only a few other sites in Britain in recent years.

Many other flies, all wetland species, not recorded at Shotover since before 1939 are now considered either scarce or rare in Britain. The three rarest are Black-legged Horsefly, the fungus gnat *Sceptonia concolor* and the short-palped cranefly *Ormosia bicornis*.

The future for flies at Shotover

The great diversity of flies at Shotover is as impressive as it is important for the ecology of the Hill. The vast majority of species do not have particularly demanding habitat requirements and, considering the diversity of micro-habitats on the Hill, most fly species should continue to thrive. Yet, as is evident from species such as Black-legged Horsefly, the very rare fruit-flies (*Amiota* spp.) and the prey-dependent predatory flies of heathland, complex interdependences easily become a vulnerability as habitats change, especially if the habitats decline.

Clearly it would be impossible to take into account all the intricate requirements of the Diptera, or even of just the scarcer species, in managing a site like Shotover for optimal diversity. Life will go on for the common species. As for the future prospects of the vulnerable fly species on the Hill, the types of fly would appear to fall into two general groups: those for which it is still possible to maintain uncommon habitats (such as dry acidic heathland) in good ecological condition, and those that are relicts of an era when relatively large areas of bog or extensive traditional stock grazing were more widespread. The lingering species of bygone habitats will probably continue to decline. Yet for the scarcer species whose complex biology is closely interwoven with the extant flora and fauna of the Hill, their future security will depend upon maintaining the ecological quality of the key habitats — marsh, heath, acidic grassland, old woodland and dead wood.

Ivan Wright and Lawrence Bee

Dragonflies and damselflies

The Odonata are a primitive order of insects that, with the exception of size, have changed little in appearance since the Carboniferous period (300 million years ago), when there were species with a wingspan as broad as that of pigeons today. In Britain, the Odonata are divided into two suborders: dragonflies (Zygoptera), of which there are 40 species, and damselflies (Anisoptera), of which there are 22. Damselflies tend to be smaller and more slender than dragonflies but the most noticeable difference is that, when at rest, a damselfly folds its wings back over its long abdomen, whereas a dragonfly's wings remain outstretched on each side.

The eggs of Odonata are laid in or near water as the larvae of all species are predatory on other aquatic animals — mostly invertebrates but also amphibians. With their very large eyes and four independently articulated wings, adults combine exceptional binocular vision with aerial agility for catching other flying insects on the wing. The common names of the different types of dragonfly — hawkers, skimmers, chasers and darters — reflect their various hunting strategies.

Shotover is predominantly a sandy hill and lacks many of the wetland habitats that would support a rich diversity of Odonata, such as large shallow ponds or lakes with a diversity of flora around their margins. Yet the hydrology of the Hill does at least provide some marshland and surface water for species whose demands are not too specialized. In the distant past, before the marshes of Shotover Hill were drained for agriculture, dragonflies and damselflies would have been much more abundant, and there would probably have been a greater range of species than today.

Fortunately, since the 18th century, landscaping and quarrying have left a legacy of water bodies, particularly on the north side of the Hill, and it is around these that most of the dragonfly and damselfly species have been recorded. Even the small ponds in the SSSI, many of which are less than 20 years old, can provide breeding habitat and are often quickly colonized

Ruddy Darter dragonfly Roger Wyatt

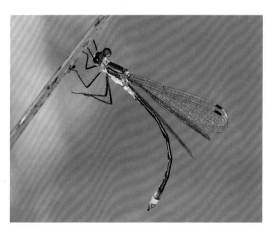

Emerald Damselfly Roger Wyatt

by common species. In the summer, when adult Odonata range widely for prey, the abundance of flying insects at Shotover ensures a good food supply and dragonflies and damselflies can be seen anywhere, even in the drier habitats.

Of the 62 British species of Odonata, 13 dragonfly and four damselfly species have been recorded at Shotover. Of these, only the Club-tailed Dragonfly *Gomphus vulgatissimus* has not been recorded since before 1939. This is a species that frequents large slow-running streams — more typical of tributaries of the River Thames — and would not be expected to breed at Shotover.

Four-spotted Chaser at The Octagon Pond Ivan Wright

However, it may still be an infrequent visitor on the Hill as it is known to forage widely from its breeding grounds.

Species most frequently seen on the Hill in summer are Common Blue Damselfly *Enallagma cyathigerum* and the dragonflies Brown Hawker *Aeshna grandis*, Common Hawker *A. juncea*, Migrant Hawker *A. mixta*, Southern Hawker *A. cyanea* and Common Darter *Sympetrum striolatum*. Other species that are less likely to be seen without a visit to the ponds on the north side of the Hill are Azure Damselfly *Coenagrion puella*, Emerald Damselfly *Lestes sponsa*, Large Red Damselfly *Pyrrhosoma nymphula*, Broad-bodied Chaser *Libellula depressa*, Four-spotted Chaser *L. quadrimaculata* and Ruddy Darter *S. sanguineum*.

The main threats to Odonata are loss of aquatic habitat, industrial pollution, pesticides and fertilizer runoff. Fortunately, water quality in Britain has improved over recent decades and consequently the abundance and distribution of many common species have been increasing since 1980 (Powney *et al.*, 2015). Habitat loss, however, remains a problem for scarcer species and those with more exacting habitat requirements. Although Shotover makes only modest provision for dragonflies and damselflies, and does not support any species of particular note, the water quality and tranquil wetland habitats do provide an ideal environment for the common Odonata.

Grasshoppers, bush-crickets and ground-hoppers

If, while walking on Shotover during the summer, you see a large slim insect suddenly fling itself through the air, it is most likely to be a grasshopper. Closer observation of the creature — which is easily located by following its trajectory — will confirm this if it has the characteristic long and muscular back legs which propel it into space. The soft repetitive buzz of stridulating grasshoppers is one of the familiar sounds of a warm summer's afternoon in the countryside [see box, page 163]. In Britain, there are several species of grasshopper within the Orthoptera group of insects; however, the order extends more widely to include ground-hoppers and various types of cricket which all have the same general shape. The Orthoptera are also closely related to three other orders of insect: cockroaches (Dictyoptera), earwigs (Dermaptera) and stick insects (Phasmida).

Of the 48 species of Orthoptera listed for Britain, 30 of these are native; the remaining 18 are migrant or introduced, some of which are naturalized and permanently resident. The crickets of Shotover are all bush-crickets (Tettigonioidea) and these differ from grasshoppers (Acridoidea) in two easily identifiable respects: the antennae of bush-crickets are much longer than their body whereas grasshopper antennae are less than half the length of the body; and the ovipositor of female bush-crickets is long and sabre-like whereas the grasshopper has no such device. Two of the three British species of ground-hoppers (Tetrigoidea) can be found at Shotover; these are more closely related than any other

Field Grasshopper Peter Creed

British Orthoptera to grasshoppers, and are distinctive in being only half the length of a typical adult grasshopper.

Grasshoppers

Only the two most common species of grasshopper have been recorded at Shotover: Field Grasshopper *Chorthippus brunneus* and Meadow Grasshopper *Pseudochorthippus parallelus*. Both lay their eggs encased in small protective pods, each containing a small number of eggs. As part of the egg-laying process, the pods are placed in shallow holes dug into loose soil using the tip of the female's abdomen. For this reason, both species of grasshopper at Shotover have a beneficial association with the ant hills of Yellow Meadow Ant, which are characterized by relatively loose soil particularly suitable for egg laying.

Songs and stridulations

Most grasshoppers and crickets can produce a sound by stridulation, that is, by rubbing one part of their body against another. Stridulating grasshoppers rub a row of minute pegs on the inside of each hind femur against strengthened veins in the forewings; in most bush-crickets the pegs are on a modified vein on the left forewing and are scraped against the rear edge of the right forewing.

Of the British species of Orthoptera that stridulate strongly enough to be heard 'singing', each has a different call. These can be useful for identification, even if, as with the soft stridulations of the Speckled Bush-cricket *Leptophyes punctatissima*, they are at a frequency that is too high for most people to hear. In this case species can often be identified using a bat detector to modulate the sound. Most of the species that are audible within the normal range of hearing are male grasshoppers; female grasshoppers are rarely loud enough and female bush-crickets do not stridulate.

The predominant sounds from both grasshoppers and crickets are the contact and territorial calls prior to courtship, and the males of most species have several different 'songs' corresponding to the various stages of attracting a female and mating. Some Orthoptera, however, create sounds by other methods. For instance, the Oak Bush-cricket *Meconema thalassinum*, a species that is common on the Hill, makes a clicking sound by striking a hind leg against a leaf or other suitable sounding board.

The Field Grasshopper flies quite well for a grasshopper and is able to range more widely than the Meadow Grasshopper over small areas of short vegetation. It feeds on grass and is often found in urban gardens as well as more natural grasslands. The Meadow Grasshopper also feeds on grass; it favours coarser grassland but can be seen in the short sward of Shotover's acidic grassland. This species is normally flightless but a population can produce individuals that are able to fly when environmental stresses, such as overcrowding, require the population to disperse.

Bush-crickets

Shotover hosts four of the 10 species of native bush-cricket: Oak Bush-cricket *Meconema thalassinum*, Speckled Bush-cricket *Leptophyes punctatissima*, Dark Bush-cricket *Pholidoptera griseoaptera* and Roesel's Bush-cricket *Roeseliana roeselii*.

The Oak Bush-cricket and Speckled Bush-cricket are more associated with trees and woodland than are other Orthoptera on the Hill. However, neither species is strongly associated with a particular species of tree and both will feed on a variety of common plants. Both species lay their eggs in the cracks and crevices of tree bark, and the Dark Bush-cricket will oviposit in soft and partially rotting wood.

Roesel's Bush-cricket, with its distinctive U-shaped yellow side-marking, was once rare in Britain and only found around the coast of the Thames estuary. Over the past century the species has spread slowly inland, reaching Oxfordshire in 1990, yet it currently remains restricted to south-east and central England. In general, it feeds mostly on grasses and lays its eggs in rush stems.

Roesel's Bush-cricket Peter Creed

Slender Ground-hopper Paul Brock

Ground-hoppers

Ground-hoppers are small inconspicuous relatives of the grasshoppers, often referred to as Pygmy Grasshoppers. There are only three British species and Shotover has records of two: Common Ground-hopper *Tetrix undulata* and Slender Ground-hopper *T. subulata*. They lay their eggs in the ground but, unlike grasshoppers, feed on algae and mosses and have no stridulation mechanism. The forewings are nothing more than a pair of small lobes and so flight is only possible with the hind pair of wings. In general, they are insects of wetter areas and muddy ground, and can skate over the surface of open water.

The Common Ground-hopper can be found in dry as well as wet habitats, as long as there is bare ground and low vegetation. Thus, for instance, it has been recorded in Mary Sadler Field, although it is more typically encountered in mossy woodlands and clearings. This species is widespread and common, whereas Slender Ground-hopper is a species of southern Britain and more restricted to wetter habitats. It can swim under water as well as skate on the surface. Most records of Slender Ground-hopper at Shotover are from the undisturbed stream lines on Horspath Common.

True bugs

It is unfortunate that a large, distinct and ecologically important order of insects should be called 'bugs', since the word is also popularly used for almost any unspecified insect. Furthermore, the name 'true bugs' — the correct vernacular term for the Hemiptera — does not greatly help to distinguish this group of invertebrates, for example, from bees or beetles.

In Britain, true bugs are generally small to medium-sized insects and many have curious shapes or bright colours — not unlike the beetles, for which they are often mistaken. However, unlike beetles which have jaws for biting, the mouth-parts of all true bugs are in the form of a piercing tube — the rostrum — which in most species is used to suck sap from plants. There are about 1,700 species in Britain including the well-known shieldbugs (Pentatomoidae) and the Pondskater *Gerris lacustris*, as well as common horticultural pests such as aphids (Aphididae) and whiteflies (Aleyrodidae).

The true bugs (Hemiptera) are divided into three suborders — Heteroptera, Auchenorrhyncha and Sternorrhyncha. In the Heteroptera the rostrum is long and the fore-wings have a hard, leathery section at the base (almost like a beetle's wings, in some species) but there is a distinctly membranous section towards the tip. Many Heteroptera are the largest of the true bugs, including shieldbugs and squashbugs (Coreoidea). Although most Heteroptera are herbivores, some aquatic species are predatory, and a few terrestrial species are carnivorous bloodsuckers — including the Bedbug *Cimex lectularius*.

Auchenorrhyncha usually have a short rostrum, reduced antennae and the wings are of various uniform textures — hard or membranous — and include the cicadas (Cicadidae) and leafhoppers (Cicadellidae). Sternorrhyncha are smaller with longer antennae and include the aphids and whiteflies. All Auchenorrhyncha and Sternorrhyncha are herbivores and most feed by sucking plant sap; however, to ingest enough protein for their growth, these bugs must

Gorse Shieldbug *Piezodorus lituratus* Peter Creed

Corizus hyoscyami, a Heteroptera bug showing the characteristic wing structure Paul Brock

Evacanthus interruptus, an Auchenorrhyncha bug showing the typically short beak or rostrum Tristan Bantock

consume and excrete a relatively large volume of sugary sap as it is so low in protein. The sugary excretion is the well-known honeydew, produced by innumerable tiny bugs, which forms the sticky layer on leaves (and parked cars) in summer. In this way, however, bugs provide an important source of easily digested sugars for a wide range of other insects. Indeed, some ants exploit this process by 'farming' aphids to their advantage.

Hemiptera data are seldom available for a site, mainly because there are so few specialist identifiers. However, Shotover is fortunate in having records of 117 species from the early 20th century (China, 1939: p. 69) mostly from survey work before 1918 by William Holland and Harry Britten, the latter leaving Oxford around that time to become an eminent entomologist at Manchester Museum. No further recording was undertaken until the 1970s, when David Steel and Pond Action (now the Freshwater Habitats Trust) began surveying the C.S. Lewis Community Nature Reserve for aquatic Heteroptera. Work on

the terrestrial species resumed in 1999 when John Campbell of the Oxfordshire Biological Record Centre visited Shotover to survey for bugs, as well as to help and encourage members of Shotover Wildlife to record invertebrates. Since 2013, collaborations between Shotover Wildlife, Darren Mann (Oxford University Museum of Natural History) and Jim Flanagan (British Bugs Recording Scheme) have supplemented the work of John Campbell and together have found a further 170 true bug species. Of the 287 species recorded on the Hill, 200 are Heteroptera, of which 31 have not been seen since before 1939, and 77 are Auchenorrhyncha, five of which have not been recorded since then. There are no recent records of Sternorrhyncha.

The majority of species of true bugs recorded on the Hill are common in Britain and would be found in most woodlands or meadows in Oxfordshire. A small number of species at Shotover, however, are sufficiently scarce to have been given a national status. *Psallus albicinctus* was caught in 2013 in the upper canopy of Brasenose Wood; this Heteropteran is nationally scarce and has been recorded in only a few other sites in Oxfordshire. In the same year, *Psammotettix nodosus* (Auchenorrhyncha) was caught in a net near The Sandpit. Although the species appears to be widely distributed in Britain, little is known about its habits and, with so few British specimens found, its status is listed as 'insufficiently known'. *Graptopeltus lynceus* (Heteroptera) is associated with sandy places and old quarries, and its preferred food plants are of the borage family, especially Viper's-bugloss *Echium vulgare*. It was recorded in several places around the county 100 years ago, including at Shotover, but is now nationally scarce. Despite suitable open habitat, neither *G. lynceus* nor Viper's-bugloss has been recorded on the Hill for many decades.

The bugs of heath and dry grassland are well represented at Shotover, with 38 associated species recorded. Both *Kleidocerys ericae* (Heteroptera) and Heath Damsel Bug *Nabis ericetorum* have been added to the known fauna. *K. ericae* has been found in the SSSI several times in recent years, yet when netted by John Campbell in 1999 it was the first record for this species in pre-1974 Oxfordshire. As it feeds almost entirely on Heather it will always be a scarce bug in the county but it should continue to thrive on the Hill while its food plant remains. A single Heath Damsel Bug was netted in 2013 from the Heather in Mary Sadler Field.

Of the remaining bugs on the Hill, the majority are equally divided between grassland and woodland species, including 70 (25 per cent)

Kleidocerys ericae **was new to Oxfordshire when recorded at Shotover in 1999** Tristan Bantock

Lacebugs

The lacebugs — Heteroptera in the family Tingidae — are remarkably sculptured. The upper surface of the insect has a rigid net-like structure on both the thorax and the wing cases, and the interstices of the 'net' are wholly or partly transparent, giving the appearance of a fragile lacy filigree. In general, the lacebugs are small insects, ranging from about two to five millimetres in length.

Eight of the 25 British species of lacebug have been identified at Shotover, and most of these appear in both early and recent records. The only species that has not been recorded since the earlier 20th century — *Kalama tricornis* — is 3.5 millimetres long and beautifully sculptured. Although it is not considered to be particularly scarce, there are very few Oxfordshire records and little is known about its life cycle or its preferred food plants.

The lacebug *Kalama tricornis*
Drawing by Jacqueline Wright

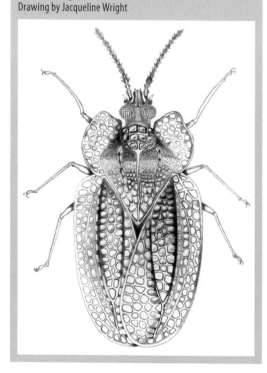

Eupteryx tenella, **an Auchenorrhyncha bug** Tristan Bantock

that are specifically associated with a particular species of food plant. All such associations are with plants that are common, with one exception: *Pinalitus viscicola* (Heteroptera), which feeds exclusively on Mistletoe and which was recorded around 1980 by David Steel [see also page 80].

Less common bugs associated with common plants at Shotover include *Pseudoloxops coccineus* (Heteroptera) found on Ash and *Eupteryx tenella* (Auchenorrhyncha) on Yarrow. Although these two species are not considered to be particularly scarce, there appear to be no other records of either species in Oxfordshire.

Thrips

In Britain thrips are particularly small insects, usually about one to two millimetres long, most of which live hidden in the flower heads of various plants, where they feed on pollen or sap. They are seldom noticed except on stormy days in summer when they swarm into the air, some of them catching in people's hair. At such times we know them as the familiar and irritating Thunder Flies or Thunder Bugs.

Shotover, however, is a special place for these creatures. In 1916, Harry Britten caught a thrips at Shotover which remained unidentified until 1923; when the specimen was eventually examined by specialist Richard Bagnell, it was declared to be a species new to science: *Thrips fulvipes*.

Thrips are in the order Thysanoptera (meaning 'fringed wings') and over 100 species are native to Britain. Although many are economic pests, it is thought that some may have a role as pollinators. Many species are wingless but on those that are winged, the four wings are very narrow and fringed with bristles on both the front and rear edges, making them look feathery. The body of a thrips is quite slender and the species range in colour from light brown to black; a few are colourfully banded. Unlike most

insects, the head is strongly asymmetrical having only one functional mandible.

Few observers record thrips in Britain; however, with the prospect of refinding *T. fulvipes*, specialist Dominic Collins visited Shotover in 2013 on a national field day hosted by Shotover Wildlife. Unfortunately, after a day spent examining the food plant of *T. fulvipes*, Dog's Mercury, it could not be found. Nevertheless, since 2013 — with the help of Darren Twort of Oxford Brookes University — a number of species new to the Hill have been recorded, bringing the total of thrips species known for Shotover to 17.

Snakeflies

The distinctive long-necked shape of a snakefly is unique and unmistakable. Although these slender insects are not especially small — typically a centimetre long for British species — they are seldom seen and little known, mostly because they spend their entire life cycle high in the tree canopy and almost never come to the ground. As with the saproxylic beetles, the discovery of snakeflies at Shotover affords yet another glimpse of tree-top wildlife revealed by the use of upper-canopy vane traps [see page 132].

Snakeflies belong to their own taxonomic order, the Raphidioptera, and structurally have changed very little since the early Jurassic — in effect, they are 'living fossils'. About 200 species of snakefly are known worldwide but only four species in Britain, all of which have been recorded in the SSSI in recent years. Perhaps the most common, *Xanthostigma xanthostigma*, has been found several times in oak trees, and the pine tree species, *Atlantoraphidia maculicollis*, was caught in 2016 on a Scots Pine on Horspath Common.

Thrips fulvipes, just two millimetres long, was caught at Shotover and declared a new species to science in 1923
Drawing by Jacqueline Wright

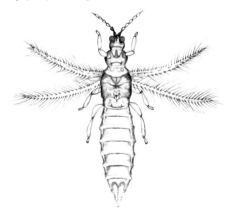

Snakeflies live high in the trees and are rarely seen; *Subilla confinis* was caught in Holme Ground in 2015
Drawing by Bonnie Collins

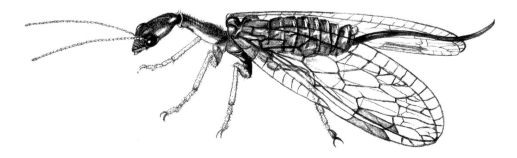

Gall causers: invertebrates and other organisms

Many visitors to Shotover will be familiar with oddly shaped growths such as Oak Apple and Marble Galls on young oak trees, and Robin's Pincushions on wild rose bushes. These are just a few of the great variety of plant galls that can be found on the trees and plants growing on the Hill. Although galls may appear to be part of the plant's growth, in fact they predominantly result from invertebrate activity, usually the laying of eggs. To a lesser extent, infestation by fungi (especially rusts and smuts), bacteria and viruses also induce gall production by the host plant. The nature of a gall has been the object of much discussion among those who study galls — cecidologists — but a generally accepted definition is *"an abnormal growth produced by a plant under the influence of another organism"* which *"involves enlargement and/or proliferation of the host's cells or vascular tissue, and provides both protection and nutrition for the gall causer"* (Redfern and Shirley, 2011: p. 1).

Galls found on oak trees

In Britain, over 70 different galls are known to form on oaks and of these 90 per cent are caused by tiny gall wasps of the Cynipidae family; the

The characteristic distortion of an oak twig galled by the wasp *Andricus inflator*

remaining galls are formed mostly by flies and true bugs. Twenty-one oak-associated galls are known to occur at Shotover and all have been recorded since 2005.

Many of the cynipid gall wasps have a life history which involves two alternating generations: an asexual generation of females whose eggs hatch into both males and females, constituting the sexual generation whose offspring are all female — thereby completing the life cycle. The galls caused by the egg laying of the two generations are quite different. Those containing the developing asexual generation are usually more robust in their structure and better protected by where they are located on the host tree. In a few cases each generation requires a different species of oak; for example, the gall wasp *Andricus lignicola*, which arrived in Britain in the 1970s, lays gall-forming eggs on the non-native Turkey Oak *Quercus cerris* for the sexual generation and on Pedunculate Oak for the asexual; on the latter, its eggs induce the formation of Cola-nut Galls.

Three types of small disc-like 'spangle' galls can be seen on the underside of oak leaves in the late summer and early autumn. Of these, Common Spangle Gall is perhaps the most widespread at Shotover. These galls, which contain the larvae of the asexual generation of the wasp *Neuroterus quercusbaccarum*, fall from the leaves just before the leaves themselves fall to the ground. The galls are then protected during the winter months by the covering of dead leaves and the following spring an all-female generation of adult wasps emerges. These females lay unfertilized eggs in the catkins of the oak tree, causing the formation of small red 'currant' galls. A sexual generation of males and females emerges from these galls and the mated females complete the cycle by laying eggs on the underside of oak leaves. Two other spangle galls are less commonly found on the oaks of Shotover: Smooth Spangle Gall and Cupped Spangle Gall which are often found alongside Common Spangle Galls on the same leaf.

Knopper Galls are a relative newcomer to Britain, first recorded in the south-west in the 1960s and quickly spreading throughout the whole country. The gall, harbouring the asexual larvae of *A. quercuscalicis*, distorts the acorn to a shiny-green growth, often sticky and pyramidal in shape. This eventually turns brown and

Spangle Galls on the underside of oak leaves

Marble Galls showing the exit holes of *Andricus kollari*

Acorns of Pedunculate Oak distorted by the Knopper Gall Lawrence Bee

woody, and can often be found on the ground during the winter. The sexual generation causes galls in the catkins of Turkey Oak. The aptly named Oak Apple Gall, caused by the sexual generation of the wasp *Biorhiza pallida,* is a soft growth found at the end of young twigs and at first closely resembles a small pinkish green apple, later turning brown and spongy. A single gall can contain a large number of developing larvae in separate chambers, which are often accompanied by a complex community of associated parasites and inquiline (cohabiting) herbivore insects.

The Marble Gall is caused by the wasp *Andricus kollari* and hardens into a woody brown 'marble' which usually remains on the twig long after the adult wasp has emerged via the clearly visible exit hole. The wasp was introduced into the West Country in the 1830s — perhaps from the Middle East — for dyeing

and tanning, as the tannin content of the galls is around 15 per cent. The galls were also ground into powder to make ink for writing legal documents and parliamentary statutes. Eventually, Marble Gall as a raw material for long-lasting inks was superseded in Britain by imported Aleppo Galls, native to southern central Europe, which have a tannin content of up to 65 per cent.

Other common galls induced by gall wasps on the oaks of Shotover include Cherry Gall caused by *Cynips quercusfolii* and Artichoke Gall caused by *A. fecundator.* Two much more recent additions to the British gall fauna, appearing in the 1990s, are Hedgehog Gall caused by *A. lucidus* and Ramshorn Gall caused by *A. aries,* which have both been recorded in recent years on the Hill.

Galls of other trees and woody shrubs

The dense entanglements of small twigs on birches — Witch's Broom [see page 170] — are caused by the fungus *Taphrina betulina.* A similar growth on willows, which has been seen in Brasenose Wood, was originally thought to be caused by the mite *Eriophyes triradiatus* but recent research has suggested that it may be induced instead by a virus or phytoplasma (bacterium) within the catkins. Dog-rose and Field-rose often act as host to the distinctive Robin's Pincushion [page 170], also known as Bedeguar Gall, caused by the gall wasp *Diplolepis rosae.* This common gall can reach a diameter of six centimetres and is characterized by a tangle of long wiry reddish-green hairs. The core of the gall can house a very complex micro-community of insects as well as the primary inducer of the gall. These include herbivorous inquilines which feed directly on the gall tissue, as well as insect-eating primary parasitoids which prey on the inquilines and which in turn may themselves be preyed upon by secondary parasitoids (hyperparasitoids), forming a miniature ecosystem within just a single gall.

Sloe berries on Shotover's Blackthorn are occasionally galled by the fungus *Taphrina pruni*. The fruit is deformed into the shape of a jellybean and is often called a pocket plum because the fungus destroys the developing stone within the fruit, leaving an empty pocket. Blackthorn is also galled by the leaf-rolling sawfly *Pristiphora monogyniae* and two gall mites, *Eriophyes prunispinosae* and *E. similis*, both of which produce reddish-green pimples on the leaves. A further nine species of tree at Shotover have been

shown to host gall-forming insects including mites, beetles, flies and the Pine Resin-gall Moth *Retinia resinella*.

Galls found on herbaceous plants

Many conspicuous galls can be seen on the trees of Shotover but numerous herbaceous plants also act as host to a variety of gall-causing organisms. Creeping Thistle is host to the gallfly *Urophora cardui*; the gall swells in the thistle stem to form a large hard mass up to 10 centimetres long, containing one or more chambers in which the larvae overwinter. Moschatel, popularly known as Town Hall Clock [see page 63], is the host for two rust galls caused by the fungi *Puccinia adoxae* and *P. albescens*. The former induces leaf and stem distortion and forms darkish spots on the leaves; the latter also distorts the leaves but appears as tiny daisy-like growths on the leaf surface. A gall midge, *Jaapiella veronicae*, galls Germander Speedwell, causing the serrated edges of the two terminal leaflets to bond together to form a greenish-red hairy pouch which can contain a number of orange larvae.

Additional gall-causing invertebrates

Most often, a gall-causing species is recorded after finding the gall but without seeing the fungus or invertebrate that has induced it, yet a gall cannot be taxonomically recorded, as it is an abnormality of growth and not a species. Fortunately, many symbioses between gall and inducer involve a specific pairing, allowing the unseen inducing species to be recorded with confidence. Conversely, there are instances where the invertebrate is more likely to be found than the obscurely located gall — for example, those in roots or stem bases. The list of invertebrates recorded on the Hill includes 38 gall-causers which are in addition to the 37 detected by finding their gall, although 23 of these have not been seen since before 1939. Most of these additional galls are hidden, or partially hidden, in a wide range of common herbs and the gall-causers are almost entirely beetles or flies that gall a specific host plant.

All of the beetles that cause galls are weevils of the families Apionidae and Curculionidae, and most are closely associated with a single plant species or a group of closely related plants. The gall weevils, like most other weevils, are characterized by a long snout which they use to

Witch's Broom on Downy Birch *Betula pubescens*

Robin's Pincushion on Field-rose

Apion frumentarium **showing the typical long snout of a weevil; at the tip of the snout the mouth-parts are all neatly formed in miniature** Drawing by Jacqueline Wright

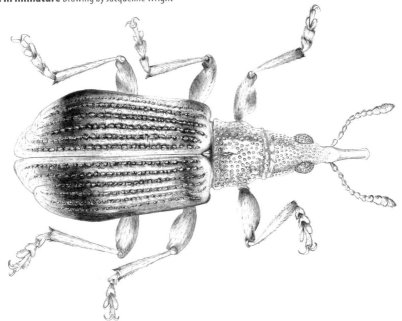

chew a hole into the soft tissue of the plant in which to lay their eggs. Perhaps, therefore, it is not surprising that some weevils have developed a gall-causing effect to aid the development of their larvae. For example, *Apion frumentarium* bores into the stem-base of docks for egg laying but it is easier to find the weevil by using a sweep-net on Broad-leaved Dock *Rumex obtusifolius* than to notice the entry hole or gall swelling at the base of the plant's stem. *A. frumentarium* stands out among the Apionidae weevils for its colouration and size; it is entirely orange and, at over four millimetres long, is one of the largest in the family.

Most of the galls that have been found on the Hill are common, yet among the unseen galls of herbaceous plants are a few that are scarce in Britain. In some cases both the insect and the gall are uncommon, such as the gallfly *Oxyna nebulosa* [see also page 157] which galls Oxeye Daisy, and in many such cases the gall-causing insects have not been recorded at Shotover since before 1939. However, looking for abnormal plant growth can still yield results; in 2016 the rare gall of Cat's-ear, caused by the cynipid wasp *Phanacis hypochoeridis*, was found near The Plain.

In all, 82 galls have been recorded at Shotover: 37 by direct observation, 38 by recording the invertebrate gall-causer and seven by unambiguous association with other life-cycle evidence, such as the tracery in leaves made by leaf-mining insects. Of the 76 species of invertebrate gall-causer at Shotover, 53 have been recorded in recent years (since 1995). Furthermore, species new to Britain are regularly recorded and, given careful examination of trees, shrubs and herbs on the Hill, the total number of recorded galls could continue to rise.

Hedgehog Gall on oak acorns, caused by the wasp *Andricus lucidus*, was first found in Britain in 2000 and at Shotover in 2006

Woodlice, waterlice, millipedes and centipedes

Steve Gregory

Insects have six legs and spiders have eight but woodlice, waterlice, millipedes and centipedes have considerably more. All these creatures have segmented bodies with pairs of jointed legs and a hard external skeleton but that is where the structural similarities end. Woodlice and waterlice (Isopoda) and millipedes and centipedes (Myriapoda) belong to different classes of animal and their respective evolutionary pathways are as distinct from each other as, for example, spiders are from snails. Also, unlike many other invertebrates, the Isopods and Myriapods lack a waxy outer layer and so tend to hide away in damp places, such as under leaf litter, to avoid dehydration. The species found in Britain are ideally adapted to the moist British climate and their distributions are mostly restricted to the wetter western parts of Europe, where summers are cool and winters relatively warm. This contrasts with many insects (butterflies, for example) which thrive on the hot dry summers typical of central Europe and often struggle in our damp climate.

Woodlice, waterlice and millipedes — but not the carnivorous centipedes — are detritivores and play a number of underappreciated roles in the environment. In woodland, for example, the several hundred individuals that are usually to be found per square metre can consume up to 25 per cent of the annual leaf fall, making a significant contribution to decomposition and nutrient recycling. Vegetable matter is chewed into small pieces, allowing rapid colonization and decomposition by bacteria and micro-fungi and thereby indirectly speeding up the recycling of nutrients back into the soil for new vegetative growth. Where they occur in large numbers, woodlice and waterlice are also an important food resource. Waterlice are consumed by amphibians, fish and other aquatic invertebrates; woodlice are eaten by a wide variety of animals, including shrews, toads, ground beetles, centipedes and some spiders.

Certain species of woodlice are useful bioindicators of pollution by heavy metals

Rough Woodlouse Keith Lugg

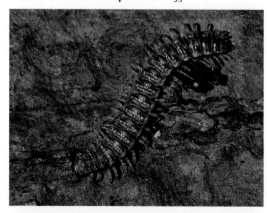

Common Flat-back Millipede Keith Lugg

The centipede Common Cryptops Keith Lugg

such as lead, copper, zinc and cadmium. The concentrations of these metals found in woodlice have been shown to correlate very closely with the levels of contamination in their environment.

History of recording at Shotover

The recording of Isopods and Myriapods has never been as popular as that of many other groups of invertebrates. At Shotover, it was not until 1953 that the first woodlouse, Rosy Woodlouse *Androniscus dentiger*, was recorded by the Oxford University Bureau of Animal Population Studies' Wytham Survey. Between 1982 and 1990, Pond Action (now the Freshwater Habitats Trust) recorded waterlice from the various ponds across the Hill. Then in 1992 the first millipede and centipede records were collected for Shotover as part of a wide-ranging survey of Oxfordshire's Isopods and Myriapods (Gregory and Campbell, 1995 and 1996).

Over half of all Isopod and Myriapod species recorded during Gregory and Campbell's survey of Oxfordshire have been found subsequently at Shotover Hill. However, the majority of the current records date from 1999 or later, and result from survey work coordinated by Shotover Wildlife using a wide range of sampling methods, and from which a good diversity of species have been recorded. However, although the SSSI and C.S. Lewis Community Nature Reserve are relatively well surveyed for these invertebrates, much of the rest of the Hill is virtually unexplored.

Woodlice and waterlice

Woodlice and waterlice belong to the Crustacean order Isopoda. The name, meaning 'equal feet', refers to their seven pairs of more or less identical legs. Isopods were originally all sea creatures, and globally most still live in the marine environment. Woodlice evolved from their ancestors relatively recently, around 50 million years ago, to colonize dry land and freshwater habitats. Britain's inland Isopods are divided into two suborders: the aquatic waterlice (Asellota) and the terrestrial woodlice (Oniscidea). Only four species of waterlice are known in Britain, two of which have been recorded at Shotover: Water Slater *Asellus aquaticus* and One-spotted Waterlouse *Proasellus meridianus*.

Woodlice are more diverse, with 40 species occurring in the wild in Britain and 19 recorded at Shotover. About half of these are large common species, including the Pill Woodlouse *Armadillidium vulgare*, Rough Woodlouse *Porcellio scaber*, Shiny Woodlouse *Oniscus asellus* and Striped Woodlouse *Philoscia muscorum*. The remainder belong to the pygmy woodlice family, a group of elusive soil-dwelling species. The Common Pygmy Woodlouse *Trichoniscus pusillus* agg. may reach 4.5 millimetres in length but most are just two to three millimetres long.

Various strategies have been adopted by woodlice to deal with danger, all of which are demonstrated by common species at Shotover. The familiar 'rollers', such as the Pill Woodlouse, form a defensive ball, while 'clampers' like the

Rosy Woodlouse, Shotover's earliest recorded Isopod
Keith Lugg

At 2.5 millimetres, Least Pygmy Woodlouse is the smallest woodlouse recorded at Shotover Keith Lugg

Striped Woodlouse is a 'runner' species Keith Lugg

Shiny Woodlouse have broad flattened bodies to grip fast to a surface. The Striped Woodlouse is one of the 'runners', whose long legs enable them to make a speedy getaway. Finally, many of the smaller woodlice, such as the Spurred Ridgeback Woodlouse *Haplophthalmus danicus*, are 'creepers' that discreetly move into crevices when disturbed.

Millipedes and centipedes

Millipedes and centipedes have elongated bodies consisting of numerous leg-bearing segments and are grouped collectively as the Myriapods, meaning 'many-footed'. Although their common names imply that they have 1,000 or 100 feet respectively, the actual number of legs varies considerably depending on the species, and is almost always fewer than their names suggest.

In Britain, about 60 species of millipede and 50 species of centipede have been recorded outdoors (exotic species may occasionally be found in glasshouses and garden centres).

The legs of the millipede *Cylindroiulus britannicus* oscillate in a coordinated wavelike motion Keith Lugg

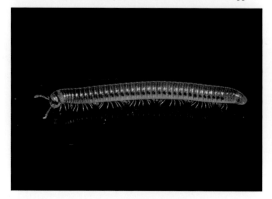

Though superficially similar, millipedes and centipedes are very different creatures and have contrasting biologies; as noted earlier, the former are vegetation detritivores and the latter carnivorous predators.

Millipedes, like woodlice, have blunt mandibles which are adapted for cutting and chewing dead and decaying plant material. Most of their body segments bear two pairs of short legs (hence their taxonomic name Diplopoda, 'twin-footed') which oscillate sequentially in a wavelike motion to force the long thin body through leaf litter and soil. They have a hard external skeleton and when threatened typically curl into a defensive spiral with further protection, if necessary, provided by noxious secretions (based on hydrocyanides, benzoquinones and alkaloids) from repugnatorial glands on the sides of the body. These secretions

Millipede world records

The fossil millipede *Pneumodesmus newmani* is the oldest known air-breathing species of land animal. At 428 million years of age (Middle Silurian period) it is about twice as old as the earliest dinosaur fossil.

Later, in the Upper Carboniferous (c. 300 million years ago), the oxygen-rich atmosphere allowed the millipede *Arthropleura armata* to grow to a colossal 2.5 metres — the largest known land invertebrate.

The female of the millipede *Illacme plenipes* — a species that can still be found in California — can have up to 750 legs (375 pairs) and yet is only about three centimetres long. It has more legs than any other known animal, though still fewer than the 1,000 legs suggested by the common name of its class.

The millipede *Illacme plenipes* Paul Marek

give many millipedes a distinctive smell when handled and can leave a yellow stain on human skin, or even a chemical burn. Unsurprisingly, few animals eat millipedes.

The 20 species recorded at Shotover represent four of the seven orders of British millipede, and each of the seven orders has a characteristic body plan. The most numerous at Shotover are the julids (Julida), which have long cylindrical bodies of 50 or more segments and repugnatorial glands indicated by brightly coloured spots. This order includes the familiar White-legged Millipede *Tachypodoiulus niger*. The second most diverse are the flat-back millipedes (Polydesmida), such as the Common Flat-back Millipede *Polydesmus angustus* with its distinctive angular projections on its sides. These millipedes have no eyes and, when adult, have 19 or 20 body segments. Silk millipedes (Chordeumatida) are able to spin nests of silk; these protective chambers are used by females in which to lay their eggs and for immature individuals to develop after hatching. The three species at Shotover have 30 body segments and, unlike most other millipedes, only attain their adult form during the winter months. Finally, pill millipedes (Glomerida) are short animals with just 12 body segments that can roll themselves into a ball; of these, only Common Pill Millipede *Glomeris marginata* has been found at Shotover.

In contrast to the woodlice and millipedes, centipedes are fearsome predators, actively hunting small insects, spiders and other invertebrates. The first pair of legs have evolved into poison claws to inject venom into its prey, giving the Chilopoda its class name, 'lip-footed'. In most species the remaining legs, with the exception of the hindmost pair, project from either side of the body, allowing them to move fast and chase down their prey. When threatened, the faster species will run for shelter, while slower ones curl into a loose ball and, like the millipedes, exude distasteful chemicals to repel an attacker.

With the exception of Common Cryptops *Cryptops hortensis*, which is in the order Scolopendromorpha, all 17 species of Shotover's centipede fauna are either earth centipedes (Geophilomorpha) or stone centipedes (Lithobiomorpha). Earth centipedes, all of which lack eyes, are long and thin with 35 to 83 pairs of legs. The Long-horned Centipede *Geophilus flavus* is a typical species, with a long flexible body

Banded Centipede showing the venomous front legs alongside its head Keith Lugg

for burrowing into soil, leaf litter or under loose bark. Stone centipedes, such as Banded Centipede *Lithobius variegatus*, have much shorter bodies, prominent eyes and 15 pairs of legs, and are fast-moving hunters of other invertebrates at the soil surface. And between these two, in terms of characteristics, comes Common Cryptops with 21 pairs of legs and no eyes.

Habitats for Isopoda and Myriapoda
Aquatic and wetland habitats
Most of the marshes and ponds on Shotover Hill are inhabited by the ubiquitous Two-spotted Waterlouse or Water Slater *Asellus aquaticus* but only the ponds on the Shotover Estate support the One-spotted Waterlouse. Woodlice characteristic of wetland habitats are Carr Slater *Ligidium hypnorum* and Rough Pygmy Woodlouse *Trichoniscoides albidus*. The latter species was found in the C.S. Lewis Community Nature Reserve in 2000 under dead wood on wet soil and, although widely distributed in

The aquatic One-spotted Waterlouse Keith Lugg

It is believed that the brightly coloured Common Shiny Woodlouse *Oniscus asellus* ssp. *occidentalis* is a subspecies which evolved in Britain, and that the associated subspecies *O. asellus* ssp. *asellus* evolved on continental Europe. However, the highly competitive 'continental' form has been inadvertently introduced at various times over the centuries and has now become dominant in Britain. Meanwhile, the native *O. asellus* ssp. *occidentalis* only survives in the extreme south-west of England — and is not known to have been found anywhere else on the planet.

Hybrids between the two subspecies *O. asellus* × *occidentalis* are able to persist in isolated fragments of semi-natural wetland habitat (Bilton *et al.*, 1999) and such relict populations have been found in the wetter parts of the SSSI (and also at the nearby Lye Valley SSSI). Thus, Shotover Hill still preserves some of the original fauna from the native woodlands that colonized Britain after the last ice age. Unfortunately, the ultimate fate of the original subspecies, *O. asellus* ssp. *occidentalis*, will be extinction by hybridization, not just at Shotover but globally.

Common Shiny Woodlouse Keith Lugg

at the interface with the soil. Some species are arboreal, climbing tree trunks, burrowing beneath loose bark or inhabiting debris inside hollow trees. The mosaic of wet woodlands and acidic soils at Shotover supports a fauna unusual for Oxfordshire (Gregory and Campbell, 1995 and 1996) with many species that are typical of ancient woodlands.

The Western Silk Millipede *Melogona gallica*, first recorded in Brasenose Wood in 2015, is characteristic of wet acidic woodland, and is known nowhere else in Oxfordshire. Large Silk Millipede *Chordeuma proximum*, which favours wetter areas, and Scandinavian Spine-tail *Julus scandinavius* are both widely recorded in the SSSI, yet elsewhere are generally restricted to ancient woodlands and are therefore rare in Oxfordshire and the surrounding counties. Of similar rarity is Western Stone Centipede *Lithobius borealis*, represented by a single specimen found in Mary Sadler Field in 2001. Other scarce woodland species of note include Carr Slater, widespread in the wetter and shadier parts of the Hill, and Broad-headed Centipede *L. muticus*. Both of these species are locally frequent in south-eastern England but Oxfordshire lies at the edge of their natural distribution and they too are rarely seen outside ancient woodland.

The dead-wood fauna is also well represented, although none of the species are particularly rare or confined to ancient woodland. The tiny Spurred Ridgeback Woodlouse, British No-tail Millipede *Cylindroiulus britannicus* and Short Earth Centipede *G. truncorum* have been

Broad-headed Centipede is an ancient woodland species
Keith Lugg

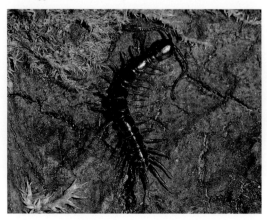

the Thames Valley (Gregory and Campbell, 1995), it is elusive and could probably be found elsewhere at Shotover. Of particular note are the records of Hybrid Shiny Woodlouse *O. asellus* × *occidentalis* collected from pitfall traps in Sandpit Field, a relict species associated with high-quality wetland habitats in central England [see box above].

Woodlands

Shotover's woodlands provide many habitat niches for Isopods and Myriapods. Most inhabit fallen dead wood or deep leaf litter, especially

found within rotting wood, and Slender Bark Millipede *Nemasoma varicorne* under loose bark. Of particular interest is the uncommon Parisian No-tail Millipede *C. parisorium* collected in 2009 from inside a hollow tree in Brasenose Wood.

Heathland and acidic grassland

Areas of Heather and acidic grassland at Shotover support a range of species different from those of the woodland. The Striped Woodlouse and Pill Woodlouse can be abundant in grassy habitats but more interesting species include Eason's Earth Centipede *G. easoni*, Embossed Flat-back Millipede *Polydesmus inconstans* and Striped Millipede *Brachyiulus pusillus*. The Black Stone Centipede *L. calcaratus*, which in Oxfordshire has a strong preference for semi-natural grasslands, has been recorded in areas where the sward is kept short by Rabbit grazing or visitors' feet, such as Mary Sadler

Ant Woodlouse is well suited to Shotover's acidic grassland Keith Lugg

Field, Sandpit Field and Horseshoe Field. Other short-turf species are widespread across the Hill, including Metallic No-tail Millipede *C. caeruleocinctus* and Ant Woodlouse *Platyarthrus hoffmannseggii* which inhabits ant nests in sunny locations.

Gardens, farmyards and other constructed habitats

Synanthropic habitats — that is, those associated with human settlement such as gardens, churchyards and farmyards — complement the semi-natural habitats discussed above. Human habitation, especially when not too tidy, can support an interesting mix of woodlice, millipedes and centipedes, among which are species that appear to prefer such locations. Many species are generalists of the wider countryside and are more typically found in naturally disturbed habitats (for example, river valleys and coastlines); others are specialists that have adapted to synanthropic environments and are less able to survive elsewhere.

Species such as Spurred Ridgeback Woodlouse, which occurs in dead wood in Shotover's woodlands, and Ant Woodlouse, found in ant nests, are equally at home in domestic gardens around the Hill. The Painted Woodlouse *Porcellio spinicornis* and Luminous Centipede *G. carpophagus* are characteristically found above ground — on garden walls in Horspath, for example — whereas in the wild they are typically associated with sea cliffs and rocky outcrops. The Plum Woodlouse *Porcellionides pruinosus*, found in the allotments next to Brasenose Farm, is a specialist synanthropic species and is rarely seen except in and around manure or compost.

The future

Isopod and Myriapod species, and their habitats, are being put under increasing pressure by modern society. Intensification of agriculture, commercial forestry and the redevelopment of brownfield sites all constitute major threats. Even in a nature reserve, such as Shotover, many scarce and vulnerable species occupy specialist habitats often perceived to be of little value for conservation: hollow trees, waterlogged flushes, short grassland and secondary woodland. It is important to appreciate, however, that the diversity of these species does not necessarily correlate with botanical richness (a common criterion for the selection of nature reserves) but more often with specific conditions at the soil surface. In common with other ground- and soil-dwelling invertebrates, microclimate and soil structure — rather than the vegetation or plant species present — are more important in determining suitability of habitat for Isopods and Myriapods.

Many organisms have naturally dynamic metapopulations that can exploit or abandon a location as the conditions fluctuate. Among such organisms are a number of Isopods and Myriapods but many of the species associated with semi-natural habitats do not disperse readily. Thus, long-term nature conservation for vulnerable species should be less concerned with preserving known colonies and should rather address species requirements more broadly. This policy would involve, in particular, allowing natural processes such as habitat succession to develop, giving time for metapopulations to disperse to their own advantage. Unfortunately, in the coming decades the impact of a rapidly changing climate will 'force the hand' of metapopulations, requiring them to expand or contract their range on a much shorter timescale. In the fragmented landscapes of today these species will be unable to migrate to suitable new sites and will therefore be vulnerable to local extinction.

Often a target for 'improvement', apparently neglected secondary woodland can be an important habitat for invertebrates (the left-hand tree is 'The Body Snatcher' [see page 56–57])

Spiders, harvestmen and allies

Lawrence Bee

In Britain, around 670 species of spider are recorded, and together with the smaller orders of harvestmen, pseudoscorpions, scorpions, mites and ticks they make up the class Arachnida. These eight-legged invertebrates are found in a wide variety of habitats in Britain throughout all seasons of the year.

Spiders

The spiders form the order Araneae, of which there are around 40,000 species worldwide. Although the total number of British spider species is small, the number of different spider families is about a third of those found globally. There is considerable variety between and within the families of British spiders but none of our native species can compare in size and appearance with some of the large, colourful and oddly shaped spiders from other parts of the world, particularly the tropics. However, the range of behaviour among British spider families — including, for example, methods of capturing prey and mating procedures — provide for a very diverse fauna.

Of the species found in Britain almost half are members of the Linyphiidae, a family of mostly very small spiders (around three to four millimetres in body length) commonly known as money spiders. Among the other 36 families are the wolf spiders, jumping spiders and crab spiders, most of which can be identified to family level in the field.

Spiders are predominantly carnivorous (and exclusively so in Britain) and their presence therefore is not dependent on particular food plants. Instead, the structure of the habitat is

Garden Spider Peter Creed

Ballooning

Although spiders do not have the wings that many invertebrates have which enable them to disperse throughout a habitat, many spiders nevertheless still have the ability to travel large distances — by 'ballooning'. This is a method of aerial dispersal achieved by spinning long threads of silk which can be caught up in rising air currents. A spider positions itself at a high point, such as the top of a grass stem or a fence post, so that it is exposed to the flow of air, and then spins strands of silk from its spinnerets. The silk is caught in the breeze and the spider is lifted away.

Adult spiders of the Linyphiidae family are light enough to be carried for very many kilometres but for larger species it is only the small immature spiders (spiderlings) which can travel

A money spider in typical ballooning posture
Tone Killick

by ballooning. The phenomenon was noted by Charles Darwin when he observed silken threads in the rigging of *HMS Beagle* some 60 miles off the Argentinian coast. *"I repeatedly observed the same kind of small spider, either when placed or having crawled on some little eminence, elevate its abdomen, send forth a thread, and then sail away horizontally, but with a rapidity which was quite unaccountable."* (Darwin, 1839: p. 188)

This also explains why some of the first organisms to be recorded on the newly emerged volcanic island of Anak Krakatau were spiders ballooning in from the surrounding mainland of Java or Sumatra.

far more relevant and a site containing a range of habitats can offer a great variety of suitable microhabitats for many different species. Shotover is rich in habitat types and consequently supports a diverse and abundant spider fauna; 198 species have been recorded in 22 families — representing 66 per cent of the spider families found in Britain. Geology also has an influence; the Victoria County History of Oxfordshire comments: *"Each one of the varied assortment of geological formations which Oxfordshire possesses has its own peculiarities of soil, elevation, aspect and humidity. These are the factors which determine its surface features and the nature and amount of covering vegetation, which in turn regulates the insect life which constitutes the food of the spiders."* (Falconer, 1939: p. 180)

These words apply well to Shotover, where the contrasting geological strata are of particular value to the arachnid fauna and add significantly to the variety of vegetation structure. The geographical location of Shotover also contributes to the diversity of spiders. As with other invertebrate groups many British spiders show a marked southern or northern distribution, and the Thames valley in Oxfordshire lies within the overlap of the northern limit of some southern species and the southernmost range of northern species.

Until Shotover Wildlife was founded in 1999, there had been no sustained effort to record the arachnid fauna on the Hill. Falconer (1939: p. 181) lists only 61 species from Brasenose Wood, Shotover Brick Pit and Shotover Hill among a total of 251 species for pre-1974 Oxfordshire. It appears that Harry Britten (1870–1954) was the only active recorder of arachnids at Shotover during the early part of the 20th century, though he would have had the best possible support from the Revd. Octavius Pickard-Cambridge (1828–1917), one of the fathers of British arachnology. Pickard-Cambridge also collected in the Oxford area, and on his death bequeathed his large collection to the Oxford University Museum of Natural History to form part of the internationally important Hope Collection. There was little recording during the remainder of the 20th century until Shotover Wildlife began working with local arachnologists and students from Oxford Brookes University.

Spider habitats at Shotover

The habitats at Shotover that have particular species of spider associated with them can be split into three main types: heathland, woodland and wetland. In addition, there are relatively common species that disperse readily by ballooning [see box above] and may be found in almost any habitat. Two such spiders are *Metellina segmentata* (Tetragnathidae) and *M. mengei*, both of which spin orb webs — the well-known flat disc of radial and spiral threads of silk [see also box, page 184] — and can be recognized by a tuning fork-shaped mark on their cephalothorax (combined head and thorax). Although the two species are very similar to each other they can be differentiated by the seasons in which they mature to adulthood: *M. mengei* in the spring and *M. segmentata* in early autumn.

Also common at Shotover is the striking Candy-striped Spider *Enoplognatha ovata* which protects its egg sac within a rolled leaf held in shape by silken threads. This spider appears in three colour forms: firstly, with a pale-yellow abdomen with a line or band of black spots on each side; secondly, with the same pattern of black spots plus a pair of pink stripes adjoining the spots; and, thirdly, with a single broad pink band down the centre of the abdomen. The plain yellow form is perhaps the commonest but the two with pink colouration give the spider its English name. Perhaps the greatest visual impact from any of Shotover's spiders comes from *Linyphia triangularis*, one of the few Linyphiid spiders that is large enough to be recognized in the field and likely to be found throughout the SSSI. In autumn, it spins fine sheets of web in the hedgerows and Gorse which are then beautifully highlighted with moisture droplets from any early-morning shroud of mist [see box, page 184].

Spiders of heathland and acidic grassland

The open acidic grassland of Sandpit Field and Mary Sadler Field and the scattered Gorse and Heather on the latter provide habitat niches for a number of spiders which spin webs to catch their prey. *Gibbaranea gibbosa* (Araneidae) is a greenish spider with distinctive humps on the shoulders of its abdomen. It spins its orb web in low, usually evergreen, vegetation; at Shotover, Gorse appears to be a favoured niche. Other orb-web spinners in the same family, such as *Cyclosa conica*, *Araneus sturmi* and Garden Spider *A. diadematus* with its distinctive white cross markings on the abdomen, also take advantage of the dense thorny foliage of Gorse. *Cyclosa conica* is one of a small number of spiders that adds a vertical wavy band of silk, the stabilimentum, across its orb web which may help to disguise the position of the spider on the web. Other striking-

Different colour forms of the Candy-striped Spider
Bruce Marlin, Wiki Commons, Peter O'Connor/Flickr

looking spiders recorded from this microhabitat include the pirate spiders *Ero furcata* and *E. tuberculata* (so called because of their piratical habit of invading other spiders' webs and preying upon their occupants) and the distinctive and colourful comb-footed spiders *Simitidion simile*, *Phylloneta sisyphia* and *Theridion mystaceum* which have a characteristic row of bristles on each hind leg.

Gibbarenea gibbosa Wim Rubers

Misumena vatia, **having changed to yellow to match the buttercup** Peter Creed

The Labyrinth Spider *Agelena labyrinthica* spins numerous tubular hollows into a large sheet web in the lower branches of Gorse. The spider itself sits in a retreat at the rear of the web, carrying its prey there for consumption. These labyrinthine webs can also be found in Heather and have been recorded in areas of grassland at Shotover, notably Slade Camp South. The Nursery-web Spider *Pisaura mirabilis* is another grassland species which also occurs on Heather. In early summer it spins a conspicuous tent-like nursery web in the upper levels of long grass, where the individual stems are used as a supporting framework for the web. The spider's egg sac is placed in the top of the web and when the young hatch they remain in the 'nursery' for a few days with the female standing guard close by.

The grassland found in Sandpit Field and Mary Sadler Field provides a suitable habitat for some of the running crab spiders (Philodromidae) and the rather more sedentary crab spiders (Thomisidae). The crab spiders do not spin a web but simply hide deep in the grass sward or wait — well camouflaged — in flower heads to pounce on prey when it comes within grasp. *Xysticus cristatus* and *X. erraticus* are both commonly found at Shotover and are typical crab spiders, being rather dumpy and crab-like with laterally inclined legs and an ability to walk sideways as well as forwards. Remarkably, a few crab spiders are able to change colour according to their surroundings. For example, *X. cristatus* normally has a mixture of dark and pale brown markings but when found in Heather it may be subtly paler, sometimes with a pinkish hue. *Misumena vatia*, recorded in Horseshoe Field, is normally white but will change colour according to where it lies in wait for prey, so that a bright yellow specimen may be found in a buttercup flowerhead. The running crab spider *Tibellus oblongus*, recorded on The Plain, is quite different in having an elongated straw-coloured

Labyrinth Spider and typical sheet web Peter Creed

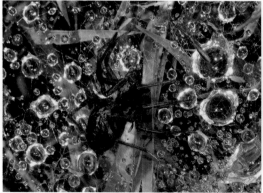

body which is extremely well camouflaged in its favoured habitat of dry grassland where it extends its legs along the grass stem to await its prey.

Spiders of woodland

Within woodland it is not just the living trees that provide habitats for spiders. Some spider species are saproxylic and therefore depend upon dead or decaying timber, both standing and fallen [see page 32]. In Brasenose Wood, the lace-web spider *Amaurobius similis* and the tube-web spiders *Segestria senoculata* and *Harpactea hombergi* have all been found underneath loose bark or on fallen timber — both typical microhabitats for these spiders. The latter two species have just six eyes (most British spiders have eight) and *S. senoculata* has a distinctive adder-like pattern on its abdomen. The lace-like web of *A. similis* has a slightly bluish tinge when freshly woven but can become rather untidy over time; the spider adds fresh silk to the existing web each night, leaving her previous efforts littered with the remains of past meals. *Tegenaria silvestris* has also been recorded in the woodland at Shotover; although the *Tegenaria* genus includes the so-called house spiders, *T. silvestris* is not found in houses but more usually under loose bark, logs and detritus. It is similar in appearance to the house spider *T. duellica* but its body length (six millimetres) is about half that of its domestic cousin.

Brasenose Wood is home to the nationally rare spider *Tuberta maerens*, which is listed in the Red Data Book for British spiders because it is estimated to exist in fewer than 15 post-1970 ten-kilometre squares. It favours cracks in the bark of mature trees, often oaks, where it spins a small fragile tunnel web. Work by Clive Hambler suggests that *T. maerens* prefers the warm dry conditions on the southern and western aspects of tree trunks in places where the trees are less dense, and may benefit from coppice rotation (Hambler, 1995; Evans and Hambler, 1995). A parasite of *T. maerens* is the wasp *Gnypetomorpha tubertae* which when found by Clive Hambler in Brasenose Wood in 1994 was a species new to science [see page 149].

Zygiella stroemi is a nationally scarce species, and also found on the trunks of mature trees in Brasenose Wood. As with its more common close relative *Z. x-notata* (found in the upper corners of window and door frames around buildings), the orb web spun by *Z. stroemi* is distinctive in having a small open sector in the upper part of the web which is free of spiral threads. Bisecting this open sector is a single thread of silk which leads to the spider's retreat, where it sits with its front legs on this signal line awaiting vibrations from a struggling insect caught in the web.

The running crab spiders *Philodromus praedatus* and *P. dispar* have both been collected from the understorey foliage of Brasenose Wood. Although they still have the crab-like appearance of the Thomisidae, their longer legs enable them to scuttle around rapidly. Two closely related orb-web spinners are also found among the low branches of trees in Brasenose Wood: *Araniella cucurbitina* and *A. opistographa,* both of which have a bright apple-green abdomen and spin small orb webs on the underside of suitably curved leaves.

On a warm day in late spring the woodland floor in Brasenose Wood may reveal the frantic activity of numerous spiders moving around

Segestria senoculata ©blickwinkel/Alamy Stock Photo

Zygiella stroemi ©blickwinkel/Alamy Stock Photo

A wolf spider *Pardosa* sp. carrying its egg sac Peter Creed

on sun-lit patches of leaf litter. These are wolf spiders of the genus *Pardosa* (Lycosidae) which do not spin a web to catch prey. Instead, they simply chase their prey down, appearing to be moving around in packs but in fact all hunting independently of each other. *Pardosa prativaga*, *P. pullata* and *P. saltans* have all been recorded in Brasenose Wood, with additional *Pardosa* species found in other woodland areas on the Hill. During late May and early June, *Pardosa* females are often seen running around with a small pale-coloured egg sac attached to the tip of their abdomen. After about three weeks the eggs hatch and the young spiderlings climb up onto their mother's back to be carried about for a few days before disembarking to fend for themselves.

Spiders of marshland

At Shotover, the marshy areas alongside the spring-fed streams that drain Johnson's Piece are not very extensive but do provide a permanent habitat for spiders which favour a moist environment. The long-jawed spiders of the Tetragnathidae family spin an orb web — often more horizontal than vertical — in damp marshy vegetation. In addition to having large conspicuous jaws, these spiders have an elongated abdomen with a silvery sheen and long slender legs. *Tetragnatha montana* and *T. extensa* have both been recorded in Long Marsh. *Pachygnatha clercki* and *P. degeeri*, two shorter-bodied members of the Tetragnathidae, are also associated with moist habitats at Shotover; they also have large jaws but only the juveniles are known to spin an orb web.

Some wolf spiders are associated with moist habitats; *Pirata hygrophilus* (the specific name

Spider silk

Spiders are well known for producing silken threads. While walking through Shotover, or indeed any countryside with trees and hedgerows, it is not uncommon for the threads of spider webs to be caught on one's face and hair. These threads are just one of a number of different types of silk spun by spiders and used in a great variety of ways:

- The most noticeable use of spider silk is in the construction of webs to catch prey. These may be complicated structures — as in the spiralled discs of an orb web — or a simpler loose framework of threads such as that spun by the Daddy-long-legs Spider *Pholcus phalangioides* and found in the corners of ceilings.
- Some spiders produce a cribellate silk which is woolly in texture and when combined with web silk makes a lace-like web — rather like a roughly-woven sheet of Velcro — that hooks onto the spines and hairs of ensnared insect prey.
- Once captured, prey is swathed in silk to immobilize it while the paralysing venom from the spider's bite takes effect. The spider can then feed without danger of counter-attack.
- All spiders produce egg sacs from their silk and this is probably the only use to which silk was put by primitive spiders, with the other applications evolving later.
- Many spiders lay down draglines of silk as safety lines and as a means of mapping their environment; sexually mature females may add pheromones to draglines to attract males.
- Silk is used in the construction of a retreat in which to shelter and may also be combined with small pieces of vegetation or soil granules to make the retreat more robust.
- Fine threads are spun for aerial dispersal by ballooning [see box, page 180].

Early-morning spider webs in Mary Sadler Field

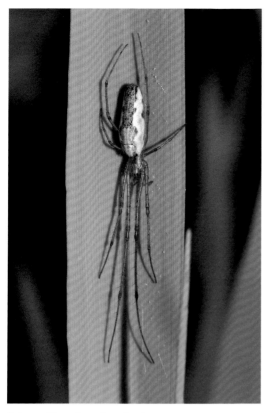

Tetragnatha extensa Peter Creed

meaning moisture-loving) and *P. latitans* have both been recorded in Johnson's Piece. They generally catch prey in the typical manner of wolf spiders but may also venture out onto small areas of still water to seize insects on or just beneath the surface. The large and distinctive orb-web spider *Larinioides cornutus*, also found in damp

Larinioides cornutus Peter Creed

habitats, spins a tough silken retreat camouflaged with seeds and plant material. Finally, although not strictly a wetland species, the uncommon *Floronia bucculenta*, one of the larger money spiders, has been recorded in Long Marsh. The female spider spins a horizontal sheet web in low vegetation and sits on the underside; if disturbed, it drops to the ground and the body colouration darkens rapidly, making it less conspicuous. Its normally pale colouring returns once the danger of predation has passed and it has returned to the web.

Harvestmen

Harvestmen (Opiliones) are often mistaken for spiders but are in fact a different order of Arachnida altogether, having only one apparent part to the body, two eyes (often located on a turret) and eight thin legs. There are 25 species in Britain, of which 15 have been recorded at Shotover. Most harvestmen have very long legs which arch over, suspending a small body above the ground at their centre. This enables freedom of movement when climbing among leaves and twigs to feed on a variety of small invertebrates. The name Opiliones derives from the Latin for shepherd and may refer to the custom in some countries, such as France, of shepherds standing on stilts high above the ground to more easily watch their flocks — rather like a harvestman with its body held high above its surroundings.

Of the species found at Shotover the majority are widespread nationally, and only two are moderately uncommon. *Oligolophus hanseni*, found in oak-tree foliage near The Sand Pit, has in fact been more commonly recorded on the east coast of Scotland, with only scattered records from the rest of Britain. A*nelasmocephalus cambridgei* — named after the Revd. Pickard-Cambridge [see page 180] — has been recorded in the acidic grassland at Shotover as well, even though it tends to prefer the calcareous regions of southern Britain.

Dicranopalpus ramosus, also found on oaks at The Sand Pit, is a harvestman easily recognized by its long pedipalps at the front of the head, which resemble a pair of tiny tuning forks. The species is relatively new to Britain, having been recorded for the first time only in 1957 near Bournemouth; however, over recent years it has spread rapidly and is now regarded as common. *D. ramosus* readily displays a behaviour that is

Dicranopalpus ramosus Peter Creed

common to all harvestmen, in that it continually uses its longest legs (the second pair) as sensory organs, in a similar way that other invertebrates use their antennae to gather information about their surroundings.

Arachnid conservation

The past 50 years have seen some spider species extending their distribution in Britain, perhaps through the effects of climate change. Very discrete populations in extreme southerly locations have now spread northwards, becoming increasingly common as warmer temperatures provide suitable environmental conditions. Conversely, more northern species may well experience changing conditions which are not suitable, forcing them out of their existing territories. Although outside the control of those managing habitats, such trends are an important influence and cannot be disregarded when considering conservation planning.

Of more concern for spiders and harvestmen is the loss of habitat as land is sought for both agricultural and urban development, and the general lack of consideration for these greatly overlooked invertebrates. Furthermore, even where valuable nature conservation sites are 'protected', management tends to favour the more obviously spectacular organisms, such as birds and butterflies. For example, coppicing in some ancient woodlands to encourage ground flora and associated butterflies is a practice of questionable value (Hambler and Speight, 1995). While coppicing may be beneficial to certain species, it can have a negative impact on those saproxylic organisms, including arachnids, that depend on naturally decaying timber which may be threatened during the coppicing process [see also page 30 and box, page 224].

Maintenance of a mosaic of habitats is critical to ensure the best conditions for arachnids. Even within a single ancient tree there will be a rich diversity of microhabitats, each of which provides appropriate conditions for individual spiders. As with other invertebrate groups the arachnids benefit more from work to conserve a wide range of habitat types than using limited resources to focus on the conservation of individual species.

Conservation for arachnids, therefore, poses many challenges. An underlying consideration is that their populations are dynamic and will remain so as long as environmental conditions continue to change. In particular, there needs to be a better appreciation of the intrinsic value of arachnid diversity, as well as their contribution to a balanced ecology.

Molluscs

Steve Gregory

The molluscs constitute a vast and diverse phylum of animals ranging from the highly intelligent octopus to the familiar slugs and snails in our gardens and allotments. A great variety of species can be found across Shotover Hill, most of which go largely unnoticed. All of Shotover's species of molluscs belong to the class Gastropoda ('stomach-foot') — muscular-footed animals with two tentacles and a shell (including the slugs [see box below]). Using their large muscular foot, lubricated by mucus, they glide effortlessly over most substrates. Characteristically, the head bears two pairs of tentacles which, in the absence of hearing and sight, are used for probing the world around them. Some 180 species of Gastropod occur in Britain and Ireland. Many have particular habitat requirements and struggle to survive in the modern intensively managed countryside, yet fortunately Shotover's unspoilt habitats provide an important refuge for many valuable and declining species.

White-lipped Snail Roger Wyatt

Shells of all shapes

Snails are well known for having a large coiled shell into which the animal may retreat but in some species it is considerably reduced. In extreme cases, the shell is a small calcified plate, usually covered by skin. We call these slugs. Thus there is no true biological distinction between a slug and a snail.

Snail shells vary in shape from the broad flattened disk of the Cellar Snail *Oxychilus cellarius* to the elongated spire of the Two-toothed Door Snail *Clausilia bidentata*. Between these two extremes is an even gradation of shapes, including the Garden Snail *Cornu aspersum* which is about

Cellar Snail Keith Lugg

as wide as it is tall. The Lake Limpet *Acroloxus lacustris*, recorded from the C.S. Lewis Community Nature Reserve, is unusual in having a conical but non-spiralled shell.

The shells of Door snails are also unusual in having a left-handed (sinistral) spiral; those of almost all other snails are right-handed (dextral) — that is, with the spiral pointing upwards, the opening is on the right when facing the observer. The rim of the opening is often reinforced by a thickened rib or lip. Some shells are covered with outgrowths; those of the Hairy Snail *Trochulus hispidus* are fine and hair-like, while the most ornate are found on the Prickly Snail *Acanthinula aculeata*.

Two-toothed Door Snail
Christian Owen

Moisture is an important factor in the distribution and activity of slugs and snails. Most species, but by no means all, frequent damp shady places. Although normally active only at night, many species may appear during the day after spells of rain. Some will climb high up among vegetation or even up tree trunks in their search for of food. In dry conditions many species become inactive until moisture returns.

Most molluscs feed on live or decaying vegetable matter, or graze on fungi, algae and lichens. Some will scavenge carrion and a few are active predators of earthworms. However, they all share the same way of feeding that is unique to molluscs, using a radula — a ribbon-like tongue with thousands of horny teeth — to scrape and rasp over food, pulling chunks into their mouth. Sometimes it is possible to see the trail of a species that has scraped clean a path through the algae on a damp wall. Large quantities of dead and decaying plant material are consumed by molluscs and their faeces are readily decomposed by soil bacteria and micro-fungi, thereby efficiently recycling nutrients essential for plant growth back into the soil.

There are many mammal and bird predators of molluscs, including Hedgehog, Badger and Song Thrush, and great quantities of slugs and snails are eaten. Also, a number of Shotover's

The ground beetle *Cychrus caraboides* with its modified mouthparts for reaching into snail shells Ivan Wright

beetle species, including ground-beetles and burying-beetles, are specialist snail predators. These beetles typically have a narrow head and elongated mandibles to reach the snail's juicy body inside its protective shell. To deter predators the tiny whorl snails (*Vertigo* spp.) have evolved protective folds, or 'teeth', just inside the shell entrance. The aptly named snail-killing flies (Sciomyzidae) produce larvae that are parasites of snails and 23 species of these flies — a third of the British fauna — have been recorded at Shotover, mostly in the marshy habitats.

Ancient deciduous woodland, unimproved grassland, undisturbed wetland and unpolluted water bodies each support a distinct and specific suite of mollusc species, often restricted to their habitat by poor powers of dispersal. Thus, the presence, or absence, of such species can inform the surveyor not only about the current quality of the habitat but also about its stability over very many years. A good example in Brasenose Wood is the Ash-black Slug *Limax cinereoniger*, an ancient woodland specialist. In contrast, other slugs and snails have readily taken to synanthropic habitats — those created through human activity — such as gardens, churchyards and waste ground. These species are typically more mobile and disperse readily, including non-native species unintentionally introduced from elsewhere. A high diversity of such species can suggest that a site may have been subjected to repeated human disturbance, and is likely to include the Worm Slug *Boettgerilla pallens*. For instance, this species was found at the C.S. Lewis Community Nature Reserve which formerly comprised a quarry, clay pit and brickworks.

Most slugs and snails are hermaphrodites, with both male and female sexual organs. Although such an individual can reproduce parthenogenetically, a mating pair allows gene exchange and is therefore more advantageous for reproduction of the species. Many species have elaborate mating rituals. Some snails produce a 'love dart', a solid calcified spike, and thrust it into the partner's body to stimulate mating. Leopard Slugs *L. maximus* will circle each other for hours prior to climbing a tree or wall and will then descend on a long string of mucus while mating. As they descend, the male organs of either slug can become irretrievably entangled and may be lost as they separate, leaving at least one of the pair entirely female.

A mating pair of Budapest Keeled Slug *Tandonia budapestensis* Christian Owen

History of mollusc recording at Shotover

The earliest record of a snail species at Shotover was made in 1853 by J.F. Whiteaves of the Ashmolean Society, who recorded Kentish Snail *Monacha cantiana* as a species new to Oxfordshire (Whiteaves, 1857). Although Whiteaves and local experts such as G.D.H. Carpenter and H.C. Napier were known to be active on the Hill, only four species were recorded during the 19th century. As with other taxa at that time, unless something 'unusual' was found, Shotover's records were simply referred to as "*in the vicinity of Oxford*" (Grensted, 1926).

Nevertheless, on this basis we can at least be confident that no great rarities were discovered.

It was not until the late 20th century that serious recording of Shotover's mollusc fauna began. Between 1971 and 1982 the ponds at the C.S. Lewis Community Nature Reserve were visited by the Ashmolean Natural History Society and staff from the Oxford University Museum of Natural History. Then in the 1980s, during their comprehensive survey of Oxfordshire, Pond Action (now the Freshwater Habitats Trust) systematically sampled all the ponds across the Hill under the leadership of Jeremy Biggs. These surveys recorded 12 species of water snail, and represent a valuable baseline record of the aquatic fauna of Shotover's numerous small water bodies.

The terrestrial slugs and snails of the SSSI were surveyed by Arthur Spriggs in 1990. Further work undertaken later in the same decade by John Campbell and Steve Gregory (for the Oxfordshire Biological Record Centre, the precursor to the Thames Valley Environmental Records Centre) extended surveying to additional parts of the Hill, including the C.S. Lewis Community Nature Reserve. This flurry of activity added over 20 species to the all-time list for Shotover Hill.

Since 2000 most of the species records have resulted from invertebrate surveys and research projects initiated by Shotover Wildlife. Of particular note was the discovery of the Ash-

Discovering wetland snails on a spring-line flush in Johnson's Piece Eleanor Hawtree

Specialist conchologists visited Shotover in 2006 to assist with the surveying and identification of molluscs.

black Slug, found in a pitfall trap in Brasenose Wood in 2006. In the same year Shotover Wildlife hosted a visit by members of the Conchological Society of Great Britain and Ireland, adding three further species including the tiny Prickly Snail *Acanthinula aculeata*.

Molluscs at Shotover

Shotover Hill lies within the Midvale Ridge diversity hot-spot for terrestrial molluscs (Gregory, 2002). However, snails require lime for shell formation and Shotover's predominantly non-calcareous geology somewhat limits the snail fauna. Nonetheless, 38 terrestrial species (including 12 slugs) have been recorded — 42 per cent of Oxfordshire's mollusc fauna (Gregory and Campbell, 2000). Water snails are better represented with 17 species, half the county fauna (Crowley and Campbell, 1984), reflecting the diversity of temporary and permenant water bodies.

Of these 55 species, the majority are pulmonates, using an internal 'lung' cavity to breathe air. Surprisingly, this includes 14 species of water snail, which return to the water's surface to breathe, and all of which were once land snails now having reverted to an aquatic existence. Just three of Shotover's species, all aquatic, belong to the Prosobranchia (or operculates), which breathe in a more primitive way using gills. These are readily distinguished by a horny plate (operculum) which seals the mouth of the shell when the body is retracted.

Most snails are small, between two and five millimetres long, living unobtrusively among leaf litter or pond weed, and are rarely seen unless searched for. However, with shells up to 40 millimetres across, the familiar Garden Snail *Cornu aspersum* and the aquatic Great Ram's-horn *Planorbarius corneus* are the giants of Shotover's snails. For slugs, 40 millimetres is an average length but the Ash-black Slug [see page 192] — typically 200 millimetres long — can reach an astonishing 300 millimetres when fully extended.

It is surprising that no bivalve molluscs have been recorded on the Hill. They are easily overlooked since some of the common pea mussels (*Pisidium* spp.) are only a few millimetres across. Surely it is only a matter of time before one is found, which would add not only a new species to Shotover but an entire class of animal (Bivalvia), equivalent to recording the first bird (Aves) or mammal (Mammalia).

Mollusc habitats at Shotover

The varied geology and hydrology of Shotover result in an intricate mosaic of semi-natural habitats, including deciduous woodland, acidic grassland, marshland and ponds. The presence of houses and farmyards also adds contrasting, though equally interesting, synanthropic habitats. This habitat diversity is reflected in the diversity of recorded species.

Aquatic and marshland habitats

Shotover's underlying geology ensures a plentiful supply of clean water from the springs that occur on all sides of the Hill [see page 20], and consequently wetland habitats and their associated species are well represented. Although the Wandering Snail *Radix balthica* can, and does, turn up anywhere, most other species have distinct habitat preferences. Truly aquatic water snails are intolerant of drying out and are only found in permanent water bodies, such as the ponds of the C.S. Lewis Community Nature Reserve and Shotover Estate. The relative purity of the water encourages plenty of aquatic vegetation which supports a large number of species. Two widely recorded examples are the Great Pond Snail *Lymnaea stagnalis* and Whirlpool Ram's-horn *Anisus vortex*.

In contrast, other water snails thrive on seasonal drought; like many other freshwater invertebrates, they rely on natural fluctuations in wetness to avoid the truly aquatic competition. The Marsh Pond Snail *L. palustris* and Button Ram's-horn *A. leucostoma* can survive months of drought, buried within mud in suspended animation (aestivation) waiting for

Great Pond Snail Bj.schoenmakers

the water to return. Amphibious species also inhabit the marshes that develop just below the spring line — Long Marsh, for example, on the south side of the Hill — where the fauna also includes 'terrestrial' species, such as Marsh Slug *Deroceras laeve*.

Woodland habitats

The damp deciduous woodlands at Shotover support a great diversity of slug and snail species. Many inhabit deep undisturbed accumulations of leaf litter, and the numerous species of tiny brown snails, such as Prickly Snail, can prove very elusive. Dead wood lying on the ground provides shelter for larger species, including Ash-black Slug, a specialist fungus feeder that is very rare in Oxfordshire beyond the well-wooded Chiltern Hills. Many woodland species will climb trees in damp weather, including the aptly named Tree Slug *Lehmannia marginata*.

Grassland habitats

Shotover's grasslands provide an interesting mix of taller grasses with contrasting areas of turf kept short by Rabbit grazing and the passage of visitors' feet. Taller grassland, such as on The Plain, can support ubiquitous species also found in large gardens. Even quite large snails, such as Kentish Snail and White-lipped Snail *Cepaea hortensis* [see page 187], can often be found high up among rank vegetation. Other, less conspicuous species, including Hedgehog Slug *Arion intermedius*, inhabit the ground below, where they find shelter in leaf litter or moss, beneath stones, or within soil crevices.

At first glance the exposed short-turf areas of Sand Pit Field and Horseshoe Field seem an inhospitable place for slugs or snails. Certainly they support fewer species but careful searching among grass roots is likely to reveal a specialist suite of tiny ground-dwelling snails such as Common Whorl Snail *Vertigo pygmaea* and Moss Chrysalis Snail *Pupilla muscorum*. Interestingly, both these species normally prefer lime-rich soils, indicating that the thin stratum of Portland Limestone at the upper spring line [see page 11] has sufficient influence to support these species.

Human habitation

To the consternation of many, some slugs and snails thrive on living vegetation in gardens and allotments, though only a few large, potentially troublesome species are the real culprits, such as Netted Field Slug *D. reticulatum*. Synanthropic habitats including gardens, farmyards and waste ground can, however, support a surprisingly large number of more benign species. Log piles, heaps of rubble, mossy walls, compost heaps and even lawns are all favoured places. Many species only have simple habitat requirements and occur widely across the Hill, including gardens; others are strongly synanthropic and are rarely found far from habitation.

Most synanthropic molluscs are not native to Britain and have been introduced unintentionally over millennia, beginning with Mesolithic traders from the Mediterranean and continuing through Roman and Medieval times into the present day. Indeed, about one in five

Hedgehog Slug Christian Owen

A wall of locally quarried limestone providing ideal habitat for molluscs

species of mollusc currently resident in Britain has been introduced. Some ancient arrivals, such as Garden Snail, are very familiar around habitation; even the Kentish Snail is now quite common although not recorded in Oxfordshire (at Shotover) until Victorian times (Gregory, 2000). On the other hand, Worm Slug, recorded at the C.S. Lewis Community Nature Reserve, was unknown in Oxfordshire until the 1990s. This species and other recently introduced slugs and snails are spreading rapidly across Britain, probably via plant nurseries and garden centres.

The future for molluscs at Shotover

Victorian shell collectors were fascinated by the wide range of forms and colours exhibited by land and water snails, and in the 19th century these amateur naturalists accumulated much information relating to the distribution and abundance of snail species around Oxford city. Since then, urban expansion and road building have encroached on habitats, and some species have shown regional decline (Gregory, 2000). The uncommon Large Chrysalis Snail *Abida secale*, for example, could be found at Headington Quarry until the 1930s, and a number of species that were once widespread, such as Desmoulin's Whorl Snail *V. moulinsiana* which was brought to public attention during the building of the Newbury bypass, are now among Oxfordshire's rarest and most vulnerable molluscs.

Around Shotover, land drainage, tree planting, farming, housing and road building

Ash-black Slug is a woodland species in decline
Armand Turpel

have all reduced the natural habitat for molluscs but, fortunately, it appears that no species has been lost since records began in the 1850s. However, earlier records, were they available, would probably reveal a different story.

Many molluscs associated with Shotover's semi-natural habitats, such as deciduous woodland, acidic grassland and undisturbed wetland, are poor dispersers and can therefore become genetically isolated. Also, for reasons not always fully understood, these species struggle to survive in alternative habitats, such as plantation woodlands, fertilized grasslands and nitrate-rich water bodies. Studies of Ash-black Slug suggest that many populations in Britain are now inbred, which does not bode well for the long-term survival of this declining species. Many other molluscs are undoubtedly in a similar position, not only because of slow dispersal but also as populations are hemmed in by an inhospitable surrounding countryside.

In contrast, many synanthropic slugs and snails have spread far beyond their natural ranges and tend to thrive in habitats created or disturbed by human activity. The close proximity of domestic gardens to the SSSI gives these species the opportunity to spread into those parts of the Hill designated for nature conservation and, worse, the fly-tipping of garden refuse can introduce species from much further afield. The danger is that those species with synanthropic tendencies will increase in abundance at the expense of species with greater conservation value. Nevertheless, if managed sympathetically, Shotover will continue to provide a safe long-term refuge for the slugs and snails associated with its semi-natural habitats.

Large Chrysalis Snail is actually only six millimetres long Steve Gregory

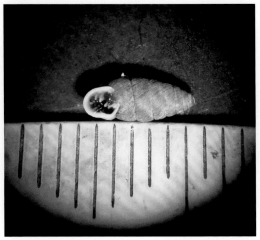

Linda Losito

Throughout history, reptiles and amphibians have often been regarded as repulsive animals to be feared and eradicated. Such revulsion is mostly based on a lack of understanding and on the way these creatures have been portrayed in myths and legends, not least on their misplaced reputation for cunning and malevolence. In the Bible, for instance, it is a serpent — "*more crafty than any other beasts of the field*" — which persuades Eve to eat the forbidden fruit (Genesis 3.1–6). Even the renowned botanist Carolus Linnaeus was not at all fond of reptiles and amphibians: he describes them as "*worst and hideous animals*" (translated from Linnaeus, 1758). Snakes in particular are commonly vilified, no doubt partly because some species are venomous. Paradoxically, they are also associated with healing, a link that can be traced back more than two millennia — not just to the cult of the Greek god of medicine Asclepius, whose staff with an entwined snake is still recognized as a symbol of the medical profession, but also to the Bible itself, where Moses makes a bronze serpent and puts it on a pole as a cure for poisonous snakebites (Numbers 21.4–9).

Of the seven native reptiles in Britain, three are confirmed residents at Shotover: Grass Snake *Natrix natrix*, Common Lizard *Zootoca*

Adult and juvenile Common Lizards in Mary Sadler Field, 2017

A serpent dichotomy
Drawing by Eleanor Hawtree

The snake is often feared and loathed and yet has been a symbol of healing for millennia.

vivipara and Slow Worm *Anguis fragilis*. The Adder *Vipera berus* has not been positively identified on the Hill for decades and there is no suitable habitat for the Sand Lizard *Lacerta agilis* or Smooth Snake *Coronella austriaca*. In 2017, the subspecies of Grass Snake, *N. natrix* ssp. *helvetica*, was promoted to species status and named Barred Grass Snake *N. helvetica*. However, observations since this announcement, and earlier photographic records, suggest that the new species is not at Shotover. Five of the six native British amphibians have been recorded at Shotover: Common Toad *Bufo bufo*, Common Frog *Rana temporaria*, Smooth or Common Newt *Lissotriton vulgaris*, Palmate Newt *L. helveticus* and Great Crested Newt *Triturus cristatus*. The Natterjack Toad *Epidalea calamita* is rarely found in Britain nowadays. All of these reptiles and amphibians have declined significantly in Oxfordshire, as in the rest of Britain, and recent recording at Shotover reflects a similar trend for most of these species.

Reptiles

The areas of sparse vegetation and warm sandy soil on the Hill are ideal for snake and lizard territories but these timid creatures are rarely seen, even in prime habitat and at times of relative abundance. In recent times, sightings by chance have been rare at Shotover, yet targeted monitoring by experienced surveyors has often revealed several individuals in quite a small area.

Reptiles are cold-blooded and rely on external warmth for all their functions. The few European species that are adapted to colder latitudes can thrive in Britain when habitat and circumstances are suitable. Warmth is obtained either directly from the sun by basking on a warm surface or from the air when the ambient temperature is sufficiently raised. When autumn comes and temperatures fall, reptiles become sluggish and are unable to venture out for food (even their eyesight is poorer in colder weather) and so they must hibernate in suitable shelters — hibernacula. Old animal burrows, cavities within rotting tree stumps, or deep gaps in living root systems can all serve as hibernacula as long as they remain dry and frost-free throughout the winter. Some individuals return to the same place to hibernate each year. Safe overwintering sites are essential for reptile survival and disturbance during hibernation can be fatal.

Grass Snake

The Grass Snake has been recorded regularly at Shotover since 1970 across a wide range of habitats and has probably thrived on the Hill for centuries. These graceful creatures grow up to 150 centimetres in length and have olive-green skin with a striking creamy-yellow 'collar' immediately behind the head and dark marks down each side of the body. Grass Snakes spend much of their time in damper places and usually feed on frogs and other amphibians; they are also

A magnificent Grass Snake in Mary Sadler Field, 2017

Reptile conservation

Since 2001, Shotover Wildlife has been investigating the distribution of reptiles at Shotover and improving their habitat in the SSSI.

To facilitate monitoring, large logs and sheets of metal and rubber are positioned in secluded sunlit places that provide shelter and warm basking opportunities for these heat-seeking animals. They habitually return to such places, making successful observations more likely and monitoring work more efficient. Grass Snake records can also be supplemented by finding their sloughed skins.

Practical conservation work to enhance habitat for reptiles has focused on developing structural diversity in the heath and surrounding low vegetation, supplemented by large log-pile refuges. The refuges are safe places where reptiles can retreat from the threat of predation and bask in the sun or take shelter when the weather is unsuitable for activity.

Another conservation measure is mowing to create a network of corridors, oriented to produce a warm microclimate along sunlit edges. This has been maintained by supplying the tractor driver (Oxford City Council) with an annual mowing plan, supplemented by more detailed work by Shotover Wildlife using a powered scythe mower. Such corridors have been particularly successful for Common Lizards in Mary Sadler Field and for Grass Snakes in the wetter areas, such as the marshy flush at The Larches.

The sloughed skin of a Grass Snake on Horspath Common

Building a log refuge for reptiles and other animals

good swimmers and will eat small fish. The Grass Snake is the only British reptile that does not give birth to live young, so it must find a warm place to lay its eggs. At Shotover, this is most likely to be in a large pile of grass cuttings, where the warmth of the decomposing vegetation helps to incubate the soft white eggs.

In recent years the number of Grass Snakes seen at Shotover has dropped dramatically. Until about 2005, on a sunny summer day, a search for a basking snake in one of their regular haunts in Mary Sadler Field was almost certain to be successful. Indeed, in 2002, a single day of intensive surveying recorded 15 individuals. However, since about 2008 they have become a much less frequent sight anywhere at Shotover. A number of factors are likely causes, including the greater number of Pheasants across the Hill (released from breeding pens on the north side from 2007 to 2014), and a management regime in the SSSI that, for a number of years, overlooked the needs of reptiles.

Common Lizard

Oxfordshire supports several localized colonies of Common Lizard but the future of this small and vulnerable reptile is by no means secure. These greyish-brown lizards, about 15 centimetres long, have markings that blend well with their natural surroundings, yet they can be seen — by a careful observer — basking in the sun on warm logs or among short dense vegetation, often shuttling between patches of sun and shade, a common habit of theirs.

Common Lizards have various predators, including toads, mustelids (such as Stoats and Weasels), birds of prey and game birds, but are rarely predated by Grass Snakes with which they will share habitat, as indeed they do at Shotover. When severely threatened, as a last resort a Common Lizard can discard its tail and make an escape while the predator focuses on the still-wriggling tail. The tail does not have to be grabbed by the predator but is self-severed

A tail-less Common Lizard at Shotover having suffered the threat of predation

(autotomy) at specifically modified vertebrae; it can also grow back but only as cartilage.

Common Lizards give birth to live young, hence their alternative name — Viviparous Lizard. The juveniles are fully formed miniatures of their parents, apart from being almost black. They receive no parental care and leave the nest only one or two days after birth to hunt and fend for themselves. Their main sources of food are spiders and small insects, supplemented by earthworms and slugs. They have excellent eyesight and a keen sense of smell for tracking their prey. However, because their energy is derived externally (from the sun's warmth) they are not so reliant on food as a source of calories which means they only need to feed occasionally — in contrast to shrews, for example, that need to feed constantly to stay alive.

Common Lizards have been recorded at Shotover in most years from 1994 to the present. The largest number of individuals recorded on the Hill in a single day was 14 in Mary Sadler Field in 2002. For the next few years records were scarce, mainly on account of inappropriate official prescriptive management [see pages 235–6] resulting in significant habitat loss in the core breeding site of the SSSI. However, since 2015, work by Shotover Wildlife to mitigate the situation has resulted in more frequent sightings — including juvenile lizards in the spring of 2017.

In addition to the SSSI and secluded field margins on the Hill, it is likely that lizards also use the larger surrounding gardens, yet the only evidence for this is unconfirmed reports. Perhaps more so than the Grass Snakes at Shotover, Common Lizards are vulnerable to predation by the game birds that are released for shooting, and those that go on to breed ferally. Common Lizards are also especially vulnerable to management activities that neglect the habitat requirements of reptiles, especially as they depend upon — and seldom range far from — places of refuge. Unfortunately, critical refugia can go unrecognized or underappreciated as such and be cleared away.

Slow Worm

Over the years, Slow Worms have been seen throughout Shotover and the surrounding area, including the C.S. Lewis Community Nature Reserve, the Shotover Estate, many private gardens, and the railway cutting and churchyard at Horspath. Though superficially resembling a native snake (Calubridae), the Slow Worm is taxonomically closer to lizards (Lacertidae) but has no legs and is in the family Anguidae. These slender creatures, which can be up to 50 centimetres long, have a smooth, metallic brown

A Slow Worm camouflaged against Heather stems on Horspath Common

Looking like a snake and closely related to lizards, these graceful reptiles are placed in a separate taxonomic family — Anguidae.

sheen and mainly eat soft-bodied prey such as earthworms and slugs. In late summer, the females give birth to up to 20 live young, each enclosed within a thin membrane which ruptures shortly after birth. They are known to breed in the nature reserves as well as in gardens around the Hill, in compost, piles of dead leaves and old underground shelters.

Slow Worms bask for warmth on stones or warm vegetation; occasionally a mass of tightly entwined bodies have been found under sun-warmed pieces of fallen fencing or corrugated iron. The sunlit slopes and varied microclimate of a disused railway cutting or embankment are especially attractive to these reptiles, although they tend to avoid habitats that are either very dry or permanently marshy.

While there are fewer dated records of Slow Worms at Shotover compared with Grass Snakes and Common Lizards, anecdotal reports have been frequent throughout the past two decades. Also, records are not so common within the Country Park as in other locations, perhaps because the south side of the Hill may be too dry and subjected to more disturbance; even sightings in the seasonal marshes and streams of the SSSI are rare. However, at The Larches, a period of specific reptile conservation and monitoring by Shotover Wildlife (2000–04) revealed frequent co-habitation with Grass Snakes. Also, in 2017 several Slow Worms were observed using the maturing Heather habitat on Horspath Common.

Adder

The Adder has a dark zig-zag mark along its top surface, as well as dark marks down each side, and is quite broad in the body. An adult Grass Snake is often similar in length but is slimmer, has its characteristic yellow collar and only has dark marks along each side of its body.

Adder populations have declined rapidly in Britain, and they may now be extinct in Oxfordshire. In the early 20th century Tucker (1939: p. 199) reported Adder to be locally common in a few areas of the county but absent everywhere else. Habitat loss has contributed to their overall decline, together with the reduced populations of small animals on which they feed. Given the general antipathy toward venomous snakes, persecution is probably a factor but perhaps no longer to the same extent now that the species is so scarce.

Perhaps one of the last Oxfordshire Adders, seen here basking at the Warburg reserve in 2006 Ivan Wright

The best anecdotal evidence of sightings of this handsome snake has been from local residents, albeit from an era when people were more familiar with the creatures of the countryside. Arthur Smith (*c*. 1925–2008) of

Arthur Smith walked regularly on Shotover thoughout his life; he was a water diviner, self-taught naturalist and remarkable source of local wildlife knowledge

Headington Quarry regularly watched the wildlife of the Hill throughout his life, and told many stories associated with local Adders. His firm view was that the last credible Adder sighting was in the 1960s just uphill from Westhill Farm, to the west of Gertie's Gap.

Over the past 20 years none of the many reported sightings of Adders at Shotover has been confirmed and no sloughed skin has been found, most likely because throughout this period there have been no Adders on the Hill.

Considering that in recent years more and more people carry a mobile phone with an inbuilt camera, that the Adder is a relatively sluggish snake, and that photographic evidence of one would rank among the most exciting finds at Shotover, it is telling that no such evidence has been forthcoming. Furthermore, since anecdotal sightings have all but ceased in recent years, there is all the more reason to conclude that the Adder is extinct on the Hill.

Amphibians

Every spring, Shotover participates in one of the great annual events in natural history, when amphibians converge on their breeding ponds to display and mate. On the Hill and in nearby gardens, the air can reverberate with the evocative croaking songs of frogs and toads.

Amphibians must have water in which to breed. Ponds were once considered an essential part of the rural landscape, especially for farm animals and horses in transit. However, through the 20th century the need for these semi-natural water bodies has diminished and their number has declined. Some have been drained and filled in; others have been lost through the natural process of succession, in which reeds and willows encroach and the pond gradually dries out. Even where a pond survives, it may only sustain minimal flora or fauna due to stagnation or toxic runoff from roads and agricultural chemicals.

At Shotover, although there is some water runoff from roads along the western boundary, the Hill benefits from having springs and seeps on all sides, which supply ponds and streams with water of high quality [see page 19]. The few wayside ponds at Shotover have limited wildlife value due to frequent disturbance by paddling dogs but otherwise amphibians have ample opportunities to find the wet habitats they need.

Common Frog

Common Frogs can be seen in any of the wetter areas across Shotover. They are beautifully camouflaged, their colour varying from brown to olive-green or yellow, often with a dark brown 'mask' across the eyes. In spring, the ponds fill with mating pairs. A receptive female will be clasped by a male ready to fertilize her eggs as they emerge. The fertilized eggs cling together in large clumps of spawn from which the tiny fish-like tadpoles will develop. Within a few weeks, they grow legs, lose their tails and emerge as froglets to spend most of their life on land.

Trees growing in the shallows of an old clay pit on the north side of the Hill

These tranquil seasonal ponds have no predatory fish and are therefore perfect habitat for amphibians.

Common Frog Richard Bartz

Common Toads are a frequent and welcome sight on conservation work days at Shotover Eleanor Hawtree

Adult frogs eat a variety of invertebrates including insects and slugs. Like reptiles, they are cold-blooded and have to hibernate during the winter. Unlike reptiles, frogs extract dissolved oxygen directly through their skin and so are able to hibernate in a protective underwater crevice or by partially burying themselves in mud at the bottom of a pond.

To date there have been no sightings of the Marsh Frog *Rana ridibunda* at Shotover. This large bright-green frog was introduced into Britain in 1935 and can spread rapidly along suitable watercourses and large marshes. It has not yet been recorded in Oxfordshire and it is not clear whether it could reach Shotover naturally and form a stable population.

Common Toad

The Common Toad is brown and warty, and will normally walk rather than hop, but its behaviour and diet are otherwise very similar to those of the Common Frog. Mating takes place in water but, unlike frogs, the eggs are produced in long strings which adhere to waterside plants. The tadpoles develop in the water but move onto dry land once they have matured. Compared with frogs, Common Toads inhabit drier places for most of the year; they cannot hibernate under water and usually spend the winter in sheltered crevices on land.

Although Common Toads have shown an alarming decline in Britain in recent years, at Shotover they seem to be widespread and thriving, breeding in the numerous small ponds and exploiting the variety of habitats for food.

During conservation work in almost any habitat on the Hill, Common Toads of all sizes are occasionally uncovered, especially in woodland, heathy ground and under Bracken, but are easily relocated to safety.

Newts

All three species of British newt have been found in the ponds at Shotover: Smooth Newt, Palmate Newt and Great Crested Newt. During the breeding season in spring, male newts develop special 'fighting' features — including strong colours — to compete for females, making the differences between species (and sexes) much more noticeable. Smooth Newt males are about 10 centimetres long and develop a temporary frilled crest along the back from neck to tail. The Palmate Newt, at nine centimetres long, is the smallest of the three, and perhaps the least impressive visually; it develops a bright pink belly stripe but the crest along the back is barely noticeable. In the breeding season, male Great Crested Newts are much more eye-catching, up to 16 centimetres long, with a well-defined spiky crest, an orange belly and a central blue or white streak on their blade-like tail. Individual Great Crested Newts can often be identified by their unique pattern of spots on the underside.

The three species of newt prefer different types of pond, which accounts for their different local distributions. The more common Smooth Newts can thrive in the smallest of garden ponds or even temporary pools that dry up in the summer. The other two species spend more of the year in water and need more permanent ponds or sluggish, vegetated streams. Palmate Newts prefer shallow, less nutrient-rich, acidic water, which explains their more restricted distribution. Adult Great Crested Newts occupy a range of habitats, including arable landscapes that may not be so suitable for other amphibians, leaving the water to live and feed among damp vegetation. Where newts are numerous, they can become the dominant amphibian predator in a pond. Consequently, they can reduce the numbers of other aquatic species, such as frogs and toads, by eating their tadpoles.

While Smooth Newts are relatively common and occur in many of Shotover's ponds, the distribution of the Palmate Newt within Oxfordshire is patchy and there are few recent records. They have been found in the ponds of the C.S. Lewis Community Nature Reserve, and in 2008 Jeremy Biggs of the Freshwater Habitats Trust recorded a male and female in an old shallow pond near the north-western boundary of Brasenose Wood. Great Crested Newts have protected status in Britain, making it illegal to disturb them without a licence, yet compared with the Palmate Newt they are relatively common, and are recorded throughout the county. Great Crested Newt and Smooth Newt have both been recorded in recent years in the small seasonal ponds of Slade Camp North and Brasenose Wood.

The future

Shotover's many spring-fed ponds, streams and wet flushes provide damp habitats of various sizes and different stages of maturity. As long as the majority remain free of pollution and major disturbance, they will continue to offer suitable all-round conditions for amphibians. By contrast, reptile populations are vulnerable to a great many threats; most species have declined sharply in recent years and could follow the Adder to local extinction.

In the countryside in general, the vital wildlife corridors that connect habitats for amphibians and reptiles are becoming fragmented, thereby hampering mobility, isolating populations and weakening genetic diversity; and reptiles are faced with the additional danger of predation by free-ranging game birds. Fortunately, at Shotover there has never been a long-established programme of breeding and releasing birds for game shooting.

However, in the years when birds were released on the Shotover Estate, from about 2007 to 2014, there was a conspicuous increase in the Pheasant population on the south side of the Hill and an expansion of feral breeding, which may well have impaired the breeding success of both Common Lizards and Grass Snakes.

A further problem for reptiles is that although the Common Lizard and Grass Snake are protected species under the planning regulations, in the public authority's conservation objectives and the citation published for the SSSI at Shotover [see the Appendix] there is no reference to these reptiles, and thus no imperative or strategy for protecting them. It is scarcely surprising, therefore, that the conservation of these largely unseen animals has not been given the priority it deserves.

Amphibians and reptiles benefit considerably from the sizeable areas of suitable habitat at Shotover, not only in the heathland and marshes but also in the meadows, streams and domestic gardens around the periphery of the Hill. The diversity of habitats and food resources in these places is ideal as long as the hibernacula and ponds remain undisturbed at the critical times of the year for breeding and hibernation. In the absence of any effective official protection for amphibians and reptiles within the SSSI itself, we must hope that the overall quality, stability and relative tranquillity of their habitats on the Hill will suffice to ensure the survival of its amphibian and reptilian residents.

The old newt pond in Brasenose Wood

Birds

Antonia Whitehead

Shotover provides a great deal of suitable territory for birds. From early spring, the residents are noisily marking their territories in preparation for breeding; later, they are joined by the migrants, and Shotover is alive with the songs of warblers and other summer visitors. In autumn, foraging parties — often of mixed species — may be seen, enjoying the cornucopia of fruit and berries, while migrating birds also drop by to roost and to feed for their continuing journey. Then the resident birds are joined by winter visitors, notably thrushes and finches, which spend the summer in the Arctic or northern Europe before overwintering in Britain, where they can congregate in substantial numbers and sizeable flocks.

Essentially, birds' needs are straightforward — the availability of food and water, together with safe places to roost and, during the breeding season, to nest. However, each species has its own dietary and nesting requirements, and some of these are quite restrictive. Shotover's diversity of habitat is a distinct advantage for birds. There is the old coppiced woodland of Brasenose Wood, successional woodland in the Country Park, ancient trees and dead timber providing both insect food and nest holes, hedges with fruit and berries, and open areas of acidic grassland and heath. On the lower slopes, there is mixed farmland and the parkland of the Shotover Estate. Water is present in the seeps and streams, together with the open water of the Shotover Estate and other old ponds around the Hill. The

farms and villages surrounding the Hill are also important. The buildings provide nesting opportunities for some birds, and many of the gardens are managed with wildlife in mind. Such gardens can be particularly beneficial in supporting birds through the winter with fruiting shrubs, winter-flowering plants and, indeed, garden feeding stations.

A major historical survey was undertaken in preparation for the writing of *The Birds of Shotover* (Whitehead *et al.*, 2003) and this now serves as a basis for comparing over 100 years of past observations with more recent data. The early sources are Aplin (1889), the reports of the Oxford Ornithological Society (OOS) from 1924 (which covered incidental observations from 1915), and Brucker *et al.* (1992). Under the auspices of the British Trust for Ornithology (BTO), a systematic census was undertaken from 1979 to 2002 to record common breeding birds in Brasenose Wood. Most of these data were collected by David Steel and, thanks to Roy Overall (OOS), the information was made available for a corresponding survey at Wytham Wood (Overall, 1988; Gosler, 1990), thus allowing a comparison between these two woods on the outskirts of Oxford. Much of the early data were collected by interested individuals, most notably by Mike Wilson who from 1980 to 2005 made systematic surveys twice a month covering the majority of the Hill. Additional data were provided by Stuart Mabbutt from 1979 and John Tomlinson from 1998.

Bird surveyors on Shotover Wildlife's West Route 'point' survey

Since 2003 data collection has continued in various ways. For rarer birds, local bird watchers are encouraged to provide records, and the Oxford Ornithological Society also shares relevant information. For more common birds, systematic surveys by Shotover Wildlife allow an estimate of numbers and trends. Since 2001, monthly point surveys have been undertaken in the SSSI; 20 points are visited for 10 minutes each and all birds identified within a 50-metre radius are noted. These point surveys are complemented by two walk-through surveys, one in Brasenose Wood and the surrounding area, the other on the east of the Hill (taking in part of the Shotover Estate and The Lake) and by systematic observations from a garden on the east side of the Hill. The regular surveys provide the best evidence for trends in the numbers of common species despite potential sources of systematic bias; understandably, surveyors participating over the years may have different skill levels and all regular observers improve their skills over time.

In all, 157 species of bird have been recorded at Shotover [see page 216]. From 2000 to 2018 the total was 125, of which 116 species were using habitat resources at the ground rather than just flying over. It is also important to establish whether birds are breeding on the Hill. Sometimes unambiguous evidence is found, such as an adult carrying food to a nest, but more often there are indications only of possible breeding, the most frequent being of a male holding territory, generally by song. Of the 116 birds recorded in terrestrial habitats since 2000, 61 species showed some evidence of breeding.

Clearly, Shotover does not exist in isolation and many of the changes in bird numbers are part of a more general picture at a national or even international level [see also page 214]. Transient effects, perhaps related to a particularly severe winter or a poor breeding season, are essentially insignificant but for some species there are marked longer-term trends. At a national level, substantial data exist concerning changes in bird numbers. The *Bird Atlas 2007–11* (Balmer *et al.*, 2013) — which includes data from Shotover — looks at changes occurring over 20 years in Britain and Ireland. The BTO's *Breeding Bird Survey 2012* (Risely *et al.*, 2013) gives trends in numbers of common breeding birds, suggesting which birds are doing well and which are in decline. For the latter, a 'red-listed' status indicates serious concern about decreasing numbers and 'amber-listed' indicates a species of moderate concern.

The birds
Water birds

Most water birds require something more substantial than seeps and streams. While there are no major bodies of water at Shotover, there are several ponds and smaller areas of water, including a large pond — known simply as The Lake or Canal — which extends for 300 metres to the east of Shotover House. Canada Geese *Branta canadensis*, Mallards *Anas platyrhynchos*, Coots *Fulica atra* and Moorhens *Gallinula chloropus* — all of which are known to breed on the Hill — can be seen on the water, while Grey Herons *Ardea cinerea* and Cormorants *Phalacrocorax carbo* visit to fish. In harsh winter conditions, The Lake can freeze over.

During the initial period of systematic surveying at The Lake (2001–05) the annual diversity of water birds was around 12 species. Black-headed Gulls *Chroicocephalus ridibundus* roosted close by, and there was always a chance of seeing something more unusual, such as Gadwall *Anas strepera*, Pochard *Aythya ferina* or Goosander *Mergus merganser*. However, since 2005 there have been fewer birds on the water, with still fewer breeding — in 2013 the only breeding success noted was a single Coot chick. Species richness has also declined markedly [see graph], with Wigeon *Anas penelope*, Pochard and Goosander not seen since 2005, 2007 and 2011 respectively, and a steady reduction in the observations of Tufted Duck *Aythya fuligula* and Little Grebe *Tachybaptus ruficollis* [see graph].

Indeed, this may be a longer-term trend. Huge winter flocks of Mallards were observed at The Lake in the 1970s and 1980s, with 350 at one time late in 1983; more recently, numbers have rarely gone into double figures. Canada

Geese reached their maximum around the turn of the last century but have declined since. While it is possible that habitat at The Lake has become less favourable, it has to be remembered that Oxfordshire has only recently become well provided with areas of open water. In the early 20th century *"the only permanent sheet of water of any size"* in Oxfordshire was the lake at Blenheim Palace (Jourdain, 1926: p. 129). In contrast, the development of the Otmoor reserve since 1997 and the conversion of numerous gravel pits into permanent lakes have provided excellent wetland habitat in the region and have greatly increased the choice for water birds. A further possible cause of local decline is predation by American Mink, particularly of the common birds such as Mallard, Coot and Moorhen that

Graph showing the decline in species richness of water birds at The Lake, 2002–16

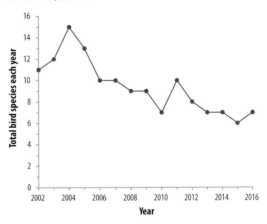

Graph showing the decline and last sightings of Tufted Duck, Little Grebe, Pochard and Goosander

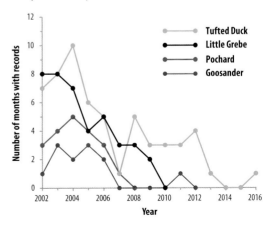

Gadwall Roger Wyatt

breed on the edges of smaller ponds. Although Mink do occur along the rivers of Oxfordshire, it cannot be assumed that they frequent the ponds of Shotover, let alone that they are responsible for the small numbers of chicks seen in recent years.

Lesser Black-backed *Larus fuscus* and Herring Gulls *L. argentatus* are not usually seen at The Lake but are observed passing over the Hill and occasionally feeding on the fields or circling to catch flying insects. Such sightings have been much more common in recent years; there are now large roosts in the neighbourhood and both these species have been breeding on roofs at the Cowley industrial complex close to the Hill. While this may seem a long way from their natural coastal habitat, it is now common for these large gulls to live in cities.

The handsome Kingfisher *Alcedo atthis* has been recorded at the larger ponds on the north side of Shotover. Most of the early sightings are from The Lake on the Shotover Estate, where there were signs of breeding in 1996; more recently, most records are from the C.S. Lewis Community Nature Reserve.

Apart from the occasional bird flying through, waders are rare at Shotover. There was an impressive flock of 500 Lapwings *Vanellus vanellus* feeding on the fields near Home Farm in December 1984, and 19 within a mixed flock, largely of Jackdaws *Corvus monedula*, in the fields west of Horspath in December 2009. This is a red-listed species and breeding numbers have suffered a substantial decline nationally, although a pair bred successfully near Monk's Farm in 1999. Winter-visiting Golden Plovers *Pluvialis apricaria* fly over Shotover fairly regularly but are seldom seen on the ground. Woodcocks *Scolopax rusticola* are increasingly infrequent winter visitors but,

being a crepuscular species, are quite likely to be overlooked; they have been noted at dusk in Brasenose Wood and Monk's Farm in particular.

Raptors

The most noticeable raptor now at Shotover is the Red Kite *Milvus milvus* and yet until recently it was a real rarity. Reintroduced into the Chilterns in 1989, Red Kites have successfully established themselves and spread outwards. They were first seen over Shotover in 1999, have bred there since 2003 and are now numerous on the Hill. Red Kites are carrion eaters and the Shotover area provides good feeding opportunities all year round. Often two or three birds will be seen together but larger groups can sometimes occur, with 10 at Bullingdon Field following the hay cut in 2003 and 16 over Horspath village early in 2013. While Red Kites have moved north-westward into the region, Buzzards *Buteo buteo* have moved eastward from their stronghold in

Red Kite has bred at Shotover since 2003 Roger Wyatt

Graph showing the upward trend in Red Kite and Buzzard from three systematic surveys, 2002–16

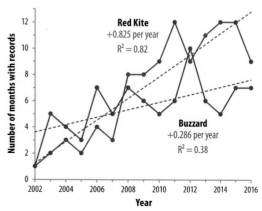

Woodcock J.J. Harrison

west Oxfordshire and, although an uncommon sight on the Hill before 1990, two or three pairs probably now nest there. Two other raptors that breed at Shotover are Sparrowhawks *Accipiter nisus* — small in size and rapid in flight, they feed mainly on small birds — and Kestrels *Falco tinnunculus*, which may be seen hovering above the field margins and road verges, seeking small mammals.

Fourteen years of continuous monthly data from three of Shotover Wildlife's systematic bird surveys give an indication of the population trends for the four breeding raptor species on the Hill [see graphs below]. The proxy for these trends is the number of months in each year that the species were observed in the upper half of the SSSI or in part of the Shotover Estate. The data show that Buzzards increased more or less steadily from 2002 to 2008 but since then may have reached a maximum, and that

the activity of Red Kites continues to increase. For Sparrowhawks and Kestrels, activity on the Hill seems to have been fairly stable until 2008 but since then Kestrels have been seen much less frequently, and then mostly by casual observation. Sparrowhawks, however, still breed regularly on Horspath Common.

Other raptors are occasionally seen at Shotover, most commonly the small summer-visiting Hobby *F. subbuteo* hunting the flocks of hirundine birds that form much of its diet. Hobbies do not nest at Shotover and it is likely that they breed in the vicinity of Otmoor.

Fluctuating raptor populations

Raptors have suffered centuries of persecution, their numbers reduced or even eliminated where their predatory nature has been thought to conflict with human activity. Remaining populations dropped sharply in the middle of the last century with the widespread introduction of organochlorine pesticides. These persistent chemicals accumulate in the bodies of predators, and raptors — which are high up the animal food chain — were particularly affected and suffered catastrophic decline. Once these pesticides were withdrawn (and with persecution no longer a great problem in southern Britain) populations of these birds recovered. The only common raptor not doing well nationally is the amber-listed Kestrel, with a 32 per cent drop in abundance between 1995 and 2010 (Balmer *et al.*, 2013); competition from Buzzards or a decline in small mammals may be the principal causes. As the Shotover data reveal a similar decline in Kestrel numbers, perhaps this species is indeed losing out to the greater population of Buzzards. Yet with the number of Red Kites on the Hill continuing to grow, further changes in the populations of these competing predators are difficult to predict.

Kestrel Roger Wyatt

Unlike other raptors, the Sparrowhawk will also hunt in small gardens for live prey Roger Wyatt

Graph showing the downward trend in Sparrowhawk and Kestel from three systematic surveys, 2002–16

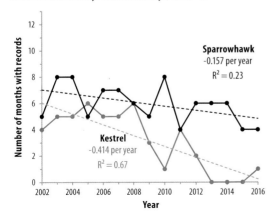

Sparrowhawk
-0.157 per year
$R^2 = 0.23$

Kestrel
-0.414 per year
$R^2 = 0.67$

Number of months with records

Year

In winter, there is an occasional Peregrine *F. peregrinus* and, during the very harsh weather of early 2012, a Merlin *F. columbarius* — a moorland species — spent a couple of weeks on the east of the Hill. There are also reports from time to time of solitary Ospreys *Pandion haliaetus* passing over the north-eastern slopes of Shotover.

Owls

The only owls that have been observed regularly at Shotover in recent decades are the Tawny Owl *Strix aluco* and Little Owl *Athene noctua*. Both species breed on the Hill — the old trees provide good nesting holes — but in what numbers is unclear. Tawny Owls are heard calling every year and at any time of day, mostly around Horspath and Westhill Farm. Sightings of Little Owls, however, have become rarer, with the most recent record from 2012. After a gap of 40 years, Barn Owls *Tyto alba* are now being seen on the Hill again, albeit infrequently. Nationally, Barn Owls had been in long-term decline until the mid-1990s, yet numbers have recovered somewhat since then, probably through constructive management. It is possible that they may once again become resident at Shotover.

Game birds

The only common game birds on the Hill are Pheasants *Phasianus colchicus*, which from about 2007 to 2014 were released on the north side for sport. During this time they were found in increasing numbers all over Shotover and they have continued to breed ferally although, as ground-nesting birds, their success rates may be low. Red-legged Partridges *Alectoris rufa* continue to be observed in small numbers, particularly on the east side of the Hill; they too were bred and released for sport but as this is no longer the case they may also be breeding naturally. Grey Partridge *Perdix perdix*, one of the fastest declining birds in Britain and mainland Europe, was noted occasionally in the 1980s and may have been breeding on the Hill (Steel, 1984: p. 113). A single bird was seen in a garden on the east side of Shotover in 2011 but all other records are from before 1995.

Woodpeckers

All three species of native British woodpeckers are found at Shotover. Green Woodpeckers *Picus viridis* are the biggest and their shrieking 'yaffle' can be heard frequently during the breeding season. They feed largely on ants and their pupae, and the sandy areas of the Hill are ideal for foraging, while rotting timber provides suitable places for nesting holes. Also common is the Great Spotted Woodpecker *Dendrocopos major*, a black-and-white bird whose drumming can be heard in spring; they feed largely on insects, supplemented during the winter by nuts from garden feeders. Much less common is the

Little Owl Roger Wyatt

Lesser Spotted Woodpecker Maris Pukitis

tiny and elusive Lesser Spotted Woodpecker *D. minor*, a species in marked decline in England, possibly losing out in competition with the Great Spotted Woodpecker, whose numbers have been increasing. Although the gentle territorial drumming of the Lesser Spotted Woodpecker has not been reported since 2009, they are thought to remain a breeding species at Shotover. Individuals have been observed almost every year for 30 years and from many different locations around the Hill.

Doves and pigeons

Woodpigeons *Columba palumbus* seem omnipresent on the Hill; they are adaptable birds, breeding at almost any time of the year, and have few predators. During the summer, groups of up to 20 males can often be heard singing within the Country Park and, in winter, moderately large flocks of over 100 can be seen. Their numbers have tended to increase during the years of systematic surveying in the SSSI in line with national trends. Collared Doves *Streptopelia decaocto* occur in much smaller numbers, especially near the villages where they nest, though sometimes in rather unlikely places, for instance, in a piece of roof guttering. It is often the Collared Dove, flying around domestic gardens, that is seen to fall victim to Shotover's Sparrowhawks. The soft cooing of Stock Doves *C. oenas* can be heard in most months; these nest in tree holes close to farmland and appear to be increasing in numbers on the Hill.

The delightful Turtle Dove *S. turtur*, with its purring song, is a summer visitor. Steel (1984: p. 113) noted that one or two pairs nested in scrub at Shotover but it has now almost certainly disappeared as a breeding species. Although one was heard singing in Brasenose Wood over several days in 2008, the last observation of likely breeding took place in 1990. A few still breed nearby at Otmoor. Nationally, Turtle Dove is a red-listed species and, like many other long-distance migrants, has declined throughout Europe.

Cuckoos

A much more noticeable summer visitor is the Cuckoo *Cuculus canorus*, whose call rings out from late April. Each year at Shotover more than one male is heard — usually three or four — but their actual breeding success is unclear, although

a juvenile bird was seen waiting to be fed in Mary Sadler Field in June 2016. The most likely local host species for these brood parasites — birds that lay their eggs in other species' nests — are Dunnocks *Prunella modularis* and Robins *Erithacus rubecula*. Cuckoos are another red-listed long-distance migrant but surveys have not indicated a decline at Shotover. The reasons for their general decline are not fully understood but may include the earlier nesting of their host species due to climate change. An overall shortage of caterpillars for food may also be a factor but this is unlikely to be a problem at Shotover and may account for the steady breeding numbers.

Swifts and hirundines

Swifts *Apus apus*, Swallows *Hirundo rustica* and House Martins *Delichon urbicum* are summer visitors from southern Africa, and are all amber-listed due to their overall decline across Britain. Although Swifts are late arriving and early departing, their piercing call is particularly evocative of summer. A few breed at Shotover — in west Wheatley — but the majority visiting the Hill breed in urban Oxford, including the colony at the Oxford University Museum of Natural History [see box, page 208]. Similarly, a few House Martins and a larger number of Swallows use barns and outbuildings in the area. However, most of these birds will visit from elsewhere,

Swallow Roger Wyatt

seeking flying insects, and towards the end of summer flocks can be large. Ninety Swifts were seen low over Mary Sadler Field in June 2011, and 50 Swallows and 100 House Martins in a mixed flock on the Shotover Estate in August 2012. The appearance of these species on the Hill is too sporadic to allow an assessment of any changes in their numbers.

The Oxford Swifts

When fledgling Swifts leave their nests in August they will fly without stopping — eating and sleeping on the wing — for the first three years of life, including an annual trip to overwinter in sub-Saharan Africa. They then return to their birth site each year to nest and breed.

Currently, many of the Swifts seen feeding on insects in the skies over Shotover belong to the famous colony in the tower of the Oxford University Museum of Natural History. In some years about 60 breeding pairs arrive at the tower in the spring. The colony has bred in the museum tower for decades and the behaviour of this remarkable bird has been studied there since 1948.

This may change in future. Populations of Swifts have declined in Britain since 1995 and this trend is reflected in the decreasing number of birds nesting in the museum tower. Even so, a project to provide nesting sites on buildings in Oxfordshire, including bespoke modifications to new developments, has been particularly successful, and it is hoped that Swifts will remain a common sight over Shotover for many years to come.

Swift Roger Wyatt

Larks

Even when David Steel was writing in 1984 there were comparatively few Skylarks *Alauda arvensis* at Shotover. Small numbers continue to sing every year over various fields across the Hill but there is little suitable land that does not suffer from disturbance, so breeding success may be very low. Woodlarks *Lullula arborea* bred on or near The Plain in the early 1950s but by 1962 no evidence of breeding could be found. Since then they have only rarely been recorded flying over, with the last observation in 1985. Both of these larks are red-listed species and have suffered greatly from changes in agricultural practice and a general increase in public access to the open land on which they breed [see also box, page 210].

Pipits, wagtails and Waxwings

Formerly known as a reliable breeder at Shotover, the red-listed Tree Pipit *Anthus trivialis* is now very rarely observed and there has been no evidence of breeding since 1968. During winter migration, however, Meadow Pipits *A. pratensis* visit and feed on the Hill, sometimes in large flocks with over 40 recorded near Westhill Farm in March 2006. Pied Wagtails *Motacilla alba* bred regularly near The Lake from 1988 until 2002, the last year of confirmed breeding on the Hill; however, small numbers can be seen foraging in winter, especially on the roofs of houses. There are occasional sightings of the amber-listed Grey Wagtail *M. cinerea* near water, sometimes accompanying Pied Wagtails, and very occasionally the red-listed summer-visiting Yellow Wagtail *M. flava* is seen, but there has never been any evidence of these species breeding.

Waxwings *Bombycilla garrulus* arrive in large numbers from Scandinavia in some winters. The first observation at Shotover was of four at Horspath in 1965. In the winters 2004–05, 2008–09, 2010–11 and 2012–13 they were reported in scores all over Oxford but only very occasionally on the Hill, perhaps because of their preference for the winter berries of domestic gardens and, curiously, supermarket car parks. A small group was reported in Risinghurst in March 2005 and a lone bird in a garden on the east side of Shotover in March 2011.

Wren Roger Wyatt

Redwing Roger Wyatt

Wrens, Robins and Dunnocks
Wrens *Troglodytes troglodytes*, Robins and Dunnocks are all resident birds of Shotover, are not fussy about their habitat, and feed mainly on insects. Robins sing throughout the year to establish their territory — a tuneful if somewhat wistful refrain. From early spring their song is joined by the rapid warble of the Dunnocks and the tirelessly repetitive song of the Wrens, surprisingly loud for such a small bird. The three species breed throughout the Hill and the systematic surveying by Shotover Wildlife has shown that typically over 30 male Robins, 40 Wrens and 15 Dunnocks may be heard singing on a spring morning in the SSSI. The numbers of all three species seem to be holding fairly steady, and Wrens and Robins are among the most numerous birds at Shotover.

Thrushes
All thrushes feed largely on invertebrates, supplemented by fruits such as berries. The melancholy song of the Mistle Thrush *Turdus viscivorus*, often sung from a treetop, may be heard from mid-winter and is soon joined by the repeated but more sophisticated phrases of the Song Thrush *T. philomelos*. Both are red-listed but are resident and breed on the Hill in small numbers. The population of Song Thrushes appears to be constant, with up to nine singing males heard during the monthly point surveys on the upper part of the SSSI [see page 202]; Mistle Thrushes are less numerous and have declined both at Shotover and in Oxfordshire, although an unusually large flock of about 20 were recorded near Home Farm in 2016. Blackbirds *T. merula*, also members of the Thrush family, whose

tuneful songs are heard from mid-spring, are much more common. Often 16 to 18 males have been heard holding territory during summer point surveys on the upper reaches of the SSSI.

During the winter, these resident birds are joined by overwintering Redwings *T. iliacus* and Fieldfares *T. pilaris*, together with additional Blackbirds which have bred on the continent, and it is during this season that flock sizes on the Hill tend to reach their maximum. For example, a flock of 66 Redwings was recorded near The Lake in early 2013.

Nightingales and Redstarts
Throughout most of the 20th century the Nightingale *Luscinia megarhynchos*, a summer visitor and beautiful songster, was a regular breeding bird at Shotover but the last successful attempt to breed is thought to have been in 2002 in Slade Camp North, where at least one male was heard singing every year from 1993 to 2003. From 2008 to 2010 the song was heard around Johnson's Piece and Horseshoe Field but the singer apparently failed to attract a mate. The breeding range of the Nightingale in Britain has been contracting in recent decades, and with Oxfordshire close to its northern limit it is thought that they no longer breed in the county and may disappear from Oxfordshire altogether (Oxford Ornithological Society, 2012: p. 9).

Similarly, Redstarts *Phoenicurus phoenicurus* no longer breed in the county and despite plenty of suitable oak woodland habitat — such as at Shotover — they have declined steadily in the British Midlands since the mid-20th century. On the Hill, most observations of this small and elusive bird have been of passage migrants during the 1980s, with the most recent record in 1993.

Warblers

All five species of Shotover's regular warblers are summer visitors, feeding on invertebrates and nesting in the scrub understorey. First to arrive are the Chiffchaffs *Phylloscopus collybita* with their repetitive 'chiff-chaff' song; the others all have more complex and often very beautiful songs, especially the Blackcap *Sylvia atricapilla* and Garden Warbler *S. borin*.

From 1982 to 2007 Mike Wilson recorded the numbers of singing warblers on a regular circuit encompassing much of Shotover. These 25 years of observations — of which the first 20 years were reviewed by Whitehead *et al.* (2003: p. 65–71) — provide good evidence of recent trends. During the 1980s, Chiffchaffs typically held about 15 territories each year and since then have steadily increased to 30, with over 40 singing males in 2002. Similarly, 15 Blackcap territories were noted up to the mid-1990s, thereafter increasing to between 25 and 30 each year. These increases are in line with the national upward trend for these species. Fewer Garden

Blackcap Roger Wyatt

Warblers were noted singing but over the survey period the number of territories increased from 10 to 15 with more than 20 singing males in exceptional years. Whitethroats *S. communis* were much less numerous and more variable, with up to eight territories each year. In contrast, Willow Warblers *P. trochilus* have decreased markedly at Shotover. During the 1980s over 30 singing males were counted in some years but from 1998 to 2002 the total was more typically 15. Since 2002 the continued reduction on the Hill has been particularly noticeable during the

The decline of heathland birds

Throughout the 20th century, heathland declined at an exceptional rate in Britain, including in Oxfordshire and at Shotover. Consequently it is not surprising that the breeding birds of open scrub habitats have also declined as many of them require extensive areas of heath and also nest on the ground in short sparse vegetation. Nationally the breeding ranges of most heathland birds has retracted and on the small and dwindling heaths of Oxfordshire these species have long since departed. Many local heaths have been lost to development or ploughed for cropping but on the remaining open habitat, including at Shotover, increased public usage deters ground-nesting birds

Dartford Warbler could return to Shotover Roger Wyatt

and the impact of myxomatosis in Rabbit has greatly reduced the area of short-grazed scrub vegetation.

In the 1930s it was possible to see breeding evidence at Shotover for heathland species such as Nightjar, Stonechat, Whinchat and Woodlark but within 30 years nesting had ceased — coincident with myxomatosis and the opening up of heathy areas to the public. Only Tree Pipits continued to breed on the Hill into the 1960s. Although Whinchats and Tree Pipits have continued to decline nationally, Woodlarks and Nightjars have responded to habitat restoration in Britain. However, the prospect of their return to Shotover is negligible.

Of particular interest is the Dartford Warbler, which last bred at Shotover in the 1870s. The disappearance of this species as a resident bird of Oxfordshire is partly due to habitat loss but mostly to the particularly harsh winters of the mid-20th century. Nevertheless, Dartford Warblers now breed in Berkshire and, surprisingly, might be the most likely heathland bird to return to breed at Shotover.

Wood Warbler Roger Wyatt

Shotover Wildlife point surveys [see page 202] where they are now rarely heard singing at the eastern survey points and, like Whitethroats, are most often heard on the western side of the SSSI. This decrease in Willow Warblers is in line with the trend for southern Britain and may be associated with a northward shift in their range rather than an overall decline (Balmer *et al.*, 2013: p. 530).

Lesser Whitethroats *S. curruca* have been recorded in small numbers in most years since the 1980s and although there has been no confirmed breeding since 2003, these small secretive birds probably still breed in the hedgerows and scrub of the Hill. Most of the recent records are of a singing male in and around Slade Camp South. Other warblers are occasionally observed on their migration routes, such as Wood Warblers *P. sibilatrix*, a nationally declining species that last bred at Shotover in 1975. Reed Warblers *Acrocephalus scirpaceus* and Sedge Warblers *A. schoenobaenus* also pass by, and a rare visitor in May 2009 was a Grasshopper Warbler *Locustella naevia* which sang for just two days in Mary Sadler Field.

In general, therefore, it seems that the warblers are doing reasonably well at Shotover, which is not very different from the picture for Britain as a whole. Blackcaps — the most adaptable of the warblers — and Chiffchaffs are short-distance migrants that overwinter around the Mediterranean, and both are increasing in numbers on the Hill. In addition, they are now overwintering here, as attested by occasional November and December records of each. Although the migratory birds typically breed in woodland, Blackcaps that remain through the winter appear to prefer gardens.

Goldcrests

A few Goldcrests *Regulus regulus*, with their preference for conifers, are resident at Shotover and breed there, their numbers substantially increased each year by an influx of wintering visitors. These tiny birds, with their high-pitched calls and songs, are heard as frequently around the conifers of nearby domestic gardens as in the Larches and Scots Pines of the Country Park. Firecrests *R. ignicapilla*, including singing males, have been recorded on rare occasions in the 1980s and 1990s.

Flycatchers

Spotted Flycatchers *Muscicapa striata* are agile flyers, showing an impressive aerobatic display as they hunt for insects. They often nest in creepers on a vertical face, such as the wall of a building. Until 2011 they bred regularly in the vicinity of Shotover House but no subsequent sign of breeding was evident there, or elsewhere on the Hill, until two adults were observed feeding two juveniles near the House in July 2015. A migrant from South Africa and nationally red-listed, this bird may have remained on the Hill as a breeding species, albeit in very low numbers.

Tits

All the tits are resident birds, with Blue Tits *Cyanistes caeruleus* and Great Tits *Parus major* abundant at Shotover, and Coal Tits *Periparus ater*, Marsh Tits *Poecile palustris* and Long-tailed Tits *Aegithalos caudatus* present in smaller numbers. They feed mainly on invertebrates, supplemented during winter by fruits and seeds, including those from garden feeding stations. Around 20 Great Tits may be heard singing their 'teacher' song in the Country Park during a

Spotted Flycatcher Roger Wyatt

summer survey, together with half that number of Blue Tits and up to three Coal Tits.

Willow Tits *Poecile montana* and Marsh Tits — which resemble each other closely — are both red-listed and of conservation concern but the national collapse in Willow Tit numbers has been the more serious. Willow Tits have most probably disappeared as a breeding bird at Shotover with the most recent likely indication of breeding in 2002. On the other hand, Marsh Tits seem to be holding their own at Shotover in low numbers — mostly recognized by their distinctive call. Although two or three might be heard during a two-hour point survey in the SSSI, it is not possible to estimate the number of territories held.

Nuthatches and Treecreepers

Both Nuthatches *Sitta europaea* and Treecreepers *Certhia familiaris* are resident breeders on the Hill. The distinctive twanging call of the Nuthatch is heard in all wooded areas of Shotover, and this species may be increasing in numbers. Treecreepers are less noticeable, spending most of their time scuttling up the trunks of trees seeking insects in crevices in the bark and then flying down and starting up a neighbouring tree. Being small and strictly insectivorous, they suffer during harsh winters but on the Hill, where invertebrates may be more available at such times, they have a greater chance of survival than in less diverse woodlands. Two pairs were detected with nesting materials in the SSSI in April 2014, and in May 2015 at least three nestlings were fledged from a deep crack in the Shotover Oak — just two months before this fine old tree split and fell [see box, page 52].

Nuthatch Roger Wyatt

The Raven is Shotover's largest corvid Roger Wyatt

Corvids

The corvids are successful birds not least because they are adaptable and have a catholic diet. Jackdaws are one of the commonest birds on the Hill, often seen in large flocks, gleaning invertebrates from farmland. About 500 were counted wheeling over Horspath in February 2013. They remain gregarious during nesting, using tree holes or chimneys and cracks in abandoned buildings. Rooks *Corvus frugilegus* can also be seen feeding in the fields, and a few small rookeries are to be found on the Hill, although numbers appear to have dropped in recent years. Carrion Crows *C. corone* are similar in appearance but have a more solitary habit.

The 'rattle' of Magpies *Pica pica* is heard in every habitat around the Hill. Their tendency to include other birds' nestlings in their diet — though a habit they share with other corvids — has given them an unenviable reputation. More popular, despite their grating screech, are the handsome and colourful Jays *Garrulus glandarius*. These birds are particularly fond of the abundant acorns and apples on the Hill. Like squirrels, Jays bury acorns for later consumption and thereby distribute oaks more widely. Largest of all Shotover's corvids are the Ravens *C. corax*, whose range has been expanding eastward in the county over recent decades. Since 2008 their hoarse croaking calls have been heard regularly on the Hill but no firm evidence of breeding has yet been reported.

Starlings and sparrows

Tree Sparrows *Passer montanus* at Shotover have experienced the same boom and bust as in the rest of the county. Record numbers were observed in the 1960s and they bred on the Hill until 1990 (at

The Piggery); however, they have since become rare in the county and are now probably lost from Shotover. Both Starlings *Sturnus vulgaris* and House Sparrows *P. domesticus* were formerly so common as to be regarded as pests but nationally their numbers have also plummeted and both are now red-listed. At Shotover small numbers of both species still breed on the farms and in surrounding villages. In winter, when continental Starlings join the residents, large flocks of Starlings used to feed in the fields around the Hill but now this is a rare sight, although over 150 birds were seen on a dead oak near Home Farm in November 2014. Further afield impressive 'murmurations' of Starlings gather where habitat is suitable — as at Otmoor.

Finches

Chaffinches *Fringilla coelebs* have been a common breeding resident at Shotover; in the recent past, more than 20 singing males have been recorded in some summer months. However, during the most recent 15 years of the Shotover Wildlife systematic surveys, numbers have declined by 40 per cent. Also resident and breeding in smaller numbers are Goldfinches *Carduelis carduelis* and Greenfinches *Chloris chloris*, together with a few Linnets *Linaria cannabina* (another red-listed species). Whereas Goldfinches appear to have gradually increased since 2002, Greenfinches have declined — especially since the onset of a parasitic disease in 2006. With ample scrub habitat in the SSSI, Bullfinches *Pyrrhula pyrrhula* do well at Shotover, their curious song and distinctive soft call announcing their presence all year round.

During the winter months, Chaffinch numbers increase when continental birds arrive to overwinter, and large groups can be seen feeding on the farmland. Other finches can also be found in smaller numbers, including redpolls *Carduelis* spp., Siskins *Spinus spinus* and occasional autumn Bramblings *F. montifringilla*. In December 2014 a flock of 25 Siskins was recorded at The Larches, and a flock of 12 in March 2016 on Mary Sadler Field.

Buntings

In the past, all of the three common resident British buntings bred on the Hill and Reed Buntings *Emberiza schoeniclus* still breed at The Lake. Several pairs of Corn Buntings *E. calandra*

Reed Bunting Roger Wyatt

were breeding on the south side of the Hill in the 1930s but none has been seen since the 1980s. Until recently, Yellowhammers *E. citrinella* were very common, their song — 'little bit of bread and no cheese' — ringing out until late summer; in the winter they were often seen in feeding parties. Numbers have declined rapidly, however, and they might no longer breed on the Hill. Their song is still heard along the hedgerows below Westhill Farm but the last record of likely breeding was in 2006. Corn Buntings and Yellowhammers are farmland specialists and both are red-listed nationally.

Factors affecting bird diversity at Shotover

Since systematic surveys began in 2001, around 50 common species have been recorded regularly and bird diversity overall has remained fairly constant. However, this apparent constancy masks many notable losses and gains in individual species, such as the lower diversity of water birds at The Lake [see page 203]. Moreover, the 15 years of data accumulated by Shotover Wildlife may be insufficient to uncover more subtle trends. Over the longer period that includes the Common Bird Census in Brasenose Wood (1979–2002) there was a significant drop in the diversity of breeding birds, matching a similar decline for Wytham Wood (Whitehead *et al.*, 2003: p. xi; Perrins and Gosler, 2010: p. 146).

In any given year, numbers of birds may change because of entirely transitory factors. Local habitats meet the nesting and feeding requirements of Shotover's resident birds but a cold winter may reduce populations, particularly among smaller birds or those that rely in large part on the availability of insects. A cold or wet spring can reduce breeding success, with a subsequent — though hopefully short-term — reduction in numbers. Even so, many birds are generally adaptable. The tiny Long-tailed Tits remain in family groups and roost closely together for overnight warmth; even the highly territorial Wrens do the same — seven were observed roosting in a garden nest box in Horspath in February 2009.

There are many other species whose needs are only partially satisfied locally and which therefore must travel, or migrate, to complete their annual cycle. The prevalence of these mobile species is largely dictated by factors beyond the Hill. At a national level numerous changes in farming practice have had a particular impact on bird numbers. For example, certain policies for hedge maintenance reduce nesting and feeding opportunities, and can eliminate wildlife corridors. Also, the use of herbicides and pesticides and the greater efficiency of harvesting reduce the availability of a year-round food supply of insects and seeds. Agricultural intensification has had adverse effects on more species than just the farmland specialists; this can be seen at Shotover with the decline of the buntings, including Yellowhammers, and many other birds such as Starlings and Lapwings. Ground-nesting birds are also affected, as the autumn planting of cereal crops and the use of grass for silage rather than hay create a departure from traditional harvesting times and therefore curtail the nesting season for these species.

The number of overwintering birds that arrive in Britain from elsewhere in Europe will depend on the prevailing weather or the distribution of available food over continental Europe. Waxwings only appear in Oxfordshire when driven west in search of winter berries; when conditions are particularly harsh, these birds will continue south and west. The comparatively late migration of Redwings, Fieldfares and Siskins back to Shotover in 2013 could have been due to these birds having headed further south than usual in response to the unusually cold spring in Britain.

In general, many species of long-distance migrant bird have suffered long-term decline; at Shotover, Spotted Flycatchers, Turtle Doves and Nightingales are especially notable in this respect. Many of our summer-breeding birds overwinter in warmer places, and those that spend the British winter in sub-Saharan Africa

Turtle Dove Roger Wyatt

have suffered the most. Factors contributing to the low survival rates of these long-distance migrants are likely to be drought or farming intensification in the African wintering grounds, together with a loss of suitable staging posts during migration. In some cases, the loss of a staging post could be related to climate change, itself a complex phenomenon that is affecting birds in various ways.

The future for birds at Shotover

Whether resident or migrant, many birds use habitat at Shotover for breeding and feeding, and their diversity and abundance are closely related to the quality of the habitats. Although the open water on the Hill is now less important in Oxfordshire than in earlier years, Shotover's dense woodland and heathy areas offer much to the birds that specialize in these habitats, and understanding birds' use of these areas is critical.

Change in woodland management is a national issue but also has local implications. Many birds require a deep shrub layer for breeding and this is now generally less available, partly through reduction in managed coppicing and partly through grazing by an increasing population of deer. Fuller and Steel (1990) studied the effects of the coppicing cycle on breeding birds in Brasenose Wood and noted that, particularly for warblers, breeding density was greatest four to eight years after cutting, when Bramble growth was at its maximum and there was a patchy shrub layer. Although coppicing continues at Brasenose Wood, deer populations have increased sharply since the 1990s [see page 224] and different methods to offset the effects of deer browsing have varied greatly in their effectiveness. However, high-cutting trials by Shotover Wildlife since 2010 [see box, page 224] have demonstrated that a coppice rotation which benefits wildlife, including a suitable period of scrub development, can be achieved in deer-browsed woodland (Wright and Bartel, 2017). Breeding birds at Shotover that would be encouraged by a deeper woodland shrub layer include Marsh Tits, Dunnocks, Bullfinches, Song Thrushes, Blackbirds and the majority of warbler species. Most of these birds are doing well in Brasenose Wood — the greatest exception being Willow Warblers — but the availability of a thick shrub layer would help to ensure the future of all these species. Tree Pipits, Nightingales and Willow Tits would also benefit but all are probably now lost.

The heathland habitat at Shotover is also important at both a local and wider level. Historically, the Hill has supported many heathland birds but this habitat is now greatly reduced, as it is across much of southern England, and most of these birds are rarely or never seen on the Hill. This is not a recent development; the last nesting of Dartford Warblers *Sylvia undata* at Shotover was recorded in 1878, that of Stonechats *Saxicola rubicola* in the mid-1930s, of Whinchats *S. rubetra* in the late 1950s, and of Wheatears *Oenanthe oenanthe* some time in the distant past. Stonechats, Whinchats and Wheatears are still seen occasionally during migration but it is uncertain whether attempts to increase the heathland on the Hill would enable any of these ground-nesting species to prosper — in any event, some restriction would have to be imposed on free-running dogs.

Wheatear Roger Wyatt

Since part of Shotover Hill became a public park, habitat disturbance has proved a significant problem for some wildlife. The public areas of Shotover serve a double function: apart from being a conservation area for wildlife, it is a popular and well-used recreational space. People, and dogs in particular, can pose problems for birds which nest on or close to the ground. A comparison of breeding density in Brasenose Wood with that in nearby Wytham Wood, where there is far less disturbance, has indicated that, in general, Wytham has a greater density of breeding pairs (Whitehead *et al.*, 2003: p. xi). A more complex problem is the apparent continuing loss of the song birds, a loss felt not least because they bring such delight to those who listen to them. These birds require high-quality habitat for breeding and survival, and so their well-being depends on carefully managing the area for their needs.

However, additional species continue to settle at Shotover, even though some have arrived through assisted colonization. The Red Kite is an obvious example, the result of a reintroduction programme in the nearby Chiltern Hills, and Pheasants released on the Shotover Estate have spilled over into the SSSI and surrounding gardens. Buzzards and Ravens have been moving eastwards across the county from existing strongholds. Gulls have been settling inland, and it is salutary to remember that Magpies were not recorded here until the 1940s nor Collared Doves until the 1970s. The growing population of Ring-necked Parakeets *Psittacula krameri* in the London area continues to expand outwards. These large colourful birds are now breeding in the south of the county and would find a good home on the Hill.

For many common species, such as Robin or Wren, their horizon scarcely extends beyond the local habitat and their adaptability (to utilise domestic gardens, for example) makes their position fairly secure. In contrast, migratory species, such as Cuckoo or Swift, that appear on the Hill each year have wide-ranging requirements to which Shotover may only make a small and non-critical contribution. Between these two extremes are many species that have been recorded on the Hill, of which some are lost or in decline while others are increasing or have recently colonized but all of which have used the habitats of Shotover in some way. Many of

Treecreeper Roger Wyatt

resilience is probably greatest in regard to two groups of species: those woodland birds that do well at Shotover but which are less common in the wider countryside (such as Nuthatch, Treecreeper and the woodpeckers), and those whose future prospects could be enhanced by active conservation (the warblers and heathland species). Sensitive active management, grounded in systematic recording and comprehensive background knowledge, would help secure a stable future for both of these groups of birds, as well as provide satisfactory habitat for a wide range of other species. However, the overall changes in diversity of birds and the ecological equilibrium between them may herald a more uncertain future. For example, since most of the newly arrived species are large birds, such as Pheasants, Ravens and Buzzards, competition for food could increase markedly. As the birds of Shotover form an indispensable part of the ecology of the Hill, this would affect not only their prospects locally but also those of a great many additional species in the wider food chain.

the changes in particular populations, as noted earlier, have followed national trends, such as the arrival of Buzzards or the loss of Nightingales, and these are largely independent of habitat change.

However, Shotover's contribution towards the diversity of regional bird fauna and its future

Table 14.1 Most recent records of birds observed on Shotover Hill
*Entries of names in **bold** are birds with a low probability of reoccurrence.*
Taxonomic order after Brucker *et al.* (1992).

Species	Record	Breeding	Species	Record	Breeding
Black-throated Diver *Gavia arctica*	1956		Red-breasted Merganser *Mergus serrator*	2002	
Little Grebe *Tachybaptus ruficollis*	2018	2008	Goosander *Mergus merganser*	2011	
Great Crested Grebe *Podiceps cristatus*	1993	1993	Red Kite *Milvus milvus*	2018	2011
Red-necked Grebe *Podiceps grisegena*	1979		Marsh Harrier *Circus aeruginosus*	2000	
Cormorant *Phalacrocorax carbo*	2018		Hen Harrier *Circus cyaneus*	1921	
Little Egret *Egretta garzetta*	2004		Goshawk *Accipiter gentilis*	1882	
Grey Heron *Ardea cinerea*	2018		Sparrowhawk *Accipiter nisus*	2018	2016
White Stork *Ciconia ciconia*	1986		Buzzard *Buteo buteo*	2018	2012
Mute Swan *Cygnus olor*	2014	2014	**Rough-legged Buzzard** *Buteo lagopus*	1973	
Black Swan (escaped) *Cygnus atratus*	1991		Osprey *Pandion haliaetus*	2013	
White-fronted Goose *Anser albifrons*	1985		Kestrel *Falco tinnunculus*	2018	2008
Greylag Goose *Anser anser*	2014		Merlin *Falco columbarius*	2012	
Canada Goose *Branta canadensis*	2018	2012	Hobby *Falco subbuteo*	2013	
Barnacle Goose (newly feral) *Branta leucopsis*	2018		Peregrine *Falco peregrinus*	2007	
Shelduck *Tadorna tadorna*	1962		Red-legged Partridge *Alectoris rufa*	2015	
Mandarin Duck *Aix galericulata*	2003	?1989	Grey Partridge *Perdix perdix*	2011	
Wigeon *Anas penelope*	2005		Quail *Coturnix coturnix*	1988	
Gadwall *Anas strepera*	2004		**Helmeted Guineafowl (esc.)** *Numida meleagris*	2001	
Teal *Anas crecca*	2004		Pheasant *Phasianus colchicus*	2018	2016
Mallard *Anas platyrhynchos*	2018	2006	Water Rail *Rallus aquaticus*	2000	
Pintail *Anas acuta*	1996		Moorhen *Gallinula chloropus*	2018	2015
Shoveler *Anas clypeata*	2004		Coot *Fulica atra*	2018	2016
Red-crested Pochard *Netta rufina*	2005		Oystercatcher *Haematopus ostralegus*	2005	
Pochard *Aythya ferina*	2008		Avocet *Recurvirostra avosetta*	2013	
Tufted Duck *Aythya fuligula*	2016	2008	Golden Plover *Pluvialis apricaria*	2001	

Species	Record	Breeding	Species	Record	Breeding
Lapwing *Vanellus vanellus*	2010	1999	Ring Ouzel *Turdus torquatus*	1988	
Dunlin *Calidris alpina*	1998		Blackbird *Turdus merula*	2018	2018
Snipe *Gallinago gallinago*	2014		Fieldfare *Turdus pilaris*	2018	
Jack Snipe *Lymnocryptes minimus*	2009		Song Thrush *Turdus philomelos*	2018	2018
Woodcock *Scolopax rusticola*	2018		Redwing *Turdus iliacus*	2018	
Whimbrel *Numenius phaeopus*	1991		Mistle Thrush *Turdus viscivorus*	2018	2018
Curlew *Numenius arquata*	2013		Grasshopper Warbler *Locustella naevia*	2009	?1994
Green Sandpiper *Tringa ochropus*	1927		Sedge Warbler *Acrocephalus schoenobaenus*	2002	?1980
Common Sandpiper *Actitis hypoleucos*	1988		Reed Warbler *Acrocephalus scirpaceus*	2004	?1995
Red-necked Phalarope *Phalaropus lobatus*	1834		Lesser Whitethroat *Sylvia curruca*	2014	2003
Black-headed Gull *Chroicocephalus ridibundus*	2018		Dartford Warbler *Sylvia undata*	1878	1878
Common Gull *Larus canus*	2005		Whitethroat *Sylvia communis*	2018	2018
Lesser Black-backed Gull *Larus fuscus*	2018		Garden Warbler *Sylvia borin*	2018	2018
Herring Gull *Larus argentatus*	2018		Blackcap *Sylvia atricapilla*	2018	2018
Great Black-backed Gull *Larus marinus*	1994		Wood Warbler *Phylloscopus sibilatrix*	2011	1975
Kittiwake *Rissa tridactyla*	1957		Chiffchaff *Phylloscopus collybita*	2018	2018
Black Tern *Chlidonias niger*	1994		Willow Warbler *Phylloscopus trochilus*	2018	2018
Feral Pigeon *Columba livia*	2003		Goldcrest *Regulus regulus*	2018	2018
Stock Dove *Columba oenas*	2018	2018	Firecrest *Regulus ignicapilla*	1999	?1999
Woodpigeon *Columba palumbus*	2018	2018	Spotted Flycatcher *Muscicapa striata*	2017	2015
Collared Dove *Streptopelia decaocto*	2018	2018	**Pied Flycatcher *Ficedula hypoleuca***	1992	
Turtle Dove *Streptopelia turtur*	2008	1990	Long-tailed Tit *Aegithalos caudatus*	2018	2018
Ring-necked Parakeet *Psittacula krameri*	2008		Marsh Tit *Poecile palustris*	2018	2018
Cuckoo *Cuculus canorus*	2018	2018	Willow Tit *Poecile montana*	2011	?2002
Barn Owl *Tyto alba*	2018	?1961	Coal Tit *Periparus ater*	2018	2018
Little Owl *Athene noctua*	2012	?2008	Blue Tit *Cyanistes caeruleus*	2018	2018
Tawny Owl *Strix aluco*	2018	2006	Great Tit *Parus major*	2018	2018
Nightjar *Caprimulgus europaeus*	1982	?1930s	Nuthatch *Sitta europaea*	2018	2018
Swift *Apus apus*	2018	2003	Treecreeper *Certhia familiaris*	2018	2018
Kingfisher *Alcedo atthis*	2015	?1996	Red-backed Shrike *Lanius collurio*	1944	1944
Green Woodpecker *Picus viridis*	2018	2018	**Woodchat Shrike *Lanius senator***	1981	
Wryneck *Jynx torquilla*	1964		Jay *Garrulus glandarius*	2018	2018
Great Spotted Woodpecker *Dendrocopos major*	2018	2018	Magpie *Pica pica*	2018	2018
Lesser Spotted Woodpecker *Dendrocopos minor*	2013	2009	Jackdaw *Corvus monedula*	2018	2018
Woodlark *Lullula arborea*	1985	1954	Rook *Corvus frugilegus*	2018	2018
Skylark *Alauda arvensis*	2018	2016	Carrion Crow *Corvus corone*	2018	2018
Sand Martin *Riparia riparia*	2001	'years ago'*	Raven *Corvus corax*	2018	
Swallow *Hirundo rustica*	2018	2016	Starling *Sturnus vulgaris*	2018	2018
House Martin *Delichon urbicum*	2018	2018	House Sparrow *Passer domesticus*	2018	2018
Tree Pipit *Anthus trivialis*	2006	1968	Tree Sparrow *Passer montanus*	2003	1990
Meadow Pipit *Anthus pratensis*	2009		Chaffinch *Fringilla coelebs*	2018	2018
Yellow Wagtail *Motacilla flava*	2014		Brambling *Fringilla montifringilla*	2010	
Grey Wagtail *Motacilla cinerea*	2014		Greenfinch *Chloris chloris*	2018	2018
Pied Wagtail *Motacilla alba*	2018	2002	Goldfinch *Carduelis carduelis*	2018	2018
Waxwing *Bombycilla garrulus*	2005		Siskin *Spinus spinus*	2018	
Wren *Troglodytes troglodytes*	2018	2018	Linnet *Linaria cannabina*	2014	2002
Dunnock *Prunella modularis*	2018	2018	Redpoll *Carduelis* sp.	2013	
Robin *Erithacus rubecula*	2018	2018	Common Crossbill *Loxia curvirostra*	2006	
Nightingale *Luscinia megarhynchos*	2010	?2002	Bullfinch *Pyrrhula pyrrhula*	2018	2018
Black Redstart *Phoenicurus ochruros*	2001		Hawfinch *Coccothraustes coccothraustes*	2017	
Redstart *Phoenicurus phoenicurus*	1993		Yellowhammer *Emberiza citrinella*	2018	2006
Whinchat *Saxicola rubetra*	2016	1958	Reed Bunting *Emberiza schoeniclus*	2016	2016
Stonechat *Saxicola rubicola*	2011	1936	Corn Bunting *Emberiza calandra*	1987	?1964
Wheatear *Oenanthe oenanthe*	2012	'years ago'#			

* (Mike Wilson, pers. comm., 2003).
\# Oxford Ornithological Society (1931).

Eleanor Hawtree

An unexpected rustle in the undergrowth at Shotover may well excite the hope of a moment to remember. Often it turns out to be a Blackbird earnestly tossing leaves aside to expose something to eat, or perhaps on the heath a brief glimpse of a Grass Snake. But if one is especially lucky it could be a rare sighting of one of Shotover's many wild mammals — creatures that specialize in concealment. Sometimes the encounter will be fleeting, just long enough to fully appreciate the experience; on other occasions, there may be time to savour the privilege of being an unseen spectator — for example, of a family of Red Foxes *Vulpus vulpus* in the early morning sunshine.

There are about 70 species of terrestrial wild mammal in Britain, of which 26 can be seen at Shotover, from the Pygmy Shrew *Sorex minutus*, just four centimetres long (excluding the tail), to the Fallow Deer *Dama dama*, which can grow to over a metre in height at the shoulders. Most animals in the class Mammalia have fur and give birth to live young but the defining feature common to all species is the presence of mammary glands in the female to provide milk for their young.

In prehistory many different mammals would have roamed Oxfordshire, though most are now long gone. Later, during the Anglo-Saxon period, there would have been Wolves *Canis lupus*, Red Deer *Cervus elaphus* and Wild Boar *Sus scrofa* at Shotover but these were gradually hunted to regional extinction through the late Middle Ages, with only Red Deer lingering on in the county (in Wychwood Forest) to the mid-19th century (Elton, 1939: p. 222).

The mammals of Shotover

Shotover supports an impressive diversity of mammals; the habitats both within and around the SSSI provide a wide range of niches which can be used to advantage by species both large and small. Some are found in abundance, such as the European Rabbit *Oryctolagus cuniculus* and Grey Squirrel *Sciurus carolinensis*, while others are much more scarce, for example Weasel *Mustela nivalis* and Polecat *M. putorius*. While deer and Rabbits are seen frequently, most

Red Fox
Alex White

Making eye contact with a fellow mammal induces complex thoughts of fight, flight and perhaps curiosity, followed by a carefully considered response.

Wild Boar Spencer Wright

Pigmy Shrew Philip Hay

mammals are elusive, stealthy or naturally more active during the darker hours. Consequently, it is often only signs such as droppings, well-used paths among the vegetation or footprints temporarily preserved in mud that indicate their presence, and sometimes the species.

Even though the Rabbit, Fox and European Mole *Talpa europaea* have been part of the British countryside for centuries, like many other common species they go mostly unrecorded and indeed there were no data for mammals at Shotover until recently. Sightings began to be recorded in the early 1970s, with the majority of early records coming from the C.S. Lewis Community Nature Reserve on the north side of the Hill. Then, with the exception of a Brown Long-eared Bat *Plecotus auritus* noted at the Horspath railway cutting in 1984, there were no records of mammals on the south side of the Hill until a Polecat was reported to Shotover Wildlife in 2000 [see page 223].

Hedgehogs, shrews and moles (Insectivora)
There are three species of hedgehog in Europe, of which Britain hosts only the pan-European Western Hedgehog *Erinaceus europaeus*. This species is rarely seen around Shotover, mostly due to its nocturnal habit and, in places, the abundance of predators. There is a great deal of anecdotal evidence of these prickly insectivores inhabiting the gardens around the edges of the Hill, although sightings seem to have declined since 2000. Notwithstanding the defensive spiny exterior of the Western Hedgehog, the Eurasian Badger *Meles meles* is an adept predator, which may explain why Hedgehogs are seldom found

in areas which are generally more sandy, where Badger setts can be particularly numerous — as at Shotover.

Shrews are insectivorous and many species are good swimmers, including the Common Shrew *Sorex araneus* and Pygmy Shrew, both of which can be found at Shotover. The Common Shrew is widely distributed on the Hill, especially in the wetter areas, with Shotover's lush marshes offering an ideal refuge and feeding ground. In contrast, the Pygmy Shrew is probably much less abundant and is seldom seen outside of live-trapping surveys; during such surveys, however, this tiny species turns up frequently, with the most recent record dating from 2016 in the meadows below Westhill Farm. It prefers open habitat such as heath, woodland edges and rough grassland, and has been found in all these habitats at Shotover. Unlike the Common Shrew, which is especially active throughout the night, the Pygmy Shrew scavenges both day and night in equal measure, as it must find and eat its own body weight in invertebrates every day. Dense vegetative cover allows the Pygmy Shrew to scuttle around undetected — often using the runs and trackways of other species — and is therefore vital in providing both food and protection from predators.

The European Mole is rarely seen at Shotover and seldom ventures above ground but its distinctive molehills are a very familiar sight. Moles inhabit deciduous woodland, arable fields and permanent meadows and pastures, so suitable habitats are available across the Hill and its surroundings. They feed on a broad range of invertebrates, including beetle larvae, centipedes

Molehills are part of the intricate ecology of the Hill

and slugs, and occasionally on vertebrates such as frogs. However, their main food is earthworms, which constitute more than 90 per cent of their diet during the winter and around 50 per cent in summer. For this reason, Moles are much less frequent where the soil is too acidic for most species of earthworm (acidity less than pH 4.5), as is the case for many areas on the Hill.

The molehills themselves make a valuable contribution to the overall ecology, each one creating a small area of bare soil that benefits a variety of species. Many of the scarcer plants in the SSSI, for example, are annuals whose seeds can germinate more readily in the bare soil left by a molehill, whether the seeds are transported by wind or animals, or are brought to the surface and exposed to light, thereby triggering the germination of dormant seeds. On relatively infertile soils where the molehills are overtaken more slowly by vegetation, the long-lasting patches of exposed soil are exploited by a great variety of invertebrates and contribute to Shotover's diverse ecology of soil-nesting species.

When a Mole is not sleeping (upright with its head between its forelegs) it is mostly burrowing. The invertebrates on which Moles feed, and especially the worms, are dispersed widely throughout the soil and so burrowing is its main means of foraging. Moles dig three types of tunnel: breeding runs, surface runs and permanent tunnels. Breeding runs are open, like a small ditch, whereas surface runs are just below the soil surface and create a ridge of soil or raised grass. Permanent tunnels are deeper below ground, with additional tunnels leading to the surface and culminating in the familiar

molehill. The molehills are used as exit points for collecting nesting material and for surface feeding, and as a repository of excavated soil.

Bats (Chiroptera)

Bats are the only flying mammal, with a skeletal structure highly adapted to that purpose. Their flight is fast and aerobatic, and they are most often seen at dusk as a fluttering silhouette against the evening sky, using echolocation to find and feed on flying insects. Eight of Britain's 18 species have been positively identified at Shotover: Barbastelle Bat *Barbastella barbastellus*, Brandt's Bat *Myotis brandtii*, Brown Long-eared Bat *Plecotus auritus*, Daubenton's Bat *M. daubentonii*, Natterer's Bat *M. nattereri*, Noctule *Nyctalus noctula*, Common Pipistrelle *Pipistrellus pipistrellus* and Soprano Pipistrelle *P. pygmaeus*.

Feeding habits of bats

Bats in Britain feed mostly by 'aerial hawking' — catching and eating small insects in flight. It has been estimated that pipistrelle species can eat about 3,000 insects in a single night. The Brown Long-eared Bat will also catch larger flying insects which it takes to a suitable perch before eating.

The wing membrane of all bats extends between the hind legs and the tail, and is used in a number of different ways, most notably as a form of scoop. In flight, Natterer's Bat can catch insects in the membrane scoop and then flick them into its mouth. While feeding over water, Daubenton's Bat can catch insects from the water surface using the membrane, and its hind feet may even grab small fish that break the water surface.

A Noctule bat predating an Orange Underwing moth
Drawing by Jacqueline Wright

The pipistrelles are the most common and widespread bat species in Britain, a fact reflected in the number of records for them on and around Shotover. The Soprano Pipistrelle is Shotover's smallest bat, with a wing span of 20 centimetres and weighing as little as three grams. It has only been recognized as a separate species since 1999; until then it was considered a subspecies of the Common Pipistrelle. The two species are usually identified by using a bat detector, which can distinguish the different frequencies of their echolocation calls.

As for the less common British bats found at Shotover, in 2003 there was a single sighting of Brandt's Bat in the C.S. Lewis Community Nature Reserve, and a Barbastelle Bat has been recorded in the disused railway tunnel between Horspath and Littleworth. Since 2001, the western end of the tunnel has been adapted specifically for bats and regularly monitored. In the cutting that approaches the tunnel entrance, spring water has been shallowly impounded behind earth dams, creating small ponds over which bats may feed for invertebrates. Inside, the walls of the tunnel have been modified to make provision for roosting, nesting and hibernation.

Shotover's extensive woodland habitats play a major role in supporting bat populations, as all species use older trees for summer roosting. This is particularly true of the Noctules, the largest bat at Shotover, which rarely uses buildings. A Noctule maternity roost was found in Brasenose Wood in 2009, the bats making use of a woodpecker hole in an oak tree. Bats seek out such nooks and crevices for their roosts; buildings with old cracked beams and other small spaces are often utilised but at Shotover it is the trees which play a dominant and vital role. Woodpecker holes, rot holes, loose bark and hollow trunks all provide prime habitat for bat colonies. Summer bat roosts may be fairly small, typically 20 individuals in the case of Brown Long-eared Bat. Roosts of other species can be much bigger where there are cavities of a suitable size; over 1,000 individuals are known to exist in some British colonies of Soprano Pipistrelle.

In winter most bats hibernate. In southern Britain, Pipistrelles do not always hibernate but may remain active through the winter, roosting in hollow trees and old buildings. Brandt's Bat, Daubenton's Bat and Natterer's Bat hibernate from around September to April and require

A rot hole in a Brasenose Wood oak tree; Shotover is rich in opportunities for roosting bats

hibernacula with a stable microclimate, such as cellars, caves or tunnels. There are very few natural hibernacula around Shotover and so the Horspath–Littleworth railway tunnel and other long-abandoned brick or concrete structures — many left over from World War II — are particularly valuable.

The proximity of a bat's feeding grounds to its roosting habitat varies between species. Daubenton's Bats, for example, generally feed within six kilometres of their roost, whereas Noctules have been known to fly over 10 kilometres to feed. In the case of Daubenton's Bat, their choice of roost may be dependent on their physiological need for more drinking water than most other bats. As it is possible that Daubenton's Bats regularly use the Horspath–Littleworth tunnel, the numerous wetlands and water bodies found at Shotover — all within six kilometres of Horspath — are likely to be among the feeding grounds for this species. Other bat species found on and around Shotover are not associated as strongly with water, yet the local water bodies remain an excellent source of flying insects, especially in periods of dry weather.

Foxes and mustelids (Carnivora)

The Red Fox inhabits the woodlands and fields around Shotover, ranging over the whole Hill and thereby ensuring occasional sightings. In the past, due to their nocturnal habit and reluctance to foray into towns and villages, Foxes were not seen as often as they are today. In recent years, however, they have overcome their timidity and are more likely to be seen taking advantage of the feeding opportunities in urban areas, even during daylight hours. Indeed, Foxes have been seen trotting down local streets and through gardens in the middle of the day. The broad range of habitats on the Hill provides ample food for Foxes, supporting their varied carnivorous diet which includes Rabbit, birds and earthworms. Foxes usually dig their own burrows and breeding dens but sometimes, particularly in the sandy soils of Shotover, they will exploit a vacated Badger sett or enlarge an abandoned Rabbit burrow. During the breeding season Foxes use their dens extensively for rearing and sheltering their cubs but for the rest of the year spend most of the time above ground, finding cover in woodlands and hedgerows.

In Britain, there are eight species of mammal in the Mustelidae family; all are short-legged carnivores that use their strong scent for territorial marking and sexual communication. Four species have been recorded in natural circumstances at Shotover: Badger, Stoat *M. erminea*, Weasel and Polecat. In addition, there has been evidence of the release of Ferrets *M. furo* (the domesticated species of Polecat) and, although not seen, American Mink *M. vison* has been suggested as a possible contributor to the low numbers of common water birds on the north side of the Hill [see also page 203].

Shotover is well populated with Badgers and these large mustelids are frequently photographed at night wherever an infra-red motion-sensitive camera is deployed. Every year a few individuals are killed on the roads that surround the Hill. Badger setts occur right across Shotover, especially where the soil is sandy, and therefore easy to dig, yet sufficiently firm to withstand the many underground tunnels and cavities these animals create. The numerous entrances to a sett, sometimes just a few metres apart, lead to an extensive network of tunnels incorporating latrines and chambers for sleeping and rearing their cubs.

Where burrowing conditions at Shotover are ideal, some setts are very old and extensive. In places, years of soil movement and the resultant mounds of excavated soil have significantly modified the shape of the ground. These enormous setts may have been used by successive generations for decades and perhaps centuries. Other setts are relatively temporary and ancillary to the main sett, and abandoned setts are not uncommon — some quite large. Vacated setts are often readily adopted by other mammals, especially by Foxes and much less frequently by Rabbits. At Shotover, observations have suggested that Foxes will partially cohabit with Badgers, using part of a large multi-entrance sett. In one instance Fox cubs were seen playing in and around one of the entrances of a sett that seemed otherwise the preserve of Badgers.

One of many badger-sett entrances excavated in the soft sand of Shotover Ivan Wright

A Badger cub returns to the sett after an evening foray Ivan Wright

The elusive Stoat Roger Wyatt

It is a rare privilege to glimpse a Fallow Deer at Shotover Roger Wyatt

Stoats, with their distinctive black-tipped tail, and the smaller, closely related Weasel are recorded regularly but infrequently at Shotover. Most records are for Stoats, and these include evidence of breeding in 2018. As long as there is cover from predators, both species will use a wide range of habitats. Weasels hunt smaller prey than that of Stoats, with most victims being voles and mice. Female Stoats hunt small animals; however, the larger male Stoat is able to supplement this diet with birds and young Rabbits.

There have been three plausible sightings of Polecat since 2000 in different parts of Shotover. These nocturnal animals are found mainly in wooded areas and wetlands and around farms — all habitats represented on the Hill. The diversity of these habitats provides plenty of food for the Polecat's diet, which includes rodents, Rabbits, frogs, birds and insects. Wild Polecats are known to occur in Oxfordshire but the release of domestically bred Ferrets and Polecat–Ferret hybrids always poses a problem for identification of live sightings. Typically, the Polecat is identified by its smaller size and the dark 'goggle' markings around its eyes but unfortunately these characters can occur in Ferret hybrids. More confident identification is possible with a dead animal, such as one killed on a road, but none have been available from around the Hill. A white Ferret was seen on one occasion on The Plain, probably having been released that day.

Deer (Cervidae)

Three species of deer can be seen at Shotover. Reeves' Muntjac *Muntiacus reevesi* and Roe Deer *Capreolus capreolus* are both common, while Fallow Deer are much less frequently seen. The diminutive Reeves' Muntjac, with its distinctively hunched back, ranges across the whole Hill, and is often regarded as a pest in allotments and gardens. This deer is probably the only resident breeding species of the three at Shotover and its eerie territorial 'barking' can be heard over a considerable distance. Roe Deer also roam the Hill but appear to use the area only for grazing, as a daytime refuge and as a natural corridor for their wider movement in the countryside. No evidence of breeding has been confirmed although juveniles (with white spots) may be seen in summer. It is not uncommon to disturb an individual at rest in the Bracken, or to see a small group grazing in open woodland or the lower fields. However, frequent sightings in the valley marshes, where the rushes show signs of extensive deer grazing, indicate that these wetlands are not only a principal feeding ground for Roe Deer but probably also their main routes of passage across the Hill.

Although Fallow Deer have been known to venture to the top of the Hill, and have been observed crossing the open ground of The Plain and Mary Sadler Field, most sightings are from the lower fields. This is only to be expected; in contrast to the woodland browsing of Reeves' Muntjac and Roe Deer, Fallow Deer are natural grazers of grassland and open ground. Only very rarely has an older buck been seen — most recently on a path in Brasenose Wood in December 2015 — standing tall and handsome with a full set of palmate antlers.

The populations of deer species in Britain varied greatly through the 19th and 20th centuries due to hunting and culling policies, changes in habitat (both losses and gains) and introductions. At the beginning of the 20th century the deer fauna at Shotover would have been very different from that of today. Roe Deer, Britain's only native deer, had become almost extinct in southern Britain by this time, and was not even mentioned in the *Victoria County History of Oxfordshire* (Elton, 1939). Red Deer had disappeared from the county in the mid-19th century and Reeves' Muntjac had only just been introduced to the Woburn Estate from China. Only Fallow Deer grazed in the open fields around the Hill, possibly in greater numbers than today.

It is somewhat surprising, therefore, that as late as the 1970s, records suggest that the only deer at Shotover were Reeves' Muntjac. Shortly thereafter, David Steel (1984: p. 119) reported that Reeves' Munjac were the commonest deer on the Hill and that Fallow Deer were only seen regularly near Shotover to the north, and added that for Roe Deer "*it will be interesting to see whether they eventually return to Oxfordshire*". Steel was clearly unaware that the first Roe Deer in the county had already been reported from Chinnor in 1970 and Wychwood in 1972 (Thames Valley Environmental Records Centre — TVERC, 2016, pers. comm.), and that although the earliest records of Roe Deer at Shotover were not until 2000 (Shotover Wildlife) there were numerous sightings in eastern Oxfordshire from 1981 to 1997.

Since Roe and Reeves' Muntjac Deer are both woodland species, the rapid increase of their populations in southern Britain has naturally had a profound effect on the ecology and management of woodlands in this region. During

High-cut coppicing

Coppicing has been practised for centuries as a method of productive woodland management, and under this traditional regime a particular wildlife diversity has stabilized. Today in Brasenose Wood, as in many other woodlands, the rapid increase in the deer population is undermining the viability of the habitat through the grazing of the young Hazel by deer. This is threatening the valued community of coppice-woodland species through the consequent changes in habitat structure.

In 2008, Shotover Wildlife began investigating a coppicing technique to maximize the benefits to wildlife while minimizing the resources required, and so initiated an experiment to test this method. Hazel stools were cut at an intermediate height (0.8 metres) to give the regrowth a head-start over the detrimental effects of browsing by deer, together with control plots cut at ground level as was traditional, and at 1.2 metres from the ground to be beyond the reach of the deer. The objective is to simulate a traditional coppicing rotation frequency (about 12 years in Brasenose Wood) without the need for fencing (Wright and Bartel, 2017).

The experiment ultimately indicated that, although the method does not protect all ground flora from deer browsing, cutting at 0.8 metres resulted in much greater woodland ground flora diversity compared with cutting either lower or higher. The experimental trials also showed that, with this technique, the mortality of Hazel stems and stools was no worse than with other methods of coppicing. In Brasenose Wood, since 2015, cutting Hazel stools at 0.8 metres from the ground has been adopted as the optimal height for overall wildlife benefit.

A female Roe Deer in Brasenose Wood recorded on a motion-sensitive camera Ivan Wright

Systematic high-cut coppicing in Brasenose Wood

Part of Brasenose Wood one year after high-cut coppicing

To minimize the damage to Hazel shoots by the increasing number of browsing deer, Shotover Wildlife has researched alternative cutting heights.

the many centuries when parts of Shotover were coppiced for woodland products, the control of large herbivorous mammals would have been essential for woodland productivity and Hazel regrowth and, as a consequence, deer control would have had an influence on the woodland ground flora. However, with the current high population of browsing deer, not only is there less regeneration of ground flora but also the plants that persist become biased towards those species that are unpalatable to the deer (Hodgetts, 2009). Although Aspen is not toxic to deer, in Brasenose Wood it is almost entirely ignored in preference for Hazel, with the consequence that, without remedial measures, the suckering Aspen increases incrementally each time the Hazel is coppiced in a conventional way.

Interestingly, when David Steel revitalized systematic coppicing in Brasenose Wood in 1973 the number of deer was only a small fraction of what it has become some 40 years later. Therefore, the coppicing of Brasenose Wood as a management intervention cannot overlook the growing influence of deer if it is to maintain, let alone enhance, the wildlife diversity of the woodland. Various attempts were made by Oxford City Council to prevent deer from reaching the newly cut and sprouting Hazel, by placing either a deer fence around each block after coppicing (2000 and 2006) or a small fence around each Hazel stool (1998–99, 2003–04), but

both of these solutions are resource-intensive and, in the case of the small fences, only partially successful. However, trials by Shotover Wildlife have shown that cutting Hazel at a height well above the ground can provide a cost-effective alternative to traditional coppicing, benefitting woodland wildlife while compensating for the impact of browsing deer [see box, previous page].

Squirrels, mice, voles and rats (Rodentia)

It is now quite difficult to appreciate that not so very long ago the Red Squirrel *Sciurus vulgaris* was common in Oxfordshire — including Shotover. However, the local population of Red Squirrels suffered a dramatic decline between 1910 and 1925 following the introduction of the Grey Squirrel *S. carolinensis* from America, in spite of which Elton wrote, somewhat optimistically, "*it does, however, seem unlikely that they* [Grey Squirrels] *will be at all common* [in Oxfordshire] *for many years to come*" (Elton, 1939: p. 221–222). In the early 20th century, and prior to the introduction of the Grey Squirrel, habitat loss in Britain was already causing marked reductions in regional populations of Red Squirrel, and its grey cousin soon drove it to extinction in most of Britain. The Grey Squirrel is notorious for stripping bark from trees to eat the sappy tissue beneath, as is evident on the many birches on the Hill. Although this activity may seem detrimental to birch woodland — killing the upper canopy of some trees — in the SSSI where birches are common, the bark damage and general necrosis create additional niches for fungi and invertebrates, and therefore enhance the ecological succession without any significant effect on the tree population.

The Brown Rat *Rattus norvegicus*, although ubiquitous around habitation and farmyards, is seldom seen alive on the upper, wilder parts of the Hill. Most of the records for this unpopular rodent are of corpses of animals that have fallen victim to disease, poison or predation. Of the rodents resident at Shotover, mice and voles are by far the most frequently encountered mammals in any live-trapping survey. The Wood Mouse *Apodemus sylvaticus* is very adaptable, in part because of its varied diet which enables it to take full advantage of the many and varied habitats at Shotover. These species, along with the Bank Vole *Clethrionomys glareolus* and Field Vole *Microtus agrestis*, can all range widely, going unnoticed in the extensive ground cover across the Hill, with the arable fields and meadows meeting their dietary needs. However, these fields are especially beneficial to the Harvest Mouse *Micromys minutus* and House Mouse *Mus musculus*, both of which feed on wild seeds and cereal grain, and which have been recorded in small numbers over the years.

Hares and Rabbits (Lagomorpha)

Throughout the 20th century, Brown Hare *Lepus europaeus* declined rapidly in Britain and Oxfordshire but although it is now locally scarce it is still seen at Shotover in most years. Hares are generally nocturnal but also moderately active during the day and have been seen in the open and arable areas around the Hill, occasionally engaging in their dramatic courtship activities. This is the enchanting 'mad March hare' behaviour and 'boxing', the latter usually being the method by which an unreceptive female fights off an attentive male. Most unusually, early on an April morning in 2010, a Hare was observed in a clearing within Brasenose Wood.

One mammal found in great abundance at Shotover is the Rabbit. The sandy soils, convenient for burrowing, and the expanses of slow-growing acidic grassland make the Hill an ideal habitat. Indeed, Rabbits are an important influence on Shotover's ecosystem; their close grazing encourages the establishment of fine-leaved grasses and suppresses the development of scrubland. Where they are numerous, their burrows form warrens which can support several very large colonies. Shotover's Rabbit population is not easy to estimate; the many free-running dogs in the daytime mean that Rabbits are accustomed to grazing during the darker, more

The neatly woven nest of a Harvest Mouse found on the edge of Lower Close during a survey in 2016

Brown Hare Dominic Regan

A large and healthy Rabbit population is critical for Shotover's grassland ecology

In the future the potential development of endemic diseases in Rabbits could have a profound impact on best management for acidic grassland.

tranquil hours, so that in all likelihood only a very small proportion is ever seen.

As with deer in the woodlands and marshes, Rabbit grazing has a notable impact on the grasslands of the Hill. The extent of unmown short-sward grassland at Shotover is correlated with the abundance of Rabbits, as was most dramatically demonstrated when Rabbits were almost eliminated by myxomatosis and many grasslands were subsequently lost to secondary woodland. This devastating disease was introduced into France in 1952 and arrived in Kent the following year; within the following two years the British Rabbit population had plummeted by 95 per cent. With sheep grazing also declining at Shotover in the mid-20th century, much of the scrub growth and secondary woodland on the Hill dates from this threshold era.

The extent and quality of acidic grassland at Shotover are therefore strongly influenced by the Rabbit population and have the potential to increase. Although the number of Rabbits has partially recovered since the destructive years of myxomatosis, the Hill is most unlikely to regain any of the former extent of acidic grassland without some conservation assistance. Indeed, in some areas, the extremely intensive Rabbit grazing, whatever its underlying cause, indicates that some colonies are confined and unable to expand. In such places the grass is insufficient for the population and the Rabbits have resorted to

eating the tougher Gorse on the periphery of the grassland — evident by a distinct browse line on the Gorse at 40 centimetres from the ground.

The future for mammals at Shotover

The prospects for the wild mammals of Shotover depend on their adaptability to the broad range of threats that they face. Those mammals that do not have highly specific requirements for food, shelter or habitat should continue to thrive. The species most at risk are those unable to adapt to the loss of habitat caused partly by agricultural policies and practices in the wider countryside (as with the Harvest Mouse) but also by wildlife management that fails to appreciate the habitat requirements for mammals. For example, in the SSSI the quality of ground cover for small mammals may be overlooked when managing scrub habitat, or during woodland work older trees may go unassessed for roosting bats. It is remarkable, for example, how little attention is paid to bat roosts in the management of ancient woodlands, in stark contrast to the high level of concern and protection for bats roosting in buildings. An additional threat for bats results from the widespread use of pesticides and artificial fertilizers, which depletes the numbers and diversity of their insect food — though fortunately, the Hill still provides bats and indeed the whole insectivorous food web with an abundance of pesticide-free insects and relatively uncontaminated spring water.

Even where pesticides do not reduce the food supply, they pose a serious risk to the majority of wild mammals in the countryside — especially carnivores and insectivores — because these chemicals accumulate in their bodies when ingested over time. At Shotover, mammals that scavenge more widely in the surrounding fields or those that prey on animals from outside the area (such as a Fox eating a bird) are more susceptible than those with much smaller ranges.

Direct human intervention also has an influence when mammals are considered to be a pest; some species can legally be shot or poisoned. In addition, although much less frequently in recent decades, some larger mammals are shot as game. Rats are universally despised and most people would prefer eradication. Rabbits, Grey Squirrels and deer can also be a target for persecution, especially in places where they harm crops and trees, but at Shotover any eradication measures are unlikely to have a significant impact on their populations. As there is currently no large-scale poultry or game-bird rearing on the Hill, the Fox may not be quite so hounded as in the past.

The fragmentation of the countryside is now widely recognized as a problem for many species, including mammals, restricting their ability to disperse and resulting in isolated populations whose genetic resilience is compromised. One principal asset of Shotover, however, is the age and quality of the hedgerow network, both on the Hill and to the south and east. With sufficient vegetation as cover from predation, many mammals are able to find adequate opportunities for dispersal.

Despite the occasional bouts of myxomatosis, Rabbits are not currently an endangered species on the Hill and, as noted earlier, since the mid-20th century they have remained a major controlling influence on one of Shotover's regionally scarce habitats — acidic grassland. This could change in the future with the arrival of Rabbit Haemorrhagic Disease. Knowledge of how to increase sustainably the area of Rabbit grazing is therefore indispensable to the conservation of the grassland which supports much of Shotover's distinctive flora and fauna. For example, it is critical that Rabbits do not lose grazing territory while their populations are temporarily reduced by disease, thereby leaving an opening for the encroachment of scrub and secondary woodland. On the other hand, it would be unwise to expand acidic grassland in the expectation that Rabbit grazing will then provide the subsequent maintenance, especially if the expansion exceeds the rate at which the local Rabbit population can increase to take up the space — notwithstanding popular notions of the rate at which Rabbits can breed.

In general, the extensive natural area of Shotover Hill is a vital resource for mammals, providing cover, food and territory. Given considerate management, and no ecologically damaging new roads or detrimental changes to agricultural and building development policy, the Hill will continue to provide for the needs of its mammals for many more years.

Matured habitat 12 years after conservation work

Undisturbed structural diversity at ground level is often underappreciated for its value to small mammals.

Shotover prospects: building on the past for the future

Ivan Wright and Jacqueline Wright

One of the veteran oaks in the nature reserve that mark the old cart track to Westhill Farm

People have been attracted to Shotover for thousands of years, for all sorts of reasons: ochre, fuel-wood, dry land for settlement, the outlook from the summit, and so on. Furthermore, the study of natural history at Shotover, benefitting greatly from the proximity of Oxford University, has spread its influence far beyond Oxfordshire. And so it continues, well into the 21st century. Today's naturalists are still finding new species on the Hill — not just to Shotover but also to Britain and even to science — and monitoring the decline of others. Their studies continue to advance understanding of the natural world and also to inspire those who care for that world and to help launch the careers of the next generation of ecologists. In every way, Shotover Hill is a natural asset to be respected and conserved.

This final chapter considers the major factors likely to influence the future for wildlife at Shotover, bringing together the views of the specialist authors and the knowledge accumulated since recording began on the Hill, and setting them in the context of our society and its institutions. For naturalists, managers, students, conservationists and more, we hope that this chapter will further an appreciation of the ebb and flow of species over time and enable an understanding of the context in which biodiversity is lost. After all, securing a future for wildlife depends on managers, advisers and politicians having a firm grasp of the major factors at play. The active commitment of members of Shotover Wildlife over 20 years, and the insights gained from working with public authorities, have produced a deeper understanding of wildlife conservation at Shotover. What follows explores the inherent problems and difficulties in achieving the best outcome for wildlife, and suggests solutions for how these insights might be taken forward.

Many people deplore the decline of wildlife and feel a sense of loss at its disappearance. In Britain, one of the reasons for that decline is that the majority of people accept the assurances of government agencies regarding species and habitat protection. In fact, however, successive recent governments have shown only

An increasing number of people appreciate the special wildlife diversity of Horspath Common as well as its tranquil beauty

a superficial concern for species protection and have accorded little intrinsic value to the broader diversity [see page 235]. Aside from species that contribute to the productivity of agriculture, medicine or commerce, the value of wildlife to central government extends little further than the countryside's important role in tourism, recreation and personal well-being — exploiting the fact that, for most people, a walk in the countryside can be thoroughly uplifting as long as the main species groups, such as trees, birds and butterflies, are present. But many also value biodiversity intuitively, beyond their level of knowledge. At Shotover, for example, many visitors are pleased to learn of the 1,000 beetle species recorded there, and express genuine appreciation to those who seek to conserve them, even though their own knowledge of beetles may extend no further than recognizing a ladybird.

A key point is that while public sector regard for wildlife has been in decline for several decades [see page 233], in recent years it has largely been communities of local people, amateur naturalists and non-governmental organizations that have championed the importance of biodiversity and its protection. And although there are many partnerships between professional managers and volunteer conservationists that have delivered effective and lasting work, it is very likely to be, above all, the strength of community feeling for nature that will secure a positive future for wildlife.

A new community at Shotover
In May 1997, Brooklime (a water speedwell with small blue flowers) was recorded near Westhill Farm by Jacqueline Wright as she set out on her first survey of wetland plants at Shotover. From that moment, through Jacqueline's enthusiasm for biological recording which was subsequently taken forward by other members of Shotover Wildlife, a journey of community activity began that has made possible the book you are now reading. Biological surveying, one of Shotover Wildlife's main activities, has also made it possible to confirm that Shotover hosts many scarce and declining species, including once-common species that are now rare or declining rapidly in the wider countryside. And, perhaps most importantly, Shotover Wildlife has been able to re-establish the Hill as regionally and nationally important for some groups of species,

Conservation at Shotover is built on a foundation of species surveying, the core activity of Shotover Wildlife Ivan Wright

and to achieve recognition as a nationally important site for others, especially beetles and the insects of dead wood [see page 132].

The many initiatives by Shotover Wildlife, whether species recording or evidence-based conservation projects, have provided the opportunity to publish and present wildlife information in a variety of ways: from public information leaflets to peer-reviewed articles, and from innumerable talks and tours for clubs and natural history societies to a Shotover conference at the Oxford University Museum of Natural History in 2014. Without doubt this output has created a much wider awareness of the importance of Shotover, bringing with it a measure of respect for wildlife from all who visit the Country Park or contribute to its management. In connection with biodiversity, for example, Shotover Hill and Shotover Wildlife are now well known by naturalists throughout the county and beyond, and community demand for leaflets and talks about Shotover is as keen now as when Shotover Wildlife was founded in 1999.

Shotover need not lose the beautiful saproxylic beetle *Callidium violaceum* ©WikiCommons

Concern for species in the future

The ways in which human activity can harm wildlife is a recurrent theme throughout this book, with authors expressing concern for the general loss of diversity and highlighting threats to species, each from their specialist perspective. Some of these threats are external and mainly beyond local control, such as climate change; other threats are site-specific and capable of local remedy. Clearly, a positive future for the wildlife of Shotover depends on understanding not only the influence of these various threats but also their combined impact.

There is great concern over climate change and the long-term effect this will have upon habitats and species, both in abundance and distribution. However, while the consequences of climate change must be faced, and concerns for wildlife are well placed, other factors such as inadequate regard for wildlife under government environmental and agricultural policies will cause a faster degradation of many species long before they are affected by the slow and unpredictable consequences of climate change. Agricultural intensification is the dominant external threat to wildlife, and over recent years has been one of the main agents of overall decline in the wider countryside (Hayhow *et al.*, 2016). Flower-rich meadows have been ploughed up for arable cropping and hedgerows removed to increase the scale of production. Also, powerful and persistent agrochemicals, such as DDT and neonicotinoids (Woodcock *et al.*, 2017), do not remain confined to their place of application and cause harm to wildlife by diffusing more widely.

The threats to species mentioned most often in this book are reduced connectivity in the wider landscape and habitat loss; both of these influences are widespread in Britain but their effect is much more local. Construction for industry, housing and national infrastructure reduces the overall area of natural habitat and also increases the isolation of the remaining wildlife sites and the distance between them, preventing the dispersal that many species depend upon. Connectivity is further reduced where hedgerows are removed for agricultural purposes or road building. At Shotover, for example, although the quality of the network of surrounding hedges to the south and east is high, the urban development and dual carriageway roads to the north and west form an impenetrable obstacle for a great many species including reptiles, small mammals and innumerable invertebrates.

The practice of burning felled trees at Shotover led to a catastrophic loss of dead-wood habitat that has now been stopped through community pressure

However, two major threats to wildlife are posed directly by site management, especially in nature reserves, and are therefore wholly avoidable. Firstly, there is the misguided tendency to 'tidy up', for example by burning or removing critical habitat such as dead wood or leaf litter. Secondly, much damage can be caused by well-intentioned work that is aimed at conserving wildlife but, through want of understanding, has the opposite effect. In particular, actions directed exclusively towards the conservation of a single popular species (or group of species) can be especially destructive to others. Examples at Shotover have been the 'weeding' of plants from an area of Heather and the ill-informed removal of scrub woodland for the benefit of butterflies, both of which have compromised rare plants. It is a sobering fact that vulnerable habitats that are widely known to be important — such as heath or ancient woodland — attract both the best and worst of conservation effort.

Many authors of these chapters have stressed how an understanding of the wider ecology is fundamental to preserving species. Wise management not only aims to conserve a scarce habitat and its component species but also pays attention to how they fit in with the surrounding landscape. The knowledge required for such conservation would seem to be limitless, and trying to take account of the full complexity of a diverse ecology is a daunting prospect; however,

as long as carefully considered evidence-based work is suitably paced and on a proportionate scale, species will be able to re-adjust without conservationists having to worry about the minutiae of multiple complex biologies.

National policy and public sector influence at Shotover

Although the understanding of ecological processes is vital for ensuring a positive future for wildlife, it is the social and commercial environment that controls the fate of all land in Britain. At the highest level, government and the democratic and bureaucratic processes decide overall policy. However, it is the actions of individuals, and how they interact with each other, that make the difference to wildlife 'on the ground' — both nationally and on the Hill. The remainder of this chapter explores the institutional and social environments out of which a positive and sustainable future for wildlife diversity at Shotover could develop.

The public sector framework

Shotover Country Park is a public-access open space managed by a public authority — Oxford City Council. In 1986, most of the park was designated as Brasenose Wood and Shotover Hill Site of Special Scientific Interest (SSSI) — a seminal moment for wildlife protection on the Hill. But institutionally the City Council has seldom

Is there a sustainable future for the complex and beautiful wildlife habitats at Shotover?

shown a strong commitment to wildlife diversity and the quality of wildlife management has relied almost entirely on the individual level of interest of the Council's managers for 'green spaces' — which has varied considerably over the years.

In order to appreciate fully the way in which habitats and species may be protected in the future, however, it is necessary to consider the central government policies purporting to address the overall state of British wildlife and, in particular, the radical changes in those policies over the past few decades. Although many of these concern agricultural land and building development, we shall focus on the directives for nature reserves, including the 6,500 designated Sites of Special Scientific Interest (SSSIs) in Britain.

In 1949, the urgent need for a government agency to safeguard British nature reserves was satisfied by a Royal Commission that founded the Nature Conservancy (NC). The NC had the authority to establish National Nature Reserves and SSSIs, employed many eminent naturalists, and was independent and generally respected. In 1973, it was replaced by the Nature Conservancy Council (NCC), which in turn was replaced in 1991 by three regional agencies, including English Nature, each also employing many specialist naturalists. Then, under the Natural Environment and Rural Communities (NERC) Act 2006, English Nature was renamed Natural England. Although the NC and NCC initiatives to conserve British habitats were underpinned by the highest of ideals, they also provoked deep tensions between environmental and economic interests, and not surprisingly wildlife has been the loser throughout (Sheail, 1998). From NCC to Natural England, each agency has been weaker and less independent than its predecessor.

Today, Natural England retains overall responsibility for wildlife management in English SSSIs but with a drastically cut budget and employing fewer specialist naturalists. Its stature has now atrophied to an administrative role within the Department for Environment, Food and Rural Affairs (DEFRA) and its activities diverted from matters of wildlife protection to assisting with economic growth (July M., 2013). Clearly, successive UK governments have sought not only to shed the cost of wildlife protection but also to weaken the conservation role of its official adviser for the natural environment.

Even before 2006, English Nature's commitment to small and medium-sized SSSIs had become somewhat lax, the scrutiny of wildlife management at some SSSIs was neglected and management schedules were allowed to lapse. At Shotover, for example, brief inspections continued at three-year intervals but the original work plan (1986) was not extended beyond 1994, following which the heath and acidic grassland deteriorated. At least in 2000 the central government had taken note of the overall poor state of the nation's SSSIs and, as a result, set targets for their improvement: in particular, for English Nature to "*bring 95 per cent of all nationally important wildlife sites into favourable condition by 2010*" (HM Treasury, 2000: section 9.3).

In the early 2000s two additional factors came into play with far-reaching consequences for biodiversity. Firstly, with diminishing resources to oversee the management of SSSIs as originally intended, English Nature, followed by Natural England, began to rely more on generalized prescriptions for habitats and less on contemporary recording, extant data or the specific needs of each site (Kirby *et al.*, 2010). Secondly, in 2006 Natural England was entrusted with the responsibility for distributing European funds which included the Higher Level Stewardship (HLS) scheme. The HLS was created in 2005 to replace a number of agricultural stewardship schemes but was also made available to landowners of SSSIs, including the commissioning of new management plans [see box, page 234]. Since Natural England was

Coordinated botanical surveying by Shotover Wildlife
Ivan Wright

under great pressure to reach over-ambitious government targets for the condition of SSSIs, yet was allowed to award HLS grants on the basis of formulaic site assessments in order to reach those targets, the scene was set for a number of strategic and regressive shifts in policy.

The redefining of public sector assessment of SSSIs

Unknown to most naturalists and managers, and after the government had set targets for the condition of SSSIs in 2000, Natural England created its own definitions for terms such as 'favourable condition' and 'recovering'. In 2005, a few months after the HLS scheme was launched in Britain, the upper part of the SSSI at Shotover — 57 per cent (62 hectares) — was declared by Natural England to be "*not currently in favourable condition*" (Natural England, 21 November 2005, letter to City Council) and in need of an HLS-funded management plan. (The lower part of the SSSI, including the ancient woodland of Brasenose Wood, was deemed in 'favourable condition' and left without a plan.) However, achieving the state of 'recovering' on the upper part was unrealistic as the set targets — for the expansion of acidic grassland,

for example — were much too ambitious and substantially mismatched to the available resources.

Similarly unattainable objectives were drafted for many other English SSSIs declared to be in 'unfavourable' condition (Kirby *et al.*, 2010). Consequently, in 2009, one year before the government's deadline for 95 per cent of SSSIs to be at least 'recovering', Natural England changed the condition definitions. Originally an SSSI could be considered as recovering from a poor state "*if it has begun to show, or is continuing to show, a trend towards favourable condition*" (JNCC, 1998 and 2004). This observation-based criterion was changed to a purely administrative one, requiring only that "*all the necessary management measures are in place*" (Kirby *et al.*, 2010; Natural England, 2017a). No longer was there a need for an SSSI to show any actual evidence of recovery, as long as the paperwork stated an intention to bring about a recovery. Hence, as far as the government was concerned, a site could deteriorate significantly but nevertheless be 'recovering'.

Furthermore, no system was put in place to ensure that HLS monies were spent on a demonstrable recovery of habitat, it being sufficient to use the grant primarily to fund management plans. At Shotover, as soon as 'recovering' was redefined, HLS money was awarded and in 2011 a basic management plan was commissioned for the upper part of the SSSI, yet such was the government pressure on Natural England to promote the site to 'recovering' condition that the SSSI was declared to be 'recovering' in 2010 (Natural England, 2017b) without a plan in place.

A flawed policy for SSSI management

It might seem that a formal reassessment of the condition of the SSSI at Shotover, followed by a new management plan, would provide a most promising way forward, especially with the accumulated data and on-site knowledge available through Shotover Wildlife. But in 2010 it became clear that Shotover Wildlife's data posed a considerable inconvenience to Natural England: firstly because an evidence-based approach would not only take too long but was also incompatible with their entrenched practice of using a basic prescriptive methodology; and secondly because the additional information exposed a serious deficiency in the public authority's regard for biodiversity in SSSIs.

Natural England revealed to Shotover Wildlife (4 February 2010, correspondence) that the conservation objectives for all SSSIs, as well as any new management plans, had to be drawn up solely on the basis of the wildlife features described in a site's original citation — the document officially designating a site as an SSSI. Incorporating new information would amount to re-designation, a measure

Silver-washed Fritillary has been resident in Brasenose Wood since 2009 Peter Creed

rarely attempted. Consequently, for the SSSI at Shotover, no additional feature or species discovered since designation could be considered, notwithstanding 30 years of additional recording and a doubling of known species. It defies belief that wildlife management should be required to proceed indefinitely as if no additions to ecological recording and understanding had been made since 1986. Clearly this policy is seriously flawed, as it presumes that the original citation is comprehensive and accurate, and places disproportionate weight on what is — in Shotover's case — a very skeletal document.

The citation for the SSSI at Shotover [see the Appendix] is just 717 words in length, of which fewer than a third deal with the upper heathy part, and includes only 115 words devoted to invertebrates. That such a sketchy document should then be used as a standard of due regard for biodiversity is particularly disturbing. Indeed, it is unlikely that the (anonymous) author of the citation would have had any notion of how their brief outline description would be ossified and misused. For example, while the citation makes no mention of the rich beetle fauna known for Shotover at that time, its reference to rare flies is based on species not seen since the 1920s. Consequently, the official conservation objectives for the SSSI — still in force in 2018 and with no prospect of change — pay no consideration to a great many important existing taxa, while imposing targets for a wetland invertebrate habitat that no longer exists at Shotover.

System failure and recovery

From 2005 to 2010, while Natural England pursued HLS money for a management plan for part of the SSSI, Shotover Wildlife worked with Oxford City Council's Countryside Service to maintain habitats and implement major conservation initiatives. This included using a sizeable grant, secured by Shotover Wildlife, to expand the acidic grassland [see box, page 98]. In 2010, however, when Natural England promised to provide Oxford City Council with advice and a partial management plan, both public authorities deemed it unnecessary to complement these with the crucial understanding of the site that Shotover Wildlife could have provided.

An outline management plan was eventually produced for the upper part of the SSSI in 2013 (by an ecological consultancy) but by this time Natural England was no longer providing sufficient guidance and Council staff were left to attempt critical habitat conservation entirely on their own. Their subsequent attempts to restore acidic grassland were mostly unsuccessful and, in places, destroyed habitat for vulnerable and protected heathland species [see pages 196 and 232]. This low point for wildlife conservation at Shotover was the inevitable consequence of an administratively driven system that had become wholly disconnected from its intended objective. In this seemingly hopeless climate of misguided management, Shotover Wildlife suspended its own practical conservation work.

Perhaps lessons will be learned from this worrying period of state intervention. As the Shotover Management Plan has proved to be of little practical use and Natural England's involvement effectively absent (satisfied that their 'recovering' target has been reached), since 2015 Oxford City Council has — after a change of management — returned to seeking the advice and assistance of local expertise. In partnership with Shotover Wildlife, careful habitat restoration, based on the best available evidence, is once more being undertaken in the SSSI. We hope that this proven method of wildlife conservation will continue well into the future. We also hope that Natural England will come to support the best possible management of an exceptional public nature reserve.

The anatomy of collaboration

Clearly, good interpersonal relationships are vital for working in partnership, especially where essential resources are provided by different contributors. However, a common problem in wildlife conservation is the marked cultural difference between professional managers and the self-motivated amateur naturalists and taxonomic specialists who work as volunteers. The interaction between these two groups can present considerable difficulties when agendas and priorities are not fully transparent, difficulties that can be exacerbated by preconceived ideas of each other's position. The problem has been recognized in recent years, at least among naturalists and social scientists in Britain, and in 2003 a study was conducted by Lancaster University specifically to investigate this social conundrum (Ellis and Waterton, 2004). Indeed, the challenges experienced by Shotover Wildlife as a newly emerging organization (2001–03) were included among Ellis and Waterton's case studies, with reference especially to the widely differing levels of respect accorded to Shotover Wildlife by various public authorities.

An important point, frequently overlooked, is that an individual volunteer seen sweating over a bow saw at a weekend may also be a nationally recognized taxonomist or an experienced and committed professional ecologist. If paid managers were the experts and there were no expertise among the unpaid volunteers, matters would be much simpler, yet — especially in aspects of species- and site-specific ecology — the best-qualified adviser in taxonomy or ecological management may well be a volunteer. Unfortunately, it is too easy

Major habitat improvements have been researched and managed by Shotover Wildlife, and delivered in partnership with contractors and Oxford City Council

Are these people 'just volunteers' — or a group of experienced conservationists and qualified ecologists?

Measuring a veteran oak on the Shotover Estate

"Amateur expert naturalists are a unique and valuable cultural element in British society ... they are the bedrock of much of the most important biodiversity protection work." Ellis *et al.* (2005)

for professional managers to believe sweeping generalizations about volunteers, often thinking in terms of 'harnessing' them solely to serve the objectives of their own workplace — rather than benefiting from a reciprocal partnership. Money is seldom a motive for volunteers, yet they do need recompense. In their summary report, Ellis *et al.* (2005: p. 20) concluded that: *"Amateur expert naturalists are a unique and valuable cultural element in British society. There needs to be more explicit recognition — by government, conservation agencies and leading NGOs — that, frequently invisible though they may be, they are the bedrock of much of the most important biodiversity protection work. Forms of recognition of their contribution are needed which reflect the values of the naturalist communities themselves."*

In the case of volunteer surveyors, professionals routinely expect that data or advice — usually the fruit of many years of committed study and demanding fieldwork — will be willingly supplied regardless of how that information might be used in professional environments. Often such data are used academically, with little relevance to the reality of conserving wildlife; however, Ellis *et al.* (2005: p. 17) noted that *"anxieties and resentments can arise if contributors feel*

they unwittingly become part of choices that have detrimental effects on the environment". Indeed, after unauthorized attempts by public authorities in 2011 to obtain Shotover Wildlife data from the Thames Valley Environmental Records Centre (TVERC), Shotover Wildlife decided to withdraw some of their data in the best interests of wildlife protection on the Hill, records that until then had been shared with the wider community.

Conversely, volunteers sometimes fail to recognize that professionals can be subject to demands that may prevent them from doing as much as they would wish for the cause of biodiversity, including budget restraints and their own institution's policies or politics. Not least is the pressure to meet targets. So when a professional manager succumbs to such demands, it does not necessarily mean that they lack commitment to habitat and species conservation.

Nevertheless, partnerships between professionals and volunteer specialists can be very effective if based firmly on respect and cooperation. In the realm of wildlife conservation, where the skills and resources of both sectors are indispensable, each sector needs to understand and respect the unescapable differences in their motives and methods.

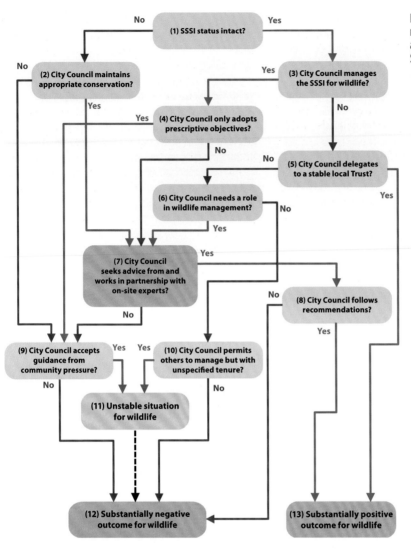

Pathways for management of wildlife at Brasenose Wood and Shotover Hill SSSI

(1) SSSI status intact?
No — Yes

(2) City Council maintains appropriate conservation?
No
Yes

(3) City Council manages the SSSI for wildlife?
Yes
No

(4) City Council only adopts prescriptive objectives?
Yes
No

(5) City Council delegates to a stable local Trust?
No
Yes

(6) City Council needs a role in wildlife management?
Yes
No

(7) City Council seeks advice from and works in partnership with on-site experts?
Yes
No

(8) City Council follows recommendations?
No
Yes

(9) City Council accepts guidance from community pressure?
Yes Yes
No

(10) City Council permits others to manage but with unspecified tenure?
No

(11) Unstable situation for wildlife

(12) Substantially negative outcome for wildlife

(13) Substantially positive outcome for wildlife

Future possibilities at Shotover

The future for wildlife in and around the SSSI depends on those with the greatest influence on conservation decisions: landowners, managers, naturalists and the public authorities. Any of these stakeholders might change their stance over the coming decades. With this in mind, the following section explores different management scenarios and the likely outcome for Shotover's biodiversity under each of them.

Shotover owes its ecological vitality to the publicly owned and officially protected nature reserve. The SSSI status of the reserve gives the wildlife a measure of security, and the diversity of rare and scarce species that have been recorded there sets it apart from the surrounding fields.

Yet the Hill — as defined in this book [see page x] — is only 12 per cent nature reserve (including the railway cuttings and the C.S. Lewis Community Nature Reserve). The remainder is private fields (58 per cent), woodland (six per cent), large gardens (seven per cent) and urban (17 per cent). And although each landowner has extensive rights over their land (within planning and building regulations), the combination of the SSSI and the surrounding countryside adds immeasurable value to that of the SSSI alone. Fortunately, many landowners take an interest in wildlife on their land; where the land is an SSSI the landowner's custodianship is critical. In fact, in protecting species their level of commitment to wildlife conservation far outweighs the impact of directives from government agencies. It would be perfectly possible for an SSSI to be adjoined by land that is better managed for wildlife than that within the SSSI itself.

The advantage of SSSI status is the relative permanence of its statutory protection for wildlife; if this status were to be cancelled, the only remaining safeguard for biodiversity would be public pressure. Although cancellation rarely happens (for example, to allow a major new road or railway), nonetheless the possibility is a useful starting point for future scenarios at Shotover [Question (1) in the flow diagram opposite]. Indeed, this is not beyond the realm of possibility since, as matters stand, those government authorities with a wildlife remit would probably be powerless to oppose it [see page 233]. In that event, Oxford City Council could decide to maintain an appropriate level of conservation (2) but it is much more likely that the quality of wildlife management would largely depend on pressure from within the community (9). Unfortunately, this would be an unstable solution

(11) as community pressure in the absence of statutory protection is difficult to sustain, with the result that the situation could easily deteriorate to be a poor outcome for wildlife (12).

On the other hand, with the SSSI status of Shotover secure, the site would retain its basic legal requirements for the overall protection of wildlife, providing a foundation on which to construct more specific management for habitats and species. With Oxford City Council continuing to manage the SSSI within legal requirements (3), wildlife security would depend on the Council's level of active involvement and commitment to its wildlife diversity. If the Council were to rely solely on the inadequate conservation prescriptions of a government authority (4) such as Natural England [see the Appendix], community pressure would almost certainly be required in order to maintain a suitably high standard of wildlife management (9) — once again landing Shotover in an unstable position.

By far the most efficient and effective route for optimal conservation management by the

Autumn colours in the mixed woodland of Holme Ground

Council is, firstly, to work in close partnership with those specialist naturalists — currently Shotover Wildlife — who have the best knowledge of the site (7) and, secondly, for the Council to follow their recommendations (8) so that the advice is translated by the manager into the best possible outcome for wildlife (13). The Council can then experience, along with the community, the pleasures resulting from a high standard of conservation and the specialists will feel respected because their advice has been implemented.

An additional scenario should be considered, in which Oxford City Council would relinquish wildlife management at Shotover and delegate or subcontract it to a competent, accountable wildlife organization (5). This scenario could be realised if the Council were able to let go of some of the prestige of managing a wildlife site which is also popular with visitors. Two possibilities then arise, both of which would require a contract lasting several years. Firstly, the local Wildlife Trust (BBOWT) could manage the site; it has a good track record, including working with volunteers and local amateur experts. However, this would require a major grant award to employ an ecologist-manager. Alternatively, a new dedicated organization could be formed, such as a Shotover Conservation

Trust, preferably with experienced naturalists forming the majority of trustees. Such a Trust would have the advantage of strong links with the local community and would require only modest funding.

However, if the Council were either uncommitted or insufficiently resourced to manage for wildlife, yet wished to retain an interest as an overseer for conservation (6), it could still work in partnership with on-site expertise but with the latter taking a more executive role (7). Finally, the Council could delegate wildlife management completely, giving conditional permission for volunteer naturalists to do conservation work independently (10), as is currently the case, for example, in north Oxford (the Trap Grounds).

A major consideration in the near future will be the availability of environmental grants, such as countryside stewardship awards, especially when the flow of European money ceases with Britain's withdrawal from the European Union. As has been demonstrated with the HLS [see page 234], such schemes offer clear incentives for both the recipient and the awarding agency but in some cases the objective has been to satisfy administrative targets rather than produce any lasting benefit to the environment.

Brasenose Wood viewed from Horspath, with part of the diverse landscape that adjoins the SSSI at Shotover

Walking, working and wildlife: all part of the life of this Oxfordshire hill

Indeed, fixation on targets can produce the opposite effect — loss of habitat, for example [see page 236]. Unfortunately, financial incentives from government agencies can be difficult for landowners to ignore, locking them into counterproductive prescriptions and leaving them either unwilling or unable to act on alternative advice (4). Nevertheless, it is important to note that optimal wildlife conservation in a SSSI such as at Shotover requires only modest financial support, especially when the volunteer infrastructure is strong. Indeed, projects planned and executed by volunteers are extremely cost-effective, as has been demonstrated frequently by wide-ranging habitat restoration work by Shotover Wildlife.

In celebration

The wildlife value of Shotover Hill is beyond question, both regionally and nationally. Shotover is also held in great affection by the local community — as it has been for generations — and visitors beyond number have felt uplifted by its wild tranquillity and its views of the surrounding countryside. For many, whether explicitly or subliminally, the fine mosaic of habitats and the fusion of flora and fauna instil deep feelings of personal well-being.

The contribution to our knowledge of the Hill over the past 20 years by Shotover Wildlife naturalists has made possible a much deeper understanding of its ecology and the importance of its wildlife. There is no better way to protect the rich diversity on the Hill than to research and communicate its uniqueness still further. For the future, Shotover needs more of the same: more individuals engaged in wildlife work, more fruitful partnerships and more community involvement, all founded on a shared passion for this historic and vibrant Hill.

In many ways, the late David Steel's comment on conservation in 1984 has lost none of its relevance today: "*Only a real appreciation of the importance of Shotover's countryside by members of the public and great vigilance can hope to ensure that none of it is damaged or destroyed.*" (Steel 1984: p. 73)

The wildlife of Shotover is profoundly worthy of such vigilance, and it will be the strength of feeling among those who appreciate this wonderful natural asset that will make all the difference in the years ahead. And there is no better community than that of local people to champion Shotover's importance, through good work proceeding from a love of place.

Appendix

Citation for Brasenose Wood and Shotover Hill SSSI

Description and Reasons for Notification

Brasenose Wood has a well defined coppice-with-standards structure and is one of the few English woods which is still actively managed by this traditional method. The greater part of the wood is an ancient remnant of the Shotover Forest with a documented history dating back to the thirteenth century. The wood lies on poorly-drained Kimmeridge clays but oolitic limestone occurs close to the south western boundary and the presence of lime-loving plants suggests that it outcrops elsewhere in the wood. The flora is exceptionally rich for a wood of this size with 211 recorded vascular plant species including 46 which are characteristic of ancient woodland.

The canopy consists mainly of mature pedunculate oak. Field maple is widespread but nowhere abundant. There are several clones of aspen and, in common with other remnants of Shotover Forest, wild cherry is frequent. Smaller amounts of silver birch, beech, rowan and yew occur, but standard ash trees are confined to Open Brasenose, a wood of relatively recent origin derived from an open common. The coppice layer is dominated by hazel with abundant blackthorn, hawthorn, Midland hawthorn, crab apple, field maple, dogwood, ash, holly and elm suckers. Smaller numbers of guelder rose, wayfaring tree and spindle are found in the southern part of the wood. The field layer is rich and varied, the composition of which is dependent on the stage of coppicing. Bramble dominates broad areas of recent coppice but in suitable places plants such as goldilocks buttercup *Ranunculus auricomus*, orpine *Sedum telephium*, nettle-leaved bellflower *Campanula trachelium*, spurge laurel *Daphne laureola*, blackcurrent *Ribes nigrum*, wood meadow-grass *Poa nemoralis* and bearded couch *Elymus caninus* occur. In recently cleared areas plants such as henbane *Hyoscyamus niger* and deadly nightshade *Atropa belladonna* may flourish for a short time.

Further variety is provided by a network of sinuous rides, with glades at the intersections, and two small ponds. Open Brasenose has a different structure from the main body of the wood, characterized by narrow, close-packed stems and few open areas. Open Magdalen is of similar composition and recent origin, but both of these woods are sufficiently close to the ancient wood to have developed a relatively rich flora and fauna. Brasenose Wood is a promising site for invertebrates and the blackthorn thickets and hedges along the northern and southern perimeter are the main habitat and foodplant of the rare Black Hairstreak butterfly. The nesting bird population is dense with an estimated average of 225 pairs representing 34 species within the 55 acres of ancient woodland. They include grasshopper warbler and tree pipit, both scarce species in the Oxford area. The Slade Camp fields are good examples of unimproved neutral or slightly acidic grassland managed for hay and pasture. Large numbers of butterflies and day-flying moths use the fields and they contain a wealth of wild flowers including characteristic species of clay soils such as grass vetchling *Lathyrus nissolia* and smooth tare *Vicia tetrasperma* as well as naturalized aliens such as goat's rue *Galega officinalis* and the rare tuberous pea *Lathyrus tuberosus*.

Shotover Hill provides one of the few extensive examples of unimproved [acidic] grassland and heath in Oxfordshire. Only a small area (1–2 acres) of heather-dominated vegetation now remains and elsewhere former heathland and bog have been replaced by bracken, birch and gorse. Current management aims at reinstating some of the former heathland area. The grassland is maintained as a short sward by rabbit grazing and human trampling, and the dry, sandy soils support a rich flora of annuals such as bird's-foot *Ornithopus perpusillus*, knotted clover *Trifolium striatum*, slender trefoil *T. micranthum*, knawel *Scleranthus annuus*, early hair-grass *Aira praecox* and squirrel-tail fescue *Vulpia bromoides*. The vegetation of Shotover has been studied by botanists for the past three hundred years and some of Britain's earliest scientific collections were made here.

The sheltered open swards, sandy banks, scrub woodland, wet flushes and stream banks of Shotover Hill are of outstanding entomological interest. A substantial number of rare species occur here, particularly among the diptera (true flies) and aculeates (bees, wasps and ants). The recorded total of 174 aculeate species is one of the highest in Britain and although many of these have not been seen in recent years, the area is still an important one. Shotover Hill is also of local importance for breeding and wintering birds.

https://designatedsites.naturalengland.org.uk/PDFsForWeb/Citation/1000351.pdf

References

Alexander H. (1912) *The place-names of Oxfordshire.* Clarendon Press, Oxford.

Alexander K.N.A. (2002) *The invertebrates of living and decaying timber in Britain and Ireland — a provisional annotated checklist.* English Nature Research Reports No. 467, Peterborough.

Alexander K.N.A. (2004) *Revision of the Index of Ecological Continuity as used for saproxylic beetles.* English Nature Research Reports No. 574, Peterborough.

Aplin O.V. (1889) *The birds of Oxfordshire.* Clarendon Press, Oxford.

Arkell W.J. (1947) *The geology of Oxford.* Clarendon Press, Oxford.

Aubrook E.W. (1939) Coleoptera. In: Salzman L.F. (ed) *The Victoria history of the County of Oxford: Volume 1.* Oxford University Press, pp. 107–135.

Avery B.W. (1980) Soil classification for England and Wales. *Soil Survey. Technical monograph 14*, Harpenden.

Balmer D.E., Gillings S., Caffrey B.J., Swann R.L., Downie I.S. & Fuller R.J. (2013) *Bird Atlas 2007–11: the breeding and wintering birds of Britain and Ireland.* BTO Books, Thetford.

Benson R.B. (1939) Symphyta. In: Salzman L.F. (ed) *The Victoria history of the County of Oxford: Volume 1.* Oxford University Press, pp. 136–139.

Bilton D.T., Goode D. & Mallet J. (1999) Genetic differentiation and natural hybridization between two morphological forms of the common woodlouse, *Oniscus asellus* Linnaeus, 1758. *Heredity* **82**: 462–469.

Botham M.S., Brereton T.M., Middlebrook I., Randle Z. & Roy D.B. (2013). United Kingdom Butterfly Monitoring Scheme report for 2012. Centre for Ecology & Hydrology, UK.

Bourdillon N.M. (1991) *A vegetation monitoring programme for Shotover Country Park.* MSc dissertation (unpublished). Oxford Brookes University.

Brewer J.S. (1920) *Letters and papers, foreign and domestic, Henry VIII*, Volume 1, 1509–1514.

Institute of Historical Research. HMSO, London.

Brucker J.W., Gosler A.G. & Heryet A.R. (1992) *Birds of Oxfordshire.* Pisces Publications, Newbury.

Buckland W. (1836) *Geology and mineralogy considered with reference to Natural Theology.* Bridgewater Treatise VI, II, 1–128, pls 1–69.

China W.E. (1939) Hemiptera. In: Salzman L.F. (ed) *The Victoria history of the County of Oxford: Volume 1.* Oxford University Press, pp. 69–77.

Coppock G.A. & Hill B.M. (1933) *Headington Quarry and Shotover.* Oxford University Press.

Crawley M.J. (2005) *The flora of Berkshire.* Bramblebee Books, Harpenden.

Crowley T.E. & Campbell J.M. (1984) *An atlas of Oxfordshire freshwater molluscs.* Occasional Paper No. 6. Oxfordshire Museum Services.

Darwin C.R. (1839) *Voyages of the adventure and Beagle, Volume III.* Henry Colburn, London.

Druce G.C. (1886) *The flora of Oxfordshire.* Parker & Co., Oxford.

Druce G.C. (1927) *The flora of Oxfordshire 2nd Ed.* Clarendon Press, Oxford.

Druce G.C. (1939) Botany. Posthumously revised: Tansley A.G. In: Salzman L.F. (ed) *The Victoria history of the county of Oxford: Volume 1.* Oxford University Press, pp. 27–55.

Ellis R. & Waterton C. (2004) Environmental citizenship in the making: the participation of volunteer naturalists in UK biological recording and biodiversity policy. *Science and Public Policy* **31**: 95–101.

Ellis R., Grove-White R., Vogel J. & Waterton C. (2005) *Nature: Who Knows?* Peterborough.

Elton C. (1939) Mammals. In: Salzman L.F. (ed) *The Victoria history of the county of Oxford: Volume 1.* Oxford University Press, pp. 217–222.

Erskine S.E., Killick H.J., Lambrick C.R. & Lee E.M. (2018) *Oxfordshire's Threatened Plants.* Pisces Publications.

Evans K. & Hambler C. (1995) The microhabitat of *Tuberta maerens* (Araneae, Agelenidae).

Bulletin British arachnological Society **10**: 101–103.

Falk S.J. (1991) A *review of the scarce and threatened bees, wasps and ants of Great Britain*. Research and Survey in Nature Conservation, 35. Nature Conservancy Council, Peterborough.

Falconer W. (1939) Arachnida. In: Salzman L.F. ed. *The Victoria history of the County of Oxford: Volume 1*. Oxford University Press, pp. 179–186.

Fitton W.H. (1836) Observation on some of the strata between the Chalk and the Oxford Oolite, in the south-east of England. *Transactions of the Geological Society of London* **4**: 103–388.

Fowles A.P., Alexander K.N.A. & Key R.S. (1999) The Saproxylic Quality Index: evaluating wooded habitats for the conservation of dead-wood Coleoptera. *The Coleopterist* **8**: 121–141.

Fowles A.P. (2017) *Saproxylic Quality Index: Evaluated sites ranked by SQI*. Version: b82e0896ed, August 2017. https://khepri.uk/rankings/

Fox R., Brereton T.M., Asher J., Botham M.S., Middlebrook I., Roy D.B. & Warren M.S. (2011) *The state of the UK's butterflies 2011*. Butterfly Conservation and the Centre for Ecology & Hydrology, Wareham, UK.

Fox R., Parsons M.S., Chapman J.W., Woiwod I.P., Warren M.S. & Brooks D.R. (2013) *The state of Britain's larger moths 2013*. Butterfly Conservation and Rothamsted Research, Wareham, UK.

Fuller R.J. & Steel D.T. (1990) Coppicing in Brasenose Wood, Oxfordshire: the response of breeding birds. *Fritillary* **1**: 5–15.

Gibbs D. & Papp L. (2006) A review of the Holarctic species of *Leiomyza* MACQUART, 1835 (Diptera: Asteiidae) with descriptions of two new species. *Studia dipterologica* **13**: 241–248.

Gilbert O.L. (2000) *Lichens*. The New Naturalist, HarperCollins.

Gordon E.O. (1894) *The life and correspondence of William Buckland, D.D., F.R.S., sometime Dean of Westminster, twice president of the Geological Society, and first president of the British Association*. John Murray, London.

Gosler, A.G. (1990) The birds of Wytham – an historical survey. *Fritillary* **1**: 29–74.

Grange D.R. & Benton M.J. (1996) Kimmeridgian metriorhynchid crocodiles from England. *Palaeontology* **39**: 497–514.

Gregory S.J. (2000) Terrestrial Mollusca in Oxfordshire: current status and distributional changes since the 19th century. *Fritillary* **2**: 45–57.

Gregory S.J. (2002) The terrestrial Mollusca of the valley-head fens of Oxfordshire. *Fritillary* **3**: 57–66.

Gregory S.J. & Campbell J.M. (1995) *An atlas of Oxfordshire Isopoda: Oniscidea*. Oxfordshire Museums Service Occasional Paper No. 17. Oxfordshire County Council.

Gregory S.J. & Campbell J.M. (1996) *An atlas of Oxfordshire Myriapoda: Diplopoda and Chilopoda*. Oxfordshire Museums Service Occasional Paper No. 19. Oxfordshire County Council.

Gregory S.J. & Campbell J.M. (2000) *An atlas of Oxfordshire terrestrial Mollusca*. Occasional Paper No. 20, Oxfordshire Museum Services.

Gregory S.J. & Wright I.R. (2005) Techniques to enhance the habitat of ground-nesting solitary bees and wasps. *British Wildlife* **6**: 408–409.

Grensted W.L. (1926) Mollusca. In: Walker J.J. (ed) *The Natural History of the Oxford District*. Oxford University Press, pp. 304–312.

Gunther R.T. (1925) *Early Science in Oxford. Vol. III. Part I. The biological sciences. Part II. The biological collections*. Printed for the subscribers, Oxford.

Hambler C. (1995) The biology of *Tuberta maerens* (Araneae, Agelenidae). *Bulletin of the British Arachnological Society* **10**: 97–100.

Hambler C. & Speight M.R. (1995) Biodiversity conservation in Britain: science replacing tradition. *British Wildlife* **6**: 137–147.

Hamm A.H. (1933) *Therioplectes micans* Mg., and other Tabanidae in and near Oxford (Dipt.). *Journal of the Entomological Society of the South of England* **1**: 66–67.

Hamm A.H. (1939) Diptera. In: Salzman L.F. (ed) *The Victoria history of the County of Oxford: Volume 1*. Oxford University Press, pp. 156–178.

Hamm A.H. (1941) Habits of *Tabanus micans* Mg (Dipt.). *Entomologist's Monthly Magazine* **77**: 235.

Harrison C. (1998) *John Malchair of Oxford.* Ashmolean Museum, Oxford.

Hayhow D.B., Burns F., Eaton M.A., Bacon L., Al-Fulaij N., Brereton T., Brookman E., Burke O., Butler J., Davis J., De Massimi S., Gambling P., Lewis S., Macadam C.R., Matthews F., Meredith C., Newson S.E., Noble D.G., O'Hara D., Pearson J., Stevenson K., Tansley D., Winder F., Wynde R.M. & Gregory R.D. (2016) *State of Nature 2016: England.* The State of Nature partnership. UK.

HM Treasury (2000) *2000 Spending Review: New Public Spending Plans 2001–2004.* HM Government.

Hodgetts S. (2009) *The effect of increasing deer presence on bird abundance and species richness in coppiced woodland.* MSc dissertation (unpublished). Oxford Brookes University.

Horstmann K. (2012) Revisionen einiger Gattungen und Arten der Phygadeuontini III (Hymenoptera, Ichneumonidae, Cryptinae). *Entomofauna* **28**: 397–424.

Horton A., Sumbler M.G., Cox B.B. & Ambrose K. (1995) *Geology of the country around Thame.* Memoir of the British Geological Survey, Sheet 237 (England and Wales). HMSO, London.

JNCC – Joint Nature Conservation Committee (1998) *A statement on Common Standards Monitoring.* JNCC, Peterborough.

JNCC – Joint Nature Conservation Committee (2004) *Common Standards Monitoring – introduction to the guidance manual.* JNCC, Peterborough.

JNCC – Joint Nature Conservation Committee (2010) *UK Priority Species pages – Amiota variegata: version 2.* JNCC, Peterborough.

Jourdain F.C.R. (1926) Ornithology. In: Walker, J.J. (ed) *The Natural History of the Oxford District.* Oxford University Press, pp. 128–160.

July M. (2013) Whither Natural England. *Ecos* **34**: 56–61.

Killick J., Perry R. & Woodell S. (1998) *The Flora of Oxfordshire.* Pisces Publications.

Kirby K.J., Jefferson R., Larwood J., Russell D., Le Bas B. & Wright R. (2010) What has the SSSI improvement programme achieved for nature conservation in England? *British Wildlife* **22**: 16–25.

Linnaeus C. (1758) *Systema Natura*, 10th edition.

Lhwyd E. (1699) *Lithophylacii Britannici Ichnographia. Sive Lapidum aliorumque Fossilium Britannicorum singulari figura insignium, quotquot hactenus vel ipse invenit vel ab amicis accepit, Distributio Classica: Scrinii sui lapidarii Repertorium cum locis singulorum natalibus exhibens. Additis rariorum aliquot figuris aere incisis; cum Epistolis ad Clarissimos Viros de quibusdam circa marina Fossilia & Stirpes minerales praesertim notandis.* First Edition. Printed for the subscribers, London.

Lobel M.D. (1957) *A history of the county of Oxford: Volume 5, Bullingdon Hundred.* Oxford University Press.

MacGregor A., Mendonça M. & White J. (2000) *Ashmolean Museum, Oxford. Manuscript Catalogues of the Early Museum Collections, 1683–1886 (Part I).* British Archaeological Reports, Oxford

Montalto N.A. (2010) *The characterisation and provenancing of ancient ochres.* PhD thesis (unpublished). Cranfield University.

Mowl T. (2007) *The Historic Gardens of England: Oxforshire.* Templus Publishing.

Natural England (2017a) *Designated Sites View: SSSI Glossary.* https://designatedsites. naturalengland.org.uk/SSSIglossary.aspx

Natural England (2017b) *Designated Sites View: Brasenose Wood and Shotover Hill SSSI.* https://designatedsites.naturalengland.org.uk/ ReportUnitCondition.aspx

National Biodiversity Network Atlas Partnership (2017) https://nbnatlas.org/

OOS (2012) *Birds of Oxfordshire 2012.* Oxford Ornithological Society.

Oostermeijer J.G.B. (1989) Myrmecochory in *Polygala vulgaris* L., *Luzula campestris* (L.) DC. and *Viola curtisii* Forster in a Dutch dune area. *Oecologia* **78**: 302–311.

Overall R. (1988) *Wytham Woods, Oxford: 1971–1987.* Oxford Ornithological Society Report 1988, Oxford

Perrins C.M. & Gosler A.G. (2010) Birds. In: Savill P.S., Perrins C.M., Kirby K.J. & Fisher N. (eds) *Wytham Woods: Oxford's Ecological Laboratory*, Oxford University Press, Oxford, pp. 145–171.

Pescott O., Simkin J., August T.A., Randle Z., Dore A.J. & Botham M.S. (2015) Air pollution and its effects on lichens, bryophytes, and lichen-feeding Lepidoptera: Review and evidence from biological records. *Biological Journal of the Linnean Society* **115**: 611–635.

Phillips J. (1871) *Geology of Oxford and the valley of the Thames.* Clarendon Press, Oxford.

Plot R. (1677) *The natural history of Oxfordshire, being an essay towards the natural history of England.* Oxford.

Powell P. (2005) *The Geology of Oxfordshire.* Dovecote Press, Dorset.

Powney G.D., Cham S.S.A., Smallshire D., Isaac N.J.B. (2015) Trait correlates of distribution trends in the Odonata of Britain and Ireland. *PeerJ* **3**: e1410. https://doi.org/10.7717/peerj.1410

Redfern M. & Shirley P. (2011*) British plant galls 2nd ed.* Field Studies Council, Shrewsbury.

Richards O.W. (1939) Aculeata. In: Salzman L.F. (ed) *The Victoria history of the County of Oxford: Volume 1.* Oxford University Press, pp. 147–156.

Richards O.W. (1951) Obituary – Albert Harry Hamm. *Entomologist's Monthly Magazine* **87**: 96–98.

Risely K., Massimino D., Newson S.E., Eaton M.A., Musgrove A.J., Noble D.G., Procter D. & Baillie S.R. (2013) *The Breeding Bird Survey 2012.* Research Report 645. BTO, Thetford.

Roberts E. (1963) The boundary and woodlands of Shotover *c.* 1298. *Oxoniensis* **28**: 68–73.

Salzman L.F. (1939) *The Victoria History of the County of Oxford: Volume 1.* Oxford University Press.

Sheail J. (1998) *Nature conservation in Britain: the formative years.* The Stationery Office, London.

Sibthorp J. (1794*) Flora Oxoniensis.* Oxonii. Typis Academicis.

Smith A.Z. (1986) *A history of the Hope Entomological Collections in the University Museum Oxford.* Clarendon Press.

Steel D. (1984) *Shotover: The natural history of a royal forest.* Pisces Publications.

Steel D. (1988) *Shotover Country Park – Management Plan.* Oxford City Council.

Stokland J.N., Siitonen J. & Jonsson B.G. (2012) *Biodiversity in Dead Wood.* Cambridge University Press.

Stroh P.A., Leach S.J., August T.A., Walker K.J., Pearman D.A., Rumsey F.J., Harrower C.A., Fay M.F., Martin J.P., Pankhurst T., Preston C.D. & Taylor I. (2014) *A vascular plant red list for England.* Botanical Society of Britain and Ireland, Bristol.

Tansley A.G. (1953) *The British Isles and their vegetation.* Cambridge University Press.

Thomas J.A., Telfer M.G., Roy D.B., Preston C.D., Greenwood J.J.D., Asher J., Fox R., Clarke R.T. & Lawton J.H. (2004) Comparative losses of British butterflies, birds, and plants and the global extinction crisis. *Science* **19**: 1879–1881.

Trudgill S. (1989) Soil types: A field identification guide. *Field Studies* **7**: 337–363.

Tucker B.W. (1939) Reptiles and Amphibians. In: Salzman L.F. (ed) *The Victoria history of the county of Oxford: Volume 1.* Oxford University Press, pp. 82–106.

Viles H. (1996) 'Unswept stone, besmeer'd by sluttish time': Air Pollution and Building Stone Decay in Oxford, 1790–1960. *Environment and History* **2**: 359–372.

Walker J.J. (1907) A preliminary list of the Coleoptera of the Oxford district. In: *Ashmolean Natural History Society Oxfordshire: Report for 1906.* Parker & Son, Oxford, pp. 49–100.

Walker J.J. (1926) *The Natural History of the Oxford District.* Oxford University Press.

Walker J.J. & Hobby B.M. (1939) Lepidoptera. In: Salzman L.F. (ed) *The Victoria history of the county of Oxford: Volume 1.* Oxford University Press, pp. 82–106.

Walker R. (1833) *The flora of Oxfordshire and its contiguous counties (comprising the flowering plants only).* Henry Slatter, Oxford

Waters E.G.R. (1929) A List of the Micro-Lepidoptera of the Oxford District. *Proceedings of the Ashmolean Natural History Society,* 1–72.

White J. (1998) *Estimating the age of large and veteran trees in Britain.* Forestry Commission.

Whiteaves J.F. (1857) *On the land and freshwater Mollusca inhabiting the neighbourhood of Oxford.* Ashmolean Society, Oxford.

Whitehead A., Wright I.R. & Gosler A.G. (2003) *The Birds of Shotover.* Oxford Ornithological Society, Oxford.

Wood A. (1890) *Survey of the antiquities of the city of Oxford, composed in 1661-6, by Anthony Wood, Vol. ii.* Printed for the Oxford Historical Society at the Clarendon Press, Oxford.

Woodcock B.A., Bullock, J.M., Shore R.F., Heard M.S., Pereira M.G., Redhead J., Ridding

L., Dean H., Sleep D., Henrys P., Peyton J., Hulmes S., Hulmes L., Sárospataki M., Saure C., Edwards M., Genersch E., Knäbe S. & Pywell R.F. (2017) Country-specific effects of neonicotinoid pesticides on honey bees and wild bees. *Science* **356**: 1393–1395.

Woodward A.S. (1885). On the literature and nomenclature of British fossil Crocodilia. *Geological Magazine* **2**: 496–510.

Wright I.R. & Bartel T.W. (2017) Effect of varying coppice height on tree survival and ground flora in Brasenose Wood, Oxfordshire, UK. *Conservation Evidence* **14**: 1–4.

Wright I.R. & Gibbs D. (2015) *Ophiomyia skanensis* (Spencer) (Diptera, Agromyzidae) new to Britain. *Diperists Digest* **22**: 21–22.

Wright I.R. & Gregory S.J. (2006) The aculeate Hymenoptera of Shotover Hill, Oxfordshire. *British Journal of Entomology and Natural History* **19**: 65–76.

Wright I.R., Roberts S.P.M. & Collins B.E. (2015) Evidence of forage distance limitations for small bees (Hymenoptera: Apidae). *European Journal of Entomology* **112**: 303–310.

Wright I.R. and Wright J.A. (2000) *Survey of Wetlands: Report No. 4.* Report for Oxford City Council (unpublished), Shotover Wildlife.

Wright J.A. and Wright I.R. (2006) The changing bryophyte flora of Chawley Brick Pit, Oxford. *Fritillary* **4**: 36–53.

Young M.T., Steel L., Rigby M.P., Howlett E.A. & Humphrey S. (2014) Largest known specimen of the genus Dakosaurus (Metriorhynchidae: Geosaurini) from the Kimmeridge Clay Formation (Late Jurassic) of England, and an overview of Dakosaurus specimens discovered from this formation (including reworked specimens from the Woburn Sands Formation). *Historical Biology* DOI: 10.1080/08912963.2014.915822.

General index

Page numbers in **bold** refer to text in figures and picture captions

Species index

Page numbers in **bold** refer to text in figures and picture captions